VOICE AND DATA INTERNETWORKING

D1299510

Voice and Data Internetworking

Gilbert Held

McGraw-Hill
New York • San Francisco • Washington, D.C. • Auckland • Bogotá
Caracas • Lisbon • London • Madrid • Mexico City • Milan
Montreal • New Delhi • San Juan • Singapore
Sydney • Tokyo • Toronto

Library of Congress Cataloging-in-Publication Data

Held, Gilbert.
    Voice and data internetworking with IP and frame relay / Gilbert Held.
        p.   cm. — (McGraw-Hill series on computer communications)
    Includes index.
    ISBN 0-07-212429-6
    1. TCP/IP (Computer network protocol) 2. Digital telephone
systems. 3. Computer networks. 4. Data transmission systems.
I. Title. II. Series.
TK5105.585.H45 1998
621.385—dc21   98-6456
                                                                     CIP

McGraw-Hill

A Division of The **McGraw·Hill** Companies

Copyright © 2000 by The McGraw-Hill Companies, Inc. All rights reserved. Printed in
the United States of America. Except as permitted under the United States Copyright
Act of 1976, no part of this publication may be reproduced or distributed in any form
or by any means, or stored in a data base or retrieval system, without the prior written
permission of the publisher.

1 2 3 4 5 6 7 8 9 0   AGM/AGM   9 0 4 3 2 1 0 9

ISBN 0-07-212429-6

*The sponsoring editor for this book was Steven Elliot, and the
production supervisor was Clare Stanley. It was set in Vendome
by North Market Street Graphics.*

Printed and bound by Quebecor/Martinsburg.

*Throughout this book, trademarked names are used. Rather than put a trademark symbol after
every occurrence of a trademarked name, we used the names in an editorial fashion only, and to
the benefit of the trademark owner, with no intention of infringement of the trademark. Where
such designations appear in this book, they have been printed with initial caps.*

Information contained in this work has been obtained by The McGraw-Hill
Companies, Inc. ("McGraw-Hill") from sources believed to be reliable. However,
neither McGraw-Hill nor its authors guarantees the accuracy or completeness of
any information published herein and neither McGraw-Hill nor its authors
shall be responsible for any errors, omissions, or damages arising out of use of
this information. This work is published with the understanding that McGraw-
Hill and its authors are supplying information but are not attempting to render
engineering or other professional services. If such services are required, the assistance of an appropriate professional should be sought.

    This book is printed on recycled, acid-free paper containing a
minimum of 50% recycled de-inked fiber.

CONTENTS

Contents

Contents

Contents

Contents

Contents

PREFACE

Imagine the cost of a long-distance or even an international call being billed at a penny a minute! At this price, even the popular "dime lady" appearing in commercials for a leading long-distance communications carrier cannot compete. Calls at a penny a minute or less with a minimum amount of organizational effort to achieve this is the driving force behind voice over data, an emerging technology that has the potential to revolutionize the manner in which both small and large corporations and government agencies construct and operate their communications networks.

The technology providing the capability to transport voice over data networks represents a natural evolution of the quest of network managers and LAN administrators to economize on the cost of organizational communications. Until recently, most organizations looked in the opposite direction, attempting to transmit data over existing voice transmission facilities. While data over voice will continue to play an important role in the creation of corporatewide integrated networks, voice over data represents a networking technology that can provide an outstanding return on your investment. In addition, unlike the use of ATM, which can require a complete change in an organization's infrastructure and severely tax existing operations during a changeover period, the switch to voice over data can be so mild that most persons are not aware of the additional capability until they've been informed of it.

As a second edition, this book builds upon the prior edition to include experiences obtained by this author testing the technology. Because the ability to transmit voice over an IP or frame relay network is very time-dependent, numerous tips and techniques are described in this new edition that may enable you to make seemingly unworkable technology work. In teaching several seminars on the topic of this book in Europe, Israel, South America, and for Interop, I became noted for the expression "save a millisecond here and a millisecond there and the technology works!" Thus, throughout this new edition you will encounter "application notes" that provide tips and techniques whose implementation could save the milliseconds necessary to successfully implement the new technology.

The advantages of voice over data are considerable. However, as with any new technology, its implementation requires appropriate planning, which is best accomplished by understanding the technology, its strengths and limitations, the options to consider, and the methods by which the technology can be implemented—all topics covered in this book. So relax, grab a Coke or a cup of coffee, and pace yourself as we explore this relatively new technology, which, as we will learn, is based on a mixture of voice and data networking technologies.

As a professional author, I highly value reader feedback. Please feel free to contact me via my publisher, whose address is at the back of this book, or send e-mail to me at gheld@mcimail.com. I welcome your comments and suggestions. For example, should a third edition contain greater detail in certain areas? Should I consider adding or perhaps removing some topics? Are there other issues you wish to bring to my attention?

Gilbert Held
Macon, Georgia

ACKNOWLEDGMENTS

Although it is a relatively easy process to select a book from a catalog or shelf in a store, the actual effort involved in its preparation and publication can be quite complex and can extend over a significant period of time. As a professional author, I learned long ago that the creation of a written work is a team effort requiring the cooperation and assistance of many persons. Thus, I would be remiss if I did not thank those who made this book possible.

First and foremost, I must thank my family for lost evenings and weekends while I worked on this new edition. It takes a considerable amount of patience and understanding to tolerate the efforts of a technical author who uses the fax machine at odd hours, fills bookshelves with reference material, and receives express packages early on Saturday mornings.

As an old-fashioned author who frequently travels to locations where even the best gadgets fail to provide the ability to recharge a notebook in hotels, I decided long ago that a pen and paper eliminates electrical-outlet incompatibilities. In addition, pens and paper are products that can be easily acquired worldwide and used on long international flights without fear of battery failure. Using pen and paper while flying through air turbulence results in some interesting examples of handwriting. Thus, once again I am grateful for the fine effort of Linda Hayes in converting my handwritten notes and drawings into a manuscript suitable for my publisher to work with.

The role of an acquisitions editor is most important in backing a writing project from its proposal and development on through the book production process. Thus, I would also like to again thank Steve Elliot, who became a father when the first edition of this book was published. Now that a second edition is in print, Steve and his wife can work on keeping up with this book!

Last but not least, the cooperation and assistance of two equipment manufacturers deserves special mention. I sincerely appreciate the efforts of Mike Vizzi of ACT Networks and Eric B. Kirsten of Nuera Communications. Both gentlemen shared detailed information that enables me to discuss the operation of their firms' voice over frame relay products and to provide extensive data concerning the cost per minute of voice transport—an economic analysis that, for many readers, will fully justify implementing this relatively new technology.

VOICE AND DATA INTERNETWORKING

Introduction

During the late 1940s, an Englishman with a fondness for cigars quoted the classic and often repeated phrase, "Jaw, jaw, jaw is better than war, war, war." Approximately 50 years later, Winston Churchill, if he could view current events from heaven, would more than likely be amazed at the amount of jawing being performed. Today, both the telephone and the personal computer are ubiquitous office and home products most of us use throughout the day, every day. The telephone is based on analog technology since it must support the analog waveforms generated by human speech. In comparison, the personal computer is based on digital technology since data is encoded and manipulated in terms of strings of binary 0s and 1s.

Until recently, the conventional wisdom associated with integrating voice and data transmission focused on two areas: integrating data transmission requirements into existing voice networks and constructing asynchronous transfer mode (ATM) networks that were designed to support the transfer of voice, data, video, and image information over a common network infrastructure. The integration of data transmission onto networks primarily constructed to transport voice calls between geographically separated organizational locations is anything but a recent phenomenon. The first generation of T1 multiplexers marketed during the 1980s provided this capability, and considerable improvement in voice digitization technology and the development of a new series of multiplexers enables corporate networks to use T1 and T3 transmission facilities and their fractional equivalents to carry router-to-router communications along with a significant amount of voice conversations plus faxes and videoconferencing. While data over voice will continue to be a viable mechanism for transporting information on a common network infrastructure, it is primarily applicable for organizations that have a significant requirement for voice communications between multiple locations.

Although ATM was proposed as a unifying technology developed to support voice, data, video, and imaging applications over a common network infrastructure, as with many technologies its hype is greater than its implementation. While the scalability of ATM, which enables LAN-based data operating at 25 or 155 Mbps to be transported as a uniform flow of cells at a T1 operating rate of 1.544 Mbps to a communications carrier's central office and at optical carrier rates up to 2.4 Gbps between carrier offices, is an admirable concept, competitive LAN technology at a significantly lower cost resulted in many organizations postponing ATM to the desktop. Instead, ATM has gained a high degree of acceptance by communications carriers as a mechanism for an assortment of other transports, ranging in scope from traditional digitized voice carried on T1 lines to frame relay and TCP/IP data networks formed literally on top of ATM. Thus, network managers and LAN administrators looking for a practical, efficient, and low-cost mechanism to transport voice and data turned to a third option, which is the focus of this book: voice over data networks.

As we turn our attention to transporting voice over IP and voice over frame relay in this book we will note that in many situations we may be able to take advantage of the ATM infrastructure used by many Internet service providers (ISPs) and communication carriers. Because ATM can provide true quality of service (QoS) that can guarantee bandwidth and latency or delay, if we can map IP and frame relay to ATM we can take advantage of the capability of ATM. Thus, while voice over data networks provides an option to ATM it can also take advantage of an existing ATM infrastructure.

1-1   Overview

Voice over data networks represents a technology developed to satisfy one of the most fundamental aspects of network management requirements: the necessity to integrate the transportation of voice and data in a cost-effective manner through the acquisition of equipment whose installation and operation limits potential disruption to ongoing organizational activities. That said, many readers may have the impression that the development of equipment to provide a voice over data network transmission capability represents a radical advance in technology. Although it is an advance in communications technology, most of the underlying technology has existed for several years. Basically, voice over data networks can be described as the application of voice digitization and compression schemes through a variety of hardware and software products to enable voice to be transported on networks originally developed to transport data. Two of these networks, which are the primary focus of equipment developers and whose use for voice over data is covered in detail in this book, are Internet Protocol (IP) and frame relay networks. As we will note later in this book, the basic concepts concerning the use of hardware and software to obtain a voice over data networking capability are applicable for both public and private networks. Thus, the information presented in this book will be applicable for voice over data occurring on the public Internet, private intranets, and public and private frame relay networks. Now that we have an overview of how voice over data fits into the methods of integrating voice and data networks and have had a very brief discussion of the underlying technology and its general benefits, let's broaden our horizon by turning our attention to the reasons that voice over data networking is one of the hottest technologies of the new millennium. Since this technology is similar to other communications technologies in that there are certain constraints and limitations associated with its use under different networking scenarios, we will also focus on potential networking problems that can adversely affect the transport of voice on data networks, and we'll discuss existing and evolving methods that may provide you with a mechanism to overcome many of these problems. Last but not least, we will conclude this chapter with a preview of succeeding chapters. This will allow you to decide if you prefer to go directly to a chapter that has information specific to your needs or if, as a newcomer to the use of voice over data networks, you should proceed sequentially by chapter to build your overall knowledge.

1-2   Rationale

Today many organizations operate separate voice and data networks based on a traditional separation of the two technologies and an initial separation of equipment developed to support voice and data networking. Other organizations integrated all or a portion of their voice and data networks by adding equipment that enables data to be transported over circuits originally installed to support voice networking, resulting in a data over voice network infrastructure. When organizations failed to integrate their voice and data networks, two of the primary reasons were economics and technology. In some situations it made sense to maintain separate networks, as the cost associated with integrating the two might exceed the potential savings or require a period of time that would result in a relatively poor return on investment. As for technology, until recently, equipment was not available to effectively and efficiently transport voice over IP and frame relay networks, thus requiring consideration of other techniques, such as time division multiplexing, that would have a permanent effect on the ability to transport both voice and data regardless of the bandwidth requirements of each.

Classical Data Over Voice Constraints

Figure 1-1 illustrates the classical method for integrating voice and data via time division multiplexing. In examining Figure 1-1, note that each

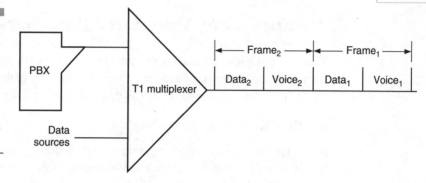

Figure 1-1

The classical method for integrating voice and data is via time division multiplexing, in which fixed segments of bandwidth are allocated to voice and data.

multiplexer frame is configured to provide a static allocation of bandwidth between voice and data sources. For example, if the PBX was configured to provide 20 PCM-encoded voice conversations, each operating at 64 Kbps, then each frame would consist of 1.28 Mbps of bandwidth allocated to the PBX (64 Kbps × 20) and the remaining bandwidth of 256 Kbps to the data sources. Since the slots in the frame are fixed by time, if the data sources became inactive the PBX could not take advantage of this fact to transmit additional PCM-digitized voice conversations. Similarly, if one or more of the 20 voice conversations supported by the multiplexer became inactive or terminated, the multiplexer could not allocate additional bandwidth to the data sources.

Another constraint associated with classical TDM operations is the requirement for organizations to construct their own networks via the installation of a series of point-to-point digital leased lines. Although this type of network is available for the exclusive use of the organization, that exclusivity is not without a price. In comparison, the cost associated with the use of packet networks that support the transmission requirements of a virtually unlimited number of different organizations can be considerably less expensive due to the sharing of the cost of the transmission facilities used to construct the packet network.

The reliability of a private leased-line network represents another constraint that must be considered. The most common way to enhance reliability is by installing additional circuits with diversity routing to ensure each circuit is routed through different central offices between source and destination, so the additional cost can be considerable—an organization would be charged for two circuits between each network location as well as a monthly fee for the diversity routing of the pair of circuits routed between locations.

Advantages of Voice Over Data Networking

The key advantages associated with the use of a packet network for the transmission of digitized voice can be considerable. Table 1-1 lists six of the advantages associated with transmitting voice over a packet-shared network.

Bandwidth Allocation

Both IP and frame relay represent packet-shared networks for which bandwidth is consumed only when transmission occurs. Thus, these networks remove the fixed bandwidth allocation associated with the first generation of T1 multiplexers. However, these networks were originally developed to transport data over relatively low-speed transmission facilities, such as 56- and 64-Kbps digital lines, with access to both of these networks only recently increased to T1 and for IP networks to a T3 operating rate, while a T3 connection rate to frame relay is being developed as this book is written.

Modern Voice-compression Techniques

Since a PCM-digitized voice conversation requires a 64-Kbps operating rate, it would make no sense to attempt to transmit the digitized conversation over a 56- or 64-Kbps digital link to an IP or frame relay network, as doing so would preclude the ability to concurrently transmit data. Recognizing this problem, equipment developers incorporated a new generation of voice-compression algorithms into their products. Today, you can consider using some frame relay access devices (FRADs) that incorporate voice-digitization modules that lower the operating rate of a voice conversation to 4 or 8 Kbps. This means you can transmit between 8 and 16 voice conversations on one 64-Kbps frame relay connection or a mixture of voice and data over a single frame relay connection.

TABLE 1-1

Advantages Associated with Transmitting Voice over a Packet Network

- Bandwidth allocation efficiency
- Ability to use modern voice-compression methods
- Sunk costs
- Ability to use a single interface
- Enhanced reliability of packet networks
- Economics associated with shared network use

Sunk Costs

The incorporation of voice compression and the development of techniques to enable compressed voice to flow effectively and efficiently through a packet network are two key mechanisms that resulted in the acceptance of the technology as a practical and economically viable mechanism for transporting voice over data networks. A similar incorporation of voice-digitization algorithms into IP equipment permits voice conversations to be transmitted using a very low amount of bandwidth on IP networks.

Since a major portion of the cost associated with the use of a frame relay network involves the monthly recurring fee for an access line and network port at the entrance to the frame relay network provider, any method that permits additional data sources to flow over a common connection becomes more cost effective. Similarly, if your organization has a connection to the Internet or you operate an internal IP network referred to as an *intranet,* the ability to use existing transmission facilities represents transmission over sunk costs. That is, you are already paying for such equipment as router ports, channel service units, and transmission facilities. Hence, transporting digitized voice without incurring additional expense other than for voice digitization can result in a very low cost per call minute.

The ability to transmit digitized voice over frame relay— and IP-based networks can provide several key advantages. Those advantages include the ability to transmit and receive information to and from multiple locations via a single connection to a packet network, enhanced transmission reliability, and the economies of scale associated with the use of packet networks shared by many organizations.

Multiple Access via a Single Network Connection

A packet network permits the flow of multiple logical connections over a single physical circuit, thus allowing an organization to support transmission to multiple locations via a single network connection. Figure 1-2 illustrates this concept, showing an intermix of packets being transmitted to locations A and B from location C via the use of a packet network access device and a single network connection from that device to the packet network. In comparison, the use of a leased-line-based network would require an organization to install separate leased lines from location C to locations A and B. This in turn would require the networking device used with the leased-line network, such as a router or multiplexer, to have two ports, since one port would be required to support the connection to each leased line.

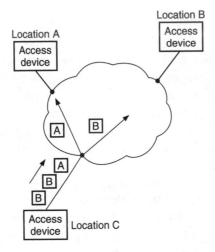

Figure 1-2
Accessing multiple connections via a single packet network.

This in turn would add to the cost of establishing a private leased-line-based network, since router and multiplexer ports can cost between $500 and $1000 or more per port. In addition, when your networking requirement expands such that you must consider the interconnection of a large number of locations, the cost of individual point-to-point networking connections and a large number of router or multiplexer ports per location can become prohibitive. In such situations, you would probably employ a different network structure—perhaps interconnecting several locations within distinct geographical areas to a single hub location and then interconnecting the hubs. Although this type of networking structure can be more economical than leased lines and routers or multiplexers, it is more appropriate for supporting a large voice-transmission internetworking requirement and a significant number of data sources than for supporting a moderate volume of voice over a data network. For the latter situation, the cost associated with using a frame relay or IP network for transmitting voice and data will usually prove to be more economical. This in turn opens up a vast number of networking possibilities, such as connecting national or international locations together via a packet network or even using a FRAD to support voice on a leased line between two locations that are required to transmit only a few data sessions of activity between locations, since the cost of adding voice support to some vendor products can be accomplished for a minimal one-time fee.

Enhanced Reliability

The backbone infrastructure of packet networks is commonly constructed based on a mesh topology. This topology, illustrated in Figure 1-3, com-

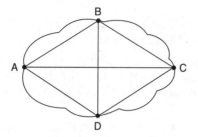

Figure 1-3
Most packet networks use a mesh structure to connect access locations, providing an enhanced level of redundancy that improves network reliability.

monly provides two or more routes or paths between network nodes. Depending on the number of network nodes between two network access points, the mesh structure can provide a large number of alternative routes between network access points. For example, if the direct line connection between locations A and C should become inoperative, transmission between those two locations could continue on paths A-B-C or A-D-C. Thus the backbone mesh structure of packet networks provides a built-in alternative routing capability whose cost to support is shared by the large number of individuals and organizational users of the network. In comparison, it could be extremely expensive for a single organization to develop a mesh network infrastructure to improve network reliability.

Economics of Use

In our prior discussion of the advantages associated with the use of packet networks, we noted that they can provide access to multiple locations via a single network connection and that their mesh infrastructure to enhance reliability would be expensive to duplicate for a private-line-based network. Both of these advantages provide an economic edge to the use of packet networks. However, a more substantial economic advantage can result from the cost structure associated with the use of different frame relay networks and the Internet. For example, the usage charge associated with some frame relay networks is based on a flat monthly fee determined by what is referred to as the *committed information rate* (CIR), which is the transmission rate the frame relay network provider guarantees will be serviced. The CIR can be less than or equal to the operating rate of the access line and is described in detail later in this book. This means that if you are not using the full CIR, you can transmit additional information in the form of conventional data or digitized voice without incurring any additional transmission charges other than a one-time expense associated with the acquisition of equipment required to transmit voice over a frame relay network. For the use of an IP network, most

Internet service providers charge organizations a monthly fee based on the operating rate of the leased line connecting an organization's location. Thus, transmission of additional information in the form of conventional data or digitized voice over the Internet may not alter the organization's communications cost (other than the one-time expenditure for equipment to support the transmission of digitized voice). If the IP network represents an organization's internal private network, the addition of voice transmission over that network can also result in significant savings. This is because the use of modern voice-compression methods can enable voice packets to flow over the excess bandwidth available on many networks. Once again, this flow of digitized voice packets does not alter the monthly cost of the organization's transmission facilities and is normally obtained as a result of the one-time expenditure for equipment to digitize and packetize voice so it can flow over an IP network. Now that we have an appreciation for some of the advantages associated with the transmission of voice over data networks, let's turn our attention to some of the networking problems that may occur. By understanding some of the potential pitfalls of transporting voice over data networks, you can make more intelligent decisions about implementing this networking technique based on your organization's current and evolving communications requirements, the existing network infrastructure used by your organization, and the potential use of different types of packet networks.

1-3   Potential Problems to Consider

The transmission of voice over data networks includes a degree of risk associated with the use of the technology. Potential problems that network managers and LAN administrators should consider can be classified into four general areas: reliability, predictability, security, and standards.

Reliability

For the purposes of this book, we will define *reliability* as the ability of a packet to reach its destination. The transmission of voice over packet networks originally developed to transmit data entails a degree of risk concerning the reliable delivery of voice-encoded packets. Some packet networks include a discard mechanism by which packets can be figuratively routed to the "great bit bucket in the sky" when the level of utilization of the network reaches a predefined level. While performance is not significantly altered by data packets transporting e-mail messages, carrying interactive query-response data, or retransmitting files of a dropped packet (or sequence of packets), the same is *not* true when digitized voice is being transported. Speech has to be reconstructed so it sounds natural, and this requires an absence of extended delays during which dropped packets are retransmitted. Thus, the ability to effectively transport voice over data networks requires a mechanism to ensure the reliable delivery of packets. As we describe and discuss the operation of certain types of equipment later in this book, we will note that vendors have increased the potential for reliable delivery of voice-encoded packets primarily by limiting the length of such packets, lessening the probability that they will be dropped by a packet network.

Another associated reliability problem with respect to transmitting voice over a data network is the manner by which a receiver performs when a voice-carrying packet is dropped. Most equipment simply does nothing, resulting in a period of silence which, if packet dropping is only occurring rarely, is more than likely impervious to the human ear. However, if several packets are transmitting digitized voice flow to the great bit bucket in the sky, the result is an audible gap of silence that becomes noticeable to the human ear. To overcome this problem, some equipment vendors generate a bit of noise, which is not as noticeable as a gap of silence.

Predictability

Although many persons might consider predictability to be similar to reliability, they actually represent two separate problems associated with the transmission of voice over data networks. *Reliability* refers to the ability of packets containing digitized voice to reach their intended destination without being dropped by the network. *Predictability* refers to the delivery of those packets without an excessive amount of delay that would result in the reconstruction of the transported conversation sounding awkward. Depending on the type of voice being transported, both reliability and predictability may or may not be an issue. To understand this, let's examine the two primary categories of voice your organization may wish to transport over a data network.

Effect on Voice Applications

There are two general categories of voice applications you can consider for transporting voice over a data network: real-time and non-real-time. A real-time voice application, such as a telephone call, requires both reliability and predictability. In comparison, the attachment of a voice message to an e-mail or the transmission of prerecorded voice mail from one location to another requires neither reliability nor predictability.

Concerning the attachment of a prerecorded voice message, reliability with respect to minimizing the dropping of packets transporting digitized voice is not required, since the eventual retransmission of dropped packets ensures the conversation arrives at its destination, where it will be listened to after the pieces of the voice message arrive and are stored as an entity. Similarly, predictability is no longer an issue, as packets arriving with random delays are not listened to in real time. Instead, the packets are assembled as an entity prior to being listened to, which removes gaps associated with their transmission over a packet network.

Techniques to Improve Predictability

There are two basic techniques that can be used to increase the predictability of packets arriving at their intended destination. The first technique involves providing a quality of service (QoS) function to provide for the reservation of network resources for the transmission of the sequence of voice packets with a guaranteed minimum delay. Although QoS is built into ATM, it has only recently been developed as a mechanism for incorporation indirectly into IP networks via the Resource ReSerVation Protocol (RSVP). Unfortunately, RSVP requires the use of RSVP-compatible devices throughout the route of packets flowing through an IP network to obtain the ability to reserve network resources from source to destination. On a public IP network like the Internet, it may be several years before a significant amount of vendor equipment is upgraded to RSVP to enable a small fraction of RSVP requests to be fully honored. Of course, if your organization has an internal IP network, you have a far greater ability to control the upgrading of equipment to support RSVP.

Recognizing that RSVP may be several years away from being useful and that an equivalent method for frame relay is lacking, equipment developers have attacked the need for predictability via the control of voice packets. In doing so, equipment vendors have introduced techniques that fragment voice packets into smaller-size packets to enhance their ability to be transported over a network, developed schemes for the prioritization of the transmission of voice packets over data so voice packets reach the network first, and initiated other techniques that are described in detail later in this book. Although such techniques do not actually guarantee that voice packets will arrive at their destinations in a timely and predictable manner, they greatly enhance the probability that they will do so.

Security

Unless you are working for the CIA, DIA, or another spook agency, chances are high that you will never have a second thought concerning the possibility of your conversation being overheard when you use the Public Switched Telephone Network (PSTN) or an internal corporate voice network. Although the probability remains slim that a voice conversation will be overheard when you use a voice over data network transmission method in which voice packets or frames flow over a public packet network, the use of a public packet network that is connected to an internal corporate network results in a new security risk—a risk with far greater potential damage to your organization than overheard conversations about a planned trip, travel arrangements, or even the potential bid on a construction project. That potential damage results from the connection of an organization's internal private network to a public packet network, which opens the internal network to access from anyone who can connect to the public network.

Although an organization will always have a degree of exposure to the contents of digitized voice packets being inadvertently or intentionally read as they are routed through a public packet network, a perhaps more significant problem is the fact that every hacker and cracker can attempt to access your organization's network once that network is connected to a public packet network. What took burglars and swindlers hours or days to accomplish, a hacker can now do in minutes using a personal computer. From a security perspective, there are three issues to be considered: barring uninvited persons from accessing your network, verifying the identity of those who access your network, and encoding the contents of packets so they are not readable. These issues involve access control, authentication, and encryption with respect to transmission over a public packet network, as illustrated in Figure 1-4.

Access Control

Access control represents a mechanism to enable or disable transmission between a public and private network, between two public networks, or between two private networks based on some predefined metric, such as the source address of a packet. One of the most common methods used

▬▬ ▬▬ ▬▬ ▬▬
Figure 1-4
Network security ele-
ments to consider.

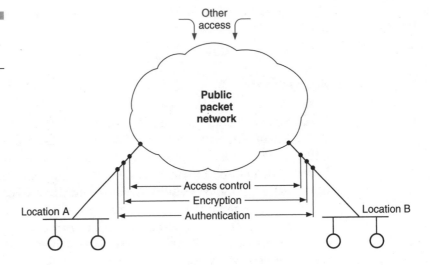

to implement access control is through the construction of an access list programmed into a router, assuming the router incorporates this feature.

One of the least understood problems associated with access control lists is the trade-off between security in a voice over IP environment and delay in the processing of the extended list that can adversely effect the intelligibility of the reconstructed piece of voice at its destination. Because the use of TCP and UDP ports for voice are not standardized, this means that if your organization supports several vendor products and uses a router access control list for security, your list more than likely includes several voice over IP—related statements. Because access lists are examined top down, sequentially, placing your voice-related statements at the bottom of the list can result in a few extra milliseconds of delay.

▬ ▬ ▬ ▬ ▬ ▬ ▬ ▬ ▬ ▬ ▬ ▬ ▬ ▬ ▬ ▬ ▬ ▬
APPLICATION NOTE If using access control lists, move your voice-related statements toward the top of the list.
▬ ▬ ▬ ▬ ▬ ▬ ▬ ▬ ▬ ▬ ▬ ▬ ▬ ▬ ▬ ▬ ▬ ▬

To gain a few milliseconds, you should consider placing your voice-related statements near the top of your access control list. Since most lists begin with statements that disallow inbound packets from your network to prevent address spoofing, a good technique is to place your voice-related statements right after your antispoofing statements in your access control list.

In examining the three elements of network security illustrated in Figure 1-4, note that access control is shown as the innermost layer with respect to the relationship between two organizational networks (A and B) communicating via the use of a public packet network. Access control is placed as the innermost layer because the most popular access control device, a router, can be considered to represent the demarcation between the public and private network. A second access control device that has gained widespread popularity is the firewall. In addition to providing an access control capability through the creation of access lists, a firewall can add a significant number of additional security features, including authentication, encryption, message alert generation, and proxy services. Both the use of router access lists and firewalls are discussed later in this book.

Encryption

Since encryption usually occurs based on the operation of a device behind a router, it is shown as the middle layer of security elements depicted in Figure 1-4. However, readers should note that encryption can be one of the optional features provided by many firewall vendors along with authentication. Thus it is entirely possible for encryption and authentication functions to be colocated on a common device. Similarly, a firewall could be used to provide authentication while a private network device, such as a program operating on a computer located on the private network, performs encryption. In this situation, authentication would be performed prior to encryption, which from a practical standpoint makes more sense when receiving packets, because the productivity of equipment would be adversely affected if, after decrypting a packet, its originator could not be authenticated and the packet was subsequently rejected.

Today you have a range of products that can be considered for use for encryption of packets. However, unlike point-to-point circuit utilization where an entire packet can be encrypted and decrypted without affecting its ability to be routed, the application of encryption for data flowing over a public packet network requires the use of an intelligent encryption device. That device must recognize the separation of the information field from the header and trailers of a packet, operating only on the information field. Otherwise the packet would not be routable through the network.

The use of encryption to hide the meaning of packets results in another delay, which by itself may not be meaningful, but in conjunction with other factors when moving voice over a data network can adversely affect the intelligibility of reconstructed voice. Because a hacker must not only intercept your voice packets but in addition must know the voice-compression algorithm, it is not a simple process to hear an unauthorized conversation. Because of this, in many situations you may wish to carefully consider the benefit of encryption prior to its use.

APPLICATION NOTE   Encryption adds to the delay of packets transporting digitized voice and should be employed only when absolutely necessary.

Authentication

The third major element of network security is verifying that the originator of a packet is the person he or she claims to be, a process more formally referred to as *authentication.* Although the sound of voice in a personal conversation may suffice to verify the originator of a call, when you connect an internal corporate network to a public packet network, there may be some data access requirements that will require authentication. If so, you will then have to consider the acquisition of equipment that can distinguish between the information transported in different types of packets and require authentication only for packets attempting to access predefined services on the private network. Now that you understand the rationale for transmitting voice over data networks and some of the potential problems, let's turn our attention to some of the key reasons you would consider adding a voice over data networking capability to your organization's network infrastructure (in addition to the economics associated with the technology). We'll look at a few of the applications that may by themselves justify adding this capability to your network infrastructure. However, prior to doing so a brief discussion of regulatory considerations and standards is in order.

Regulatory Considerations

While the transmission of voice over data networks provides a variety of productivity and economic advantages that make it a very desirable technology, readers should be aware of certain regulatory issues that can affect its implementation. These include national and international efforts aimed at precluding individual organizations from transmitting voice over their internal networks and preventing voice resellers that provide a telephone service via the use of gateways from competing with communications carriers.

Rationale

Economics is the primary reason for national and international regulations attempting to prevent or limit the ability of organizations to transmit voice over data networks. Over the past century, communications carriers invested hundreds of billions of dollars on a global basis in technology based on the use of 64-Kbps time slots to transport digitized voice. The ability to transport voice at data rates as low as 2.4 Kbps is more than competitive; it provides the eventual capability of relatively newly formed alternative communications carriers to put long-established organizations out of business. It is sort of like one widget manufacturer being able to undercut the cost of another by a factor of 8 or 16 or more!

National Events

At the national level, the Association of Telecommunications Carriers, an organization representing thousands of small telephone companies, petitioned the Federal Communications Commission (FCC) to prevent the establishment of voice calling over data networks, as their ability to earn long-distance revenue is curtailed while gateways tie up their local exchanges.

In addition, another interesting aspect of regulation involves the desire of local telephone companies to charge for the delivery of long-distance calls that are delivered to a subscriber of an Internet connection. If a friend or business associate uses MCIWorldcom, AT&T, Sprint, or another long-distance communications carrier to dial a telephone number where local access is provided by another carrier, the carrier that provides local access is rightly compensated for completing the call. Currently, in the wonderful world of Internet telephony, there is no mechanism for local access providers to be compensated, which rightly makes them angry. At the time this new edition was prepared, the FCC ruled that Internet calls represent long-distance calls; however, it remains to be seen what effect this will have on the ability of local access providers to be compensated for delivering such calls.

To understand the potential effect of charges for delivery, assume a local access provider bills calls at a nickel per minute. Vendors currently charging 4.9 cents per minute for Internet calls would go out of business because they could never earn a profit. However, for private networks based on the use of leased lines, the preceding local access delivery charge would not be applicable. Thus, a corporation that uses leased lines to form a private network or gain access to a public packet network would not be subject to local delivery charges.

International Events

At the international level, several countries have blocked access to Web sites that offer software for making international calls over the Internet. The latter situation occurred during June 1997 when the Czech Republic, Hungary, Iceland, Portugal, and Palau (an island in the South Pacific) made it unlawful for customers to access a Web site that provides software enabling voice calls to be placed over the Internet. In March 1999, Lebanon added a new wrinkle to the prevention of Internet telephony when it officially banned Internet service providers from offering overseas Internet calls to their subscribers. Since the software enables calls to be made at a cost of between 10 and 30 cents per minute, while long-distance companies in those countries charge between $2 and $4 per minute, the preceding actions could be considered one of self-preservation for the international long-distance service offered by certain national communications carriers. One vendor affected by this action asked the FCC and White House to intervene on the issue. While the potential effect of national and international actions against voice over data network applications is essentially anyone's guess, it is this author's opinion that restrictive regulations will eventually be self-defeating. Although voice over data networks are in their infancy, they represent a relatively easy-to-apply technology that is difficult to bar by the regulatory process. Instead of attempting to fight this technology, national and international communications carriers should be looking at methods to integrate the technology into their communications infrastructure. They might then be able to develop schemes to price the transmission of low-bit-rate digitized voice at a substantial discount from their regular tariff and thus encourage persons to use their facilities.

Standards

Standards can be considered the glue that enables different vendor products to interoperate. In the area of standards, voice over IP is still in its infancy, with many standards clearly lacking, thus forcing vendors to use other standards that may not be the most suitable for operation. Although voice over frame relay is presently more standardized due to the efforts of the Frame Relay Forum in developing Implementation Agreement (IA) II (covering numerous aspects of transporting voice over frame relay), there are still other areas that lack standardization. For example, frame relay providers have not standardized their service-level agreements (SLAs), how their prioritization occurs, or queuing methods used to support prioritization.

Currently, popular IP standards include the Real-Time Protocol (RTP), which involves the time-stamping and sequencing of packets; RSVP, which involves the reservation of bandwidth; and H.323, which represents an umbrella standard originally developed for conferencing but now embraced by many vendors because of control bandwidth utilization. In this book we will focus our attention upon each of those standards.

In addition to the previously mentioned standards, there are two evolving standards that, while extremely important for the success of Internet telephony, may not be necessary for an organization implementing a voice over IP capability. These two standards are the Open Settlement Protocol (OSP), which is designed to handle authorization, call routing, and call detail billing between ISPs; and iNOW!, promoted by several vendors to obtain interoperability among IP telephony platforms produced by different vendors.

1-4 Applications

When discussing potential and existing voice over data network applications, we are literally moving into a new dimension—akin to the way in which the advent of three-dimensional graphics revolutionized that industry. Table 1-2 lists five examples of voice over data network applications. We'll discuss them briefly to illustrate the potential of this relatively new technology.

Document Conferencing

Document conferencing enables multiple parties to verbally communicate while viewing the same document on their computer screens. Until recently document conferencing was based on the use of the public switched telephone network for voice communications, while software on multiple computers used the corporate network or the Internet to pro-

TABLE 1-2

Voice Over Data Network Applications

Document conferencing

Help desk access

Integrated call management

Order placement

Unified messaging

vide real-time document-editing capability. With the ability to transmit voice over data, it becomes possible to integrate voice and data communications requirements onto a common network infrastructure. This not only makes it simpler to coordinate software, but also eliminates the use of the PSTN, which could result in considerable savings, especially if document-conferencing audio and data are transported between international locations.

Help Desk Access

Imagine that a customer just bought your firm's latest software or hardware product. Suppose that during its installation the customer encounters a problem or has a question. Now further suppose that the installed hardware or software product generates an interface to the customer's favorite browser and, upon recognition that its PC is multimedia-ready, generates a screen displaying a message such as "click here to talk to our customer service representative." By clicking on an icon, the user's browser establishes a connection to the product help desk operated by your organization, which supports a digitized telephone application that enables the customer to verbally define the problem and seek assistance.

The preceding help desk operation represents a voice over data network application that makes good sense from both a customer satisfaction and an economic perspective. Such applications could forestall toll-free calls to your organization's help desk facility. In addition, since many organizations do not provide international toll-free access to their customer assistance or help desk, providing voice support via the Internet could be a marketing ploy that makes one product more valuable than an equivalent product whose manufacturer does not offer this feature. Thus, marketing and economic advantages accrue by providing voice access via a data network to an organizational help desk.

Integrated Call Management

Call management represents the routing of inbound and outbound calls using the most appropriate technique for the call to reach its intended destination. When you add the ability to transmit voice over data networks, you can integrate this capability with existing voice applications and transmission methods to obtain an integrated call management capability. For example, a PBX could be programmed to recognize the dial prefix 6 as the code to route calls from the local PBX to another location via an internal private IP network, a frame relay network, or the Internet.

Another call management technique that provides an interesting discussion topic is international callback. If you travel abroad and read the *International Herald Tribune* or scan some foreign newspapers you will more than likely note advertisements proclaiming "Cheap Callback," "Save 50% or more on international calls," and similar headings designed to get your attention. Although you might expect some sort of illicit scheme is in progress, vendors offering rates 50 percent or more below international calling rates are legitimate. They use a callback feature that lets subscribers dial their facility in the United States, which in many cases does not answer their call but reads their caller ID telephone number and dials back using much lower rates. On receiving the callback, the subscriber enters an access code and the desired telephone number, and the equipment in the United States generates a second telephone call to the destination. Since the cost of *both* U.S.-originated calls is significantly less than the cost of *one* international call originated in some overseas locations, a portion of the savings is passed along to the subscriber to encourage the use of callback.

To economize even more on the cost of international calls, many callback operators recently turned to voice-capable FRADs, using them on international circuits to transport up to 16 simultaneous calls over one 64-Kbps frame relay access line or on a leased 64-Kbps circuit. In fact, ACT Networks reported high sales of their voice-capable FRADs to callback operators due to the ability of their equipment to significantly reduce the cost of long-distance international calling.

Order Placement

Although in its infancy, the use of the Internet for ordering products ranging from books to bagels is literally exploding. The ability to communicate verbally with an order desk adds a new dimension to selling products over the Internet. Let's consider the manner in which products are currently sold and compare it to how they *could* be sold, using as an example the sale of coffee makers. Say you locate a World Wide Web page that displays a picture and description of a 12-cup coffee maker.

Let's assume you have a question concerning its filters. Normally, you might click on the e-mail icon that would generate a form with the company's e-mail address included in the "to" line. After filling out a message and clicking on the Send button, you would probably go on to check other sites, since you know the response to your query will be far from instantaneous. Now suppose that instead of clicking on an e-mail icon, you could click on a voice icon and directly communicate with a customer service representative who immediately answers your query and concludes with, "Can I process your order now?" This is obviously a more effective method for obtaining a sale.

Another possible variation of the use of voice for Internet order placement for potential customers who do not have an appropriate voice capability involves integrating an organization's call management capability with Web browsers' activity. For example, instead of clicking on a voice icon, the potential customer might also be offered the option to click on a Help icon that enables the user to enter his or her name and telephone number on the WWW page. This information is passed to the vendor, which results in the call management system dialing the number and connecting a customer representative to the dialed connection. For both methods discussed in this section, the end result is the use of voice in conjunction with data to assist potential customers and to hopefully improve the probability of closing a sale.

Unified Messaging

Unified messaging refers to the use of a system to manage all methods used to convey information, such as voice mail, e-mail, fax, and real-time voice. The addition of voice over data networks into a unified messaging system enables employees to make more effective use of all methods used to convey information. This is because it enables a common graphical user interface (GUI) to be used and learned and eliminates the need for users to spend additional time locating and retrieving messages from nonunified separate systems. In addition, by integrating voice over data network applications into a unified messaging system, the system can facilitate the use of voice application, such as real-time voice or voice mail that employees may use instead of dialing over the PSTN, resulting in both enhanced productivity and the cost avoidance associated with not having to leave real-time voice mail messages when the party called using the PSTN is not available.

1-5 Technological Success

Voice over data networks is similar to any new technology in that to be successful it must provide a certain level of customer satisfaction. We can gain an appreciation of that level of customer satisfaction by comparing telephone company circuit switching to packet switching and then turning our attention to what I call the *Rosetta stone for success*—the maximum delay you should strive to undercut prior to constructing a voice over data network transmission facility.

Circuit Switching Versus Packet Switching

Table 1-3 provides a comparison of circuit switching performed by the traditional telephone companies and packet switching. In examining the entries in Table 1-3, note that the pulse code modulation (PCM) used by telephone companies represents a "toll-quality" voice-digitization method that results in high-quality reconstructed voice. In comparison, most voice over data network equipment involves the use of low-bit-rate coders that may provide near-toll-quality reconstructed voice. However, because delays occur randomly on a packet network, the reconstruction of voice is subject to variable delays.

Although not indicated in Table 1-3, it is important to note that once you make a connection over the switched telephone network there is no nonplanned disconnection. In comparison, under periods of congestion, both routers and frame relay switches drop packets. Concerning the last entry in Table 1-3, call management features can include call waiting, call

TABLE 1-3

Comparing Circuit Swiching and Packet Switching

Parameter	Circuit Switching	Packet Switching
Dedicated bandwidth	Yes	No
Quality of service		
Voice quality	Toll-quality	Non-toll-quality
Delay latency	Minimal	Variable
Utilization level	Poor	High
Economics of Utilization	Low	High
Call management features	Numerous	Few

forwarding, caller ID, and unified billing. While most telephone companies market a full range of call management features, most voice over data network solutions presently provide few such features. In my opinion, successful packetized voice requires characteristics and features similar to those offered by the legacy telephone company.

The Rosetta Stone of Delay

Humans can endure approximately 250 milliseconds of delay before a voice conversation becomes awkward and perhaps intolerable. When voice is transmitted over a packet network, there are both fixed and variable delays that have to be considered. By understanding where these delays occur, you can consider different actions to ensure that latency on an end-to-end basis is below 250 ms; if you are not able to provide this capability, you would then want to consider temporarily abandoning your voice project until such time as you can ensure a reasonable degree of latency. Thus, understanding congestion and delay results in the Rosetta stone of implementing a voice over data network project.

Table 1-4 indicates the general range of fixed and variable packet network delays. In examining the entries in Table 1-4, note that the inter-

TABLE 1-4

Fixed and Variable Packet Network Delays

Cause	Delay in ms
Fixed Delays	
Compression (voice coding)	20—45
Interprocess at origin	10
Network access at origin	0.25—7
Network delay	20—100
Network egress at destination	0.25—7
Interprocess at destination	10
Jitter buffer (configurable)	10
Decompression (voice)	10
Fixed delay	90—199

For worst case a call can tolerate 250 – 80 to 250 – 199 or between 170 and 51 ms of variable delay.

process delays represent handoffs at routers and do not consider extra delays resulting from access list processing or encryption. Also note that network access and network egress delays are based on the line operating rate. For example, a relatively small voice packet might require 2.5 ms when access and egress occurs on a T1 line operating at 1.544 Mbps, while the delay could expand to 7 ms when access and egress occurs on a 56-Kbps line.

APPLICATION NOTE   Understanding the delays associated with access and egress lines, different voice-compression methods, and the network provides the ability to consider different techniques to reduce overall latency.

Now that we have an appreciation for the constraints that govern our ability to successfully implement voice over data network technology, let's turn our attention to the actual methods used by the technology. Since these methods are the focus of the remainder of this book, we will conclude this chapter with a preview of the topics covered in succeeding chapters.

1-6   Topic Preview

You can use the information presented in this section by itself or in conjunction with the index in this book to focus your attention on a particular topic of interest. You can read topics in the order presented, or you can tailor your reading by going directly to the material that corresponds to your specific requirements.

The Internet Protocol

In Chapters 2 through 4 we will turn our attention to obtaining a basic understanding of IP and frame relay networks and the characteristics and encoding of human voice. Some readers may find they are already familiar with the information in these chapters. If this applies to you, you may wish to skip or simply skim their contents. For other readers, the information presented in these chapters will provide a basic foundation concerning the operation of the two key types of packet networks for which the transmission of voice is both economical and practical based on the recent development of a variety of hardware and software products covered in this book.

In Chapter 2, we will discuss TCP/IP, including how the IP stack is constructed, applications that reside on the stack, and why basic IP operations lack predictability. We will also discuss the role of RSVP and how its incorporation by different networks can be expected to eventually provide a level of predictability required to transport voice over public IP networks, as well as the use of RTP and the H.323 standard.

Frame Relay

Chapter 3 will examine the rationale for frame relay with an overview of basic X.25 packet switching, noting strengths and weaknesses that have resulted from the rapidly growing market for frame relay products and services. Following the overview, we will focus our attention directly on frame relay. We'll learn how private networks are connected to this public network, define various frame relay parameters, and discuss the conventional flow of information through this type of network, including how frames can be lost and how higher layers in the protocol stack operate to ensure that frame loss does not translate into the actual loss of data.

Voice Basics

No book on voice over data networks would be complete without a detailed discussion of the characteristics, digitization, and encoding of voice, which is the focus of Chapter 4. In this chapter, we will examine the characteristics of human speech, which will serve as a foundation for discussing how voice can be analyzed and synthesized. As we discuss different voice-digitization methods, we will also cover different international standards, laying the foundation for information presented in the next three chapters.

Telephone Operations

The transmission of voice over a data network requires the selection of equipment that supports the signaling method used by organizational PBXs. Thus, it is important to obtain an appreciation of how a telephone call is routed between PBXs or over the switched telephone network and the different types of signals required to establish a call. This information is presented in Chapter 5.

Voice over IP

As previously mentioned, there are two types of packet networks applicable for transporting voice. One type of packet network is based on the IP protocol and can range in scope from private IP networks to the mother of all public IP networks—the Internet. In Chapter 6, we will turn our attention to the transmission of voice over IP—based networks, examining different techniques used to accomplish this function, including the operation of equipment from different vendors, the economics associated with transporting voice over IP, and how this technology can be integrated into existing and proposed private networks that in turn are connected over an internal corporate IP network or via a public IP network like the Internet.

Voice over Frame Relay

Continuing our practical examination concerning the transmission of voice over data networks, Chapter 7 concludes this book with a discussion of the transmission of voice over frame relay networks. After reviewing different techniques developed to perform this operation with some degree of network predictability, we will turn our attention to the operation of appropriate vendor equipment, the economics associated with this technology, and the various network integration issues you should consider. This chapter will give you an understanding of the practical issues associated with moving voice over frame relay networks, including the use of currently available equipment and its integration into existing and planned private networks.

Management

No book covering the transmission of voice over IP and frame relay would be complete without considering management tools and techniques. At the conclusion of this book we will examine several management issues and evaluate the use of different tools to help you decide prior to investing in equipment and/or line facilities whether the technology will work at an acceptable level.

IP and Related Protocols

Any discussion concerning the transmission of voice over IP networks requires a degree of knowledge concerning the Internet Protocol. Since IP represents one component of the TCP/IP family, it is difficult to discuss IP as a separate entity unto itself. Recognizing this fact and the fact that the actual implementation of voice over IP requires knowledge about setting IP addresses and subnet masks and pointing your computer to the correct gateway and domain name server, this chapter is designed to provide readers with practical information necessary to configure and operate any IP device to include voice over IP products. In addition, because knowledge of the operation of the TCP/IP protocol stack provides us with the ability to understand how certain activities adversely affect the flow of data through an IP network, we will be able to note the effect of certain network-related operations upon latency. This in turn will provide us with the ability to consider certain network adjustments that may make an otherwise unworkable voice over IP transmission method workable.

In this chapter, we will focus our attention on IP; however, since it represents a component of the TCP/IP family, we will first review the layered structure of that family with respect to the International Standards Organization (ISO) Open System Interconnection (OSI) Reference Model. Once this is accomplished, we will turn our attention to network and data link layer addressing. In doing so, we will also examine the method by which Ethernet and Token Ring frames are transmitted on local area networks and the manner in which TCP/IP uses 32-bit IP addresses. This information will then be used to discuss the need for a mapping or translating mechanism between data link and network addresses, which is accomplished through the Address Resolution Protocol (ARP). We will also discuss the role of the Domain Name Server and its use, as well as the structure of the Internet Protocol. In addition, since IP does not operate by itself, we will also move up the protocol stack, turning our attention to the transport layer and the role of the Transmission Control Protocol (TCP) and the User Datagram Protocol (UDP), as well as several evolving protocols that provide a mechanism to transport voice over IP in an effective and efficient manner.

2-1 The TCP/IP Family

The Transmission Control Protocol/Internet Protocol (TCP/IP) represents a family of protocols that evolved over a period of time to perform predefined tasks. The roots of TCP/IP can be traced to the U.S. Defense

Department Advanced Research Projects Agency (DARPA), which developed a series of communications protocols for transporting data between geographically separated networks via a common network infrastructure known as the Advanced Research Projects Agency Network (ARPANET). ARPANET research formed the basis for the development of the *Internet*, which, when used with a capital I, refers to a collection of interconnected networks.

Although ARPANET and the evolution of the Internet predate the development of the ISO's OSI Reference Model, the TCP/IP protocol family is a layered network architecture that is very similar in structure to the OSI Reference Model. Thus, prior to discussing the TCP/IP protocol family, let's quickly review the OSI Reference Model.

The OSI Reference Model

The OSI Reference Model was developed as a mechanism to subdivide networking functions into logical groups of related activities referred to as *layers*. Each network layer was designed to represent a collection of independent tasks that would be self-contained from a programming point of view but that could easily interact with another layer developed by the same programmers or even persons from a different company who followed the rules associated with creating a layer's set of tasks. Thus, another goal of the OSI Reference Model was to create an open system architecture that would facilitate interoperability between different vendor products.

Figure 2-1 illustrates the general structure of the OSI Reference Model and the relationship of each layer in the model to the other layers in the

Figure 2-1

The 7-layer OSI Reference Model.

Layer number	Layer
7	Application
6	Presentation
5	Session
4	Transport
3	Network
2	Data link
1	Physical

model. The lower four layers in the model focus on tasks required for the transmission of data. Those tasks include the creation of fields to transport data so each entity can be correctly routed to its destination via the use of addressing information, as well as the use of cyclic redundancy checking to enable the contents of each entity to be verified. In comparison, the upper layers are concerned with the manner in which the application interface is presented to the user and are not concerned with the manner by which data gets to the application. Let's briefly examine the tasks performed at each layer.

The Physical Layer

The lowest layer of the OSI Reference Model is the physical layer. This layer is responsible for the mechanical, electrical, functional, and procedural mechanisms required for the transmission of data. It can be considered to represent the physical connection or cabling of a device to a transmission medium. When we examine the TCP/IP protocol suite we will note that it does not define a physical layer. Because the TCP/IP protocol suite actually commences at the network layer, it depends on the data link layer associated with other protocols, such as Ethernet and Token Ring, for data delivery. Because such data link protocols include a physical layer, TCP/IP in effect uses the physical layer of the data link protocol for data delivery.

The Data Link Layer

The data link layer is responsible for the manner in which a device gains access to the medium specified in the physical layer. In addition, the data link layer is also responsible for the manner in which data is formatted into defined fields and the correction of any errors occurring during a transmission session. Common examples of data link protocols include the various "flavors" of Ethernet, including Fast Ethernet and Gigabit Ethernet as well as Token Ring.

The Network Layer

The network layer is responsible for the physical routing of data. To accomplish this task, the network layer performs addressing, routing, switching, sequencing of data packets, and flow control, with the latter used as a mechanism to prevent data from overflowing buffers and becoming lost during periods of network congestion. In the TCP/IP protocol suite, the Internet Protocol (IP) represents a network layer protocol. IP version 4 (IPv4) and the emerging IP version 6 (IPv6) use 32- and 128-bit addresses to identify source and destination interfaces. In addition, all routing on an IP network occurs by routers examining the destination IP address, checking its table entries, and making a routing decision concerning to which port to output a packet with a particular destination IP address.

The Transport Layer

The transport layer is responsible for ensuring that the transfer of information occurs correctly once a route is established through a network. This means the transport layer is responsible for controlling the communications session between network nodes once a path is established by the network control layer. This control includes verifying that transmitted data matches the data received.

The TCP/IP protocol suite includes two transport layer protocols, the Transmission Control Protocol (TCP) and the User Datagram Protocol (UDP). As we will note later in this chapter, TCP is a connection-oriented protocol that requires handshaking prior to the transmission of data, while UDP is a connectionless protocol that operates on a best-effort delivery basis.

The Session Layer

The session layer represents the first of three upper layers of the OSI Reference Model. This layer is responsible for establishing and terminating data streams between network nodes. Since each data stream can represent an independent application, the session layer is also responsible for coordinating communications between different applications that require communications.

The Presentation Layer

The presentation layer is responsible for isolating the application layer's data format from the lower layers in the OSI Reference Model. To accomplish this task, the presentation layer provides data transformation, formatting, and syntax conversion, converting application data into a common format for transmission and reversing the process for inbound or received data.

The Application Layer

At the top of the OSI Reference Model, the application layer functions as a window through which the application gains access to all of the services of the model. In the reverse direction, the application layer displays received information in an appropriate format. In the TCP/IP protocol suite, applications can be considered to represent a combination of layers 5 through 7 of the OSI Reference Model. Prior to turning our attention to the TCP/IP family and its relationship to the OSI Reference Model, let's briefly review the movement of data within the protocol stack and how the attachment and removal of protocol headers facilitate the layering process.

Data Flow

Within an ISO network, each layer from top to bottom appends appropriate heading information to packets of information flowing within the network while removing the heading information added by a lower layer when the data flow is in the reverse direction. In this manner layer n interacts with layer $n - 1$ as data flows through the network. Figure 2-2 illustrates the data flow within an OSI Reference Model network for an outgoing frame. For a received frame, the process would be reversed, with headers stripped or removed as the packet flows up the reference model.

It should be noted that when referring to the data link layer, the unit of transportation is referred to as a *frame*. At higher layers, the information field contained in several layer 2 frames may be combined into one larger packet. When transmission flows onto a local area network the contents of a packet whose information field exceeds the length of the information field of a LAN frame will be subdivided into segments, enabling multiple frames to transport the contents of a packet. In this book, we will refer to *frames* when a unit of transmission flows at the data link layer, while that same unit of information or grouping of units of information into a single entity flowing at and above the network layer will be referred to as a *packet*.

Figure 2-2

Data flow of outgoing packets within an OSI Reference Model.

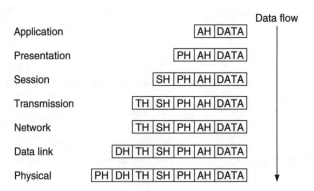

The TCP/IP Protocol Family

The TCP/IP protocol family was developed as a layered network architecture, even though its development predated the OSI Reference Model. In fact, the TCP/IP protocol suite represents the first major effort to develop a layered network architecture. As you might surmise, its development effort achieved a considerable degree of recognition, as it represents the only protocol suite used for transmission on the Internet.

Although TCP/IP predates the OSI Reference Model, at the lower layers there is a general one-to-one correspondence between the TCP/IP protocol suite and the OSI Reference Model. At the upper layers there is considerable divergence between the two, as most TCP/IP applications roughly correspond to the upper set of OSI Reference Model layers from layer 5, the session layer, through layer 7, the applications layer.

Figure 2-3 provides a general indication of the correspondence between the TCP/IP family of protocols and the OSI Reference Model. At the data link layer, the referenced figure shows how TCP/IP resides on top of various data link layers that are not in actuality part of the TCP/IP family of protocols, enabling TCP/IP to transport data between local area networks that are located in close proximity to one another or geographically separated from one another by a few miles or by thousands of miles.

Figure 2-3
A portion of the TCP/IP protocol family.

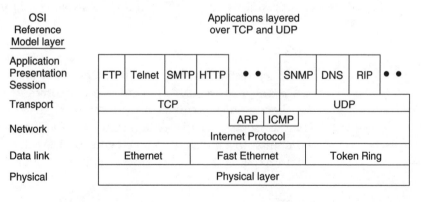

Legend:
FTP = File Transfer Protocol
SMPT = Simple Mail Transport Protocol
HTTP = HyperText Transmission Protocol
SNMP = Simple Network Management Protocol
DNS = Domain Name Service
ARP = Address Resolution Protocol

The protocols that reside above the transport layer and roughly correspond to the upper three layers of the OSI Reference Model represent some well-known applications as well as a special transport protocol mechanism developed to deliver audio and video packets. Thus, prior to focusing our attention on the lower layers of the TCP/IP protocol stack, let's briefly examine some applications and audio and video transport protocols that correspond to the upper layers of the OSI Reference Model.

FTP

The File Transfer Protocol (FTP) is a mechanism for moving data files between hosts via a TCP/IP network. FTP operates as a client-server process, with the client issuing predefined commands to the server to navigate its directory structure and to upload and download files to and from the server. Examples of client commands include GET to retrieve a file and MGET to retrieve a series of files that could be specified using a wild card such as PAY.*, where the asterisk is used to specify "any extension."

Two types of FTP access are supported by servers: anonymous and via a previously established account. Anonymous access allows any person accessing the server to enter the USER ID "anonymous" to access the server or a predefined directory on the server. When "anonymous" is used as the USER ID, no password checking is employed, although many FTP servers request the user to enter his or her e-mail address in the password field. If access is via a previously established account, password checking is employed.

Telnet

Telnet represents another TCP/IP client-server application. This application is designed to enable a client to access a remote computer as though the client were a terminal directly connected to the remote computer. There are several versions of Telnet, with TN3270 providing the client with the ability to emulate different types of IBM 3270—type terminals to obtain access to IBM mainframes operating TCP/IP.

SMTP

The Simple Mail Transport Protocol (SMTP) provides the data transportation mechanism for electronic messages to be routed over a TCP/IP network. This protocol is completely transparent to the user since there are no user commands that govern the transfer of electronic mail via SMTP.

HTTP

The HyperText Transmission Protocol (HTTP) represents a relatively recent addition to the TCP/IP family in comparison to the previously mentioned protocols. HTTP is the protocol used by Web browsers to communicate with Web servers and vice versa.

SNMP

The Simple Network Management Protocol (SNMP) provides the mechanism to transport status messages and statistical information about the operation and utilization of TCP/IP devices. In addition, under SNMP, devices can generate alarms when certain predefined thresholds are reached. Under SNMP, the client-server processes are altered, with a server becoming a network manager that controls clients, referred to as *agents*. Although the previously described members of the TCP/IP family use TCP as a transport mechanism, SNMP uses the User Datagram Protocol (UDP).

DNS

The Domain Name Service (DNS) provides a very important service by enabling "near-English" host computer names (such as ftp.xyz.com to indicate an FTP server operated by the XYZ commercial firm) to be translated into a unique IP address that represents the physical address of the interface of the FTP server on a network (in this case, the XYZ Corporation). Similar to SNMP, DNS uses the User Data Protocol (UDP) as a transport mechanism.

RTP

The Real-Time Transport Protocol (RTP) represents a special type of protocol developed to support applications requiring the real-time delivery of data such as audio and video. RTP has evolved from the Visual Audio Tool (VAT) protocol, which was used to support the first working voice-conferencing program carried over the Internet. Although many Internet telephony products use proprietary audio coding techniques and protocols, a number of products use RTP as a "transport" protocol on top of UDP. In addition, other vendors, including Microsoft and Netscape, have committed to using RTP. Because of its evolving role in the transportation of audio and video information on TCP/IP networks, we will examine this protocol in some detail later in this chapter.

Transport Protocol Overview

Returning to Figure 2.3, you will note that the familiar TCP/IP applications correspond roughly to the upper three layers of the OSI Reference Model. You will also note that there are two transport protocols in the TCP/IP protocol suite: the Transmission Control Protocol (TCP) and the User Datagram Protocol (UDP). Some applications, such as FTP, Telnet, SMTP, and HTTP, were developed to use TCP, while other applications, such as DNS and RTP, were developed to use UDP. Thus, it is important to note the differences between each transport protocol.

TCP

TCP was developed to provide a reliable, connection-oriented service that supports end-to-end transmission reliability. To accomplish this task, TCP supports error detection and correction as well as flow control to regulate the flow of packets through a network. Error checking requires the computation of a cyclic redundancy check (CRC) algorithm at a network node based on the contents of a packet and a comparison of the computed CRC against the CRC carried in the packet. The CRC carried in a packet is created by the same algorithm applied to the contents of the packet by the originating node. If the two CRCs do not match, an error is presumed to have occurred and the packet is corrected by retransmission. The request to retransmit and the retransmission process delay the flow of the packet through a TCP/IP network. Thus, although TCP is used by the File Transfer Protocol (FTP), Telnet, Simple Mail Transport Protocol (SMTP), and other applications where the integrity of data is a primary concern, it can result in unacceptable delays when transporting digitized voice and is rarely, if ever, used for voice transmission. In fact, some developers of voice over IP products prefer to drop a delayed packet containing digitized voice information and either use a period of silence or attempt to predict the contents of the packet based on a previously received packet rather than accept a delayed packet that results in a distortion to a portion of reconstructed speech.

Another characteristic of TCP that deserves mention is the fact that it is a connection-oriented protocol. This means a session between originator and receiver has to be established prior to data transfer being permitted. Although TCP is rarely, if ever, used to transport digitized voice, its connection-oriented capability results in its use for call control operations. This explains why just about all voice over IP products use

TCP for call control, including the setup of a call, while UDP is used to transfer the digitized conversation. Now that we have a general appreciation for the operational characteristics of TCP, let's turn our attention to UDP.

UDP

The User Datagram Protocol (UDP) was developed to provide an unreliable, connectionless transport service. Before we are tempted to make a nasty comment concerning its unreliability, we should note that this is not necessarily bad and adds a degree of flexibility to the protocol family. That is, if reliability is required, a higher layer, such as the application layer, can be used to ensure that messages are properly delivered.

A second property of UDP that warrants a discussion is the fact that it is a connectionless protocol. This means that instead of requiring a session to be established between two devices, transmission occurs on a best-effort basis. That is, functions associated with connection setup and the exchange of status information as well as flow control procedures are avoided. While this removes a considerable amount of overhead, there is a price paid for obtaining this capability. To understand this price, we must digress a bit and look at the two methods in which the TCP/IP protocol suite routes data between network nodes: by the establishment of virtual circuits and the use of datagrams.

VIRTUAL CIRCUIT TRANSMISSION

When transmission occurs via a virtual circuit, a temporary path is established between source and destination locations. The establishment of a virtual circuit requires each network node to maintain a table of addresses and destination routes to enable a path to be established for the duration of the communications session. This fixed path, which is established for the duration of the transmission session, can be considered as a logical linking of nodes on a temporary basis. Once the communications session is completed, the previously established path is relinquished.

The key advantage associated with the transmission of data via a virtual circuit results from the use of the same path for all transmission. Although this precludes the use of an alternate route if a circuit outage occurs on the virtual path, it also precludes the need for data sequencing. This means that the possibility of duplicate data packets occurring is eliminated, resulting in an easier mechanism for the management of data flow between source and destination.

APPLICATION NOTE Within an IP network, routers periodically transfer the contents of their routing tables, during which time the transmission of data, including voice-digitized packets, is suspended. Because edge routers commonly are connected only to an ISP router, you should consider configuring the edge router for static routing. This will preclude the transfer of router table entries and the resulting delays to traffic such table transfers cause.

DATAGRAM TRANSMISSION

Datagram transmission results in the ability of transmission at the network layer to avoid the need to establish a fixed path between source and destination. Instead, packets are subdivided into units of data referred to as *datagrams*. Datagrams are transmitted via a broadcasting technique in which they are forwarded onto every port other than the port on which they were received. While this transmission technique results in duplicate traffic occurring on some network paths, it can considerably simplify network routing. This simplification results from the fact that since there are no fixed paths between nodes, there is no requirement to support a recovery method to reestablish a path if a circuit or intermediate node should fail.

Datagram transmission represents a connectionless or best-effort type of transmission. Transmitting datagrams onto all ports other than the port data is received on is a relatively easy process to implement. Figure 2-4 illustrates the transmission of a datagram on a three-node network from LAN A to LAN B. Note that router A forwards datagrams to routers

Figure 2-4
Datagram transmission can result in duplicate packets arriving at certain network locations.

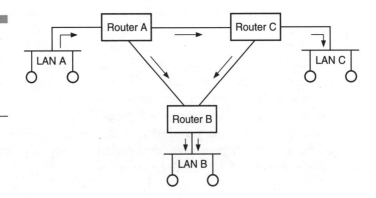

B and C. Router C in turn transmits the datagram to LAN C as well as to router B. Thus, two datagrams arrive at router B. This means that duplicate datagrams will appear on LAN B and router C, and LAN C will receive datagrams that are not destined for those locations, thus requiring a higher level of network utilization than if a virtual circuit method of transmission were used.

As previously discussed, most implementations of voice over IP networks use TCP to establish communications between network devices, while UDP is used for the flow of digitized data. Although UDP is used to transport datagrams, the actual transfer occurs via the use of virtual circuits as an IP header added to the UDP header for routing purposes. Although datagram transmission was popular during the 1960s, its generation of duplicate datagrams more than negates its ease of implementation, and all known network operations now avoid this transmission method.

2.2   The Internet Protocol

Now that we have an appreciation of TCP and UDP, let's turn to the network layer and examine the Internet Protocol. To understand the relationship of TCP and UDP to IP, let's examine Figure 2-5, which illustrates the formation of a series of headers as application data is transported via a TCP/IP network onto a local area network, with the latter resulting in the

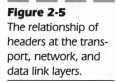

Figure 2-5
The relationship of headers at the transport, network, and data link layers.

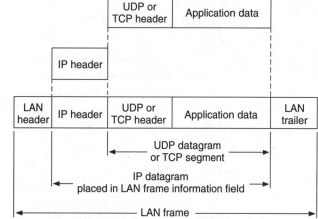

use of a LAN frame as the transport mechanism. Each of the headers is employed to facilitate the transfer of information at the indicated network layer. For example, the TCP header will contain information that allows this layer 4 protocol to track the sequence of the delivery of datagrams so they can be placed in their correct order if they arrive out of sequence.

In examining Figure 2-5, note that the layer 4 protocol results in either a TCP or UDP header appended to application data. When passed to the IP layer, an IP header is added that includes the use of source and destination fields in the form of IP addresses, enabling data to flow from source to destination. At layer 2, which commonly represents a local area network transmission facility, a LAN header such as those formed by Ethernet or Token Ring will prefix the IP header, and a LAN trailer will be added as a suffix, with the trailer typically consisting of cyclic redundancy check characters that provide a mechanism for the LAN to determine if a frame of data is received without errors.

As we will note later in this section, LANs use 6-byte addresses assigned by the Institute of Electrical and Electronics Engineers (IEEE), which results in each station on a node having a unique 48-bit address. In comparison, IP uses a 32-bit address assigned by the Internet Network Information Center (InterNIC), whose composition, as we will shortly note, identifies a network and a station or an interface node on a network. Thus, there is no correlation between a data link address and an IP address, which means that when IP enables data to be correctly delivered to a LAN, another mechanism is required to enable data to reach a destination that uses a different addressing scheme. That mechanism is the Address Resolution Protocol (ARP), which we will discuss after we cover the composition of the IP header and examine IP addressing in detail.

The IP Header

Figure 2-6 illustrates the fields contained in the IP header. Note that the header contains a minimum of 20 bytes of data, and the width of each field is shown with respect to a 32-bit word. To obtain an appreciation for the functions performed by the IP header, let's examine the functions of the fields in the header.

Vers Field

The Vers field consists of 4 bits that identify the version of the IP protocol used to create the datagram. The current version of the IP protocol is 4 and the next generation IP protocol is assigned version number 6.

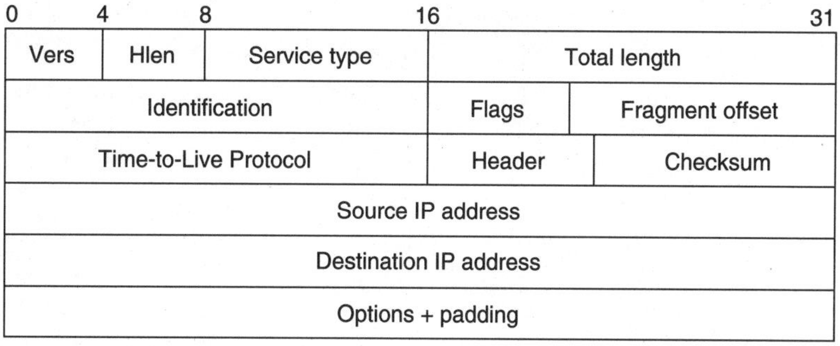

Figure 2-6
The IP header.

0   4   8   16   31

Vers	Hlen	Service type	Total length
Identification		Flags	Fragment offset
Time-to-Live Protocol		Header	Checksum
Source IP address			
Destination IP address			
Options + padding			

Hlen and Total Length Fields

The Hlen field is 4 bits in length. This field, which follows the Vers field, indicates the length of the header in 32-bit words. In comparison, the total length field indicates the total length of the datagram, including its header and higher-layer information. Since 16 bits are used for this field, an IP datagram can be up to 2^{16}, or 65,536, octets in length.

Service Type Field

The purpose of the service type field is to indicate how the datagram is processed. This field is also referred to as the Type of Service (TOS) byte and its composition is illustrated as follows:

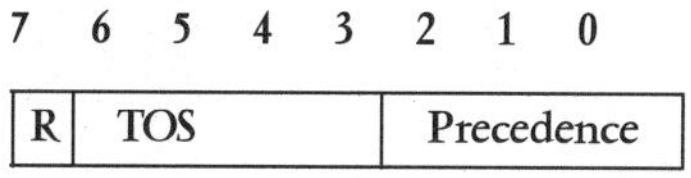

```
7   6   5   4   3   2   1   0
```

R	TOS	Precedence

where

R represents reserved.

Precedence provides eight levels, 0 to 7, with 0 normal and 7 the highest priority.

Type of Service (TOS) indicates how the datagram is handled:

0000	Default
0001	Minimize monetary cost
0010	Maximize reliability
0100	Maximize throughput
1000	Minimize delay
1111	Maximize security

Although the use of the Service Type field provides a priority mechanism for the routing of IP datagrams, it is important to note that the IP standard does not mandate the specific actions that are caused by the values of the precedence bits. However, the Service Type field provides a mechanism for mapping LAN priority settings into an IP network, enabling end-to-end precedence to be obtained if routers along the path support the use of the field settings in a common manner.

When a router runs short of memory it will discard some datagrams. If an application sets the TOS field to a value of 0010, the packets transporting the application will be less eligible for discard than other packets.

APPLICATION NOTE For transporting voice over IP, you will normally be more concerned with the effect of delay than with that of periodic packet dropping, because real-time voice cannot be transmitted. For this reason, you should configure your application to set the TOS field in the Service Type byte to a value of 1000, which minimizes delay.

Although a TCP/IP-based network is difficult to configure so that its reserved bandwidth is reliable and predictable enough to transport digitized voice, the Service Type byte provides a mechanism to overcome certain shortcomings. For example, by mapping TOS field values into ATM classes of service, it becomes possible to use IP to transport digitized voice over an ATM backbone with a quality of service that provides both reliability and predictability. When we cover voice over IP networking in Chapter 6, we will examine the previously mentioned method of transporting digitized voice contained in IP datagrams over an ATM backbone.

Identification and Fragment Offset Fields

The identification field enables each datagram or fragmented datagram to be identified. If a datagram is fragmented into two or more pieces, the fragment offset field specifies the offset in the original datagram of the data being transported. Thus, this field indicates where a fragment belongs in the complete message. The actual value in this field is an integer that corresponds to a unit of 8 octets, providing an offset in 64-bit units.

Time-to-live Field

The time-to-live (TTL) field specifies the maximum time that a datagram can exist. This field is used to prevent a misaddressed datagram from endlessly wandering the Internet or a private IP network. Since an exact time is difficult to measure, it is commonly used as a hop count field. That is, routers decrement the value of this field by 1 as a datagram flows between networks. If the value of the field reaches 0, the datagram is discarded.

Flags Field

The flags field contains 2 bits that are used to denote how fragmentation occurs, with a third bit in the field presently unassigned. The setting of one of the two fragmentation bits can be used as a direct fragment control mechanism, since a value of 0 indicates the datagram can be fragmented, while a value of 1 indicates it cannot be fragmented. The second bit is set to 0 to indicate that a fragment in a datagram is the last fragment, while a value of 1 indicates that more fragments follow.

Protocol Field

The purpose of the protocol field is to identify the higher-level protocol used to create the message carried in the datagram. For example, a value of decimal 6 would indicate TCP, while a value of decimal 17 would indicate UDP.

Source and Destination Address Fields

The source and destination address fields are both 32 bits in length. Each address represents both a network and a host computer on the network. Since it is extremely important to understand the composition and formation of IP addresses to correctly configure devices connected to an IP network, we will turn our attention to this topic. Once we understand IP addressing, we will then examine the address resolution process required to enable layer 3 packets that use IP addresses to be correctly delivered via layer 2 addressing.

IP Addressing

In this section, we turn our attention to the mechanism that enables TCP and UDP packets to be transmitted to unique or predefined groups of hosts. That mechanism is the addressing method used by the Internet Protocol, commonly referred to as IP addressing. The current version of the Internet Protocol is version 4. The next-generation Internet Protocol, which is currently being operated on an experimental portion of the Internet, is referred to as version 6 and noted by the mnemonic IPv6.

Since there are significant differences in the method of addressing used by each version of the Internet Protocol, we will cover both versions in this section. First we will focus our attention on the addressing used by IPv4. Once we have an appreciation for how IPv4 addresses are formed and used, we will turn our attention to IPv6. By first covering the addressing used by IPv4, we will have the ability to discuss address-compatibility methods that will allow IPv6 addresses to be used to access devices configured to respond to IPv4 addresses.

Overview

IP addresses are used by the Internet Protocol to identify distinct device interfaces such as interfaces that connect hosts, routers, and gateways to networks as well as to route data to those devices. Each device interface in an IP network must be assigned to a unique IP address so that it can receive communications addressed to it. This means that a multiport router will have one IP address for each of its network connections.

IPv4 uses 32-bit binary numbers to identify the source and destination addresses in each packet. This address space provides 2,294,967,296 distinct addressable devices—a number that exceeded the world's population when the Internet was initially developed. However, the proliferation of personal computers, the projected growth in the use of cable modems that require individual IP addresses, and the fact that every interface on a gateway or router must have a distinct IP address have contributed to a rapid depletion of available IP addresses. Recognizing that hundreds of millions of Chinese and Indians may eventually be connected to the Internet and also recognizing the potential for cell phones and even pacemakers to communicate via the Internet, the Internet Activities Board (IAB) in 1992 commenced work on a replacement for the current version of IP. Although the addressing limitations of IPv4 were of primary concern, the efforts of the IAB resulted in a new protocol with a number of significant improvements over IPv4, including the use of 128-bit addresses for source and destination devices. This new version of IP, which is referred to as IPv6, was finalized in 1995 and is currently being evaluated on an experimental portion of the Internet. Since this section is concerned with IP addressing, we will cover the addressing schemes, address notation, host address restrictions, and special addresses associated with both IPv4 and IPv6.

IPv4

The Internet Protocol was officially standardized in September 1981. Included in the standard was a requirement for each host connected to an

IP-based network to be assigned a unique, 32-bit address value for each network connection. This requirement resulted in some networking devices, such as routers and gateways, that have interfaces to more than one network, as well as host computers with multiple connections to the same or different network being assigned a unique IP address for each network interface. Figure 2-7 illustrates two bus-based Ethernet LANs connected by using a pair of routers. Note that each router has two interfaces, one represented by a connection to a LAN and the second represented by a connection to a serial interface that provides router-to-router connectivity via a wide area network. Thus, each router will have two IP addresses, one assigned to its LAN interface and the other assigned to its serial interface. By assigning addresses to each specific device interface, this method of addressing enables packets to be correctly routed when a device has two or more network connections.

THE BASIC ADDRESSING SCHEME

When the IP was developed, it was recognized that hosts would be connected to different networks and that those networks would be interconnected to form an internet. Thus, in developing the IP addressing scheme, it was also recognized that a mechanism would be required to identify a network as well as a host connected to a network. This recognition resulted in the development of a two-level addressing hierarchy, as illustrated in Figure 2-8.

Figure 2-7
IP network addressing requires a unique 32-bit network number to be assigned to each device network interface.

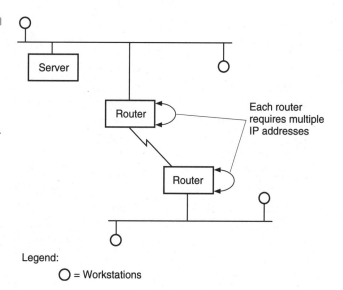

Legend:
O = Workstations

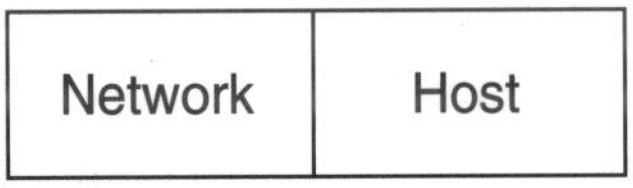

Network	Host

Figure 2-8
The two-level IP addressing hierarchy. Under the two-level IP addressing hierarchy, the 32-bit IP address is subdivided into network and host portions. The composition of the first 4 bits of the 32-bit word specifies whether the network portion is 1, 2, or 3 bytes in length, resulting in the host portion being either 3, 2, or 1 bytes in length.

Under the two-level IP addressing scheme, all hosts on the same network must be assigned the same network prefix, but they must have a unique host address to differentiate one host from another. Similarly, two hosts on different networks must be assigned different network prefixes; however, the hosts can have the same host address.

ADDRESS CLASSES

When IP was standardized, it was recognized that the use of a single method of subdivision of the 32-bit address into network and host portions would be wasteful with respect to the assignment of addresses. For example, if all addresses were split evenly, resulting in 16 bits for a network number and 16 bits for a host number, the result would allow a maximum of 65,534 ($2^{16} - 2$) networks with up to 65,534 hosts per network. In that case, the assignment of a network number to an organization that had only 100 computers would result in a waste of 65,434 host addresses, which could not then be assigned to another organization. Recognizing this problem, the designers of IP decided to subdivide the 32-bit address space into different address classes, resulting in five address classes being defined. Those classes are referred to as Class A through Class E.

Class A addresses are for very large networks, while Class B and Class C addresses are for medium-size and small networks, respectively. Class A, B, and C addresses incorporate the two-level IP addressing structure previously illustrated in Figure 2-8. Class D addresses are used for IP multicasting, where a single message is distributed to a group of hosts dispersed across a network. Class E addresses are reserved for experimental use. Both Class D and Class E addresses do not incorporate the two-level IP addressing structure used by Class A through Class C addresses.

Figure 2-9 illustrates the five IP address formats, including the bit allocation of each 32-bit address class. Note that the address class can be easily

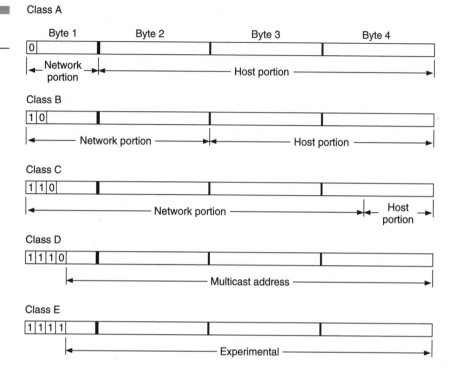

Figure 2-9
IP address formats.

determined by examining the values of one or more of the first 4 bits in the 32-bit address. Once an address class is identified, the subdivision of the remainder of the address into the network and host address portions is automatically noted. Let us examine the composition of the network and host portion of each address when applicable, as doing so will provide some basic information that can be used to indicate how such addresses are used. Concerning the allocation of IP addresses, it should be noted that specific class addresses are assigned by the InterNIC.

Class A. A Class A IP address is defined by a 0-bit value in the high-order bit position of the address. This class of addresses uses 7 bits for the network portion and 24 bits for the host portion of the address. As a result of this subdivision, 128 networks can be defined, with approximately 16.78 million hosts capable of being addressed on each network. Due to the relatively small number of Class A networks that can be defined and the large number of hosts that can be supported per network, Class A addresses are primarily assigned to large organizations and countries that have national networks.

Class B.   A Class B network is defined by the setting of the 2 high-order bits of an IP address to 10. The network portion of a Class B address is 14 bits in width, while the host portion is 16 bits wide. This results in the ability of Class B addresses to be assigned to 16,384 networks, with each network having the ability to support up to 65,536 hosts. Due to the manner by which Class B addresses are subdivided into network and host portions, such addresses are normally assigned to relatively large organizations with tens of thousands of employees.

Class C.   A Class C address is identified by the first 3 bits in the IP address being set to the value 110. This results in the network portion of the address having 21 bits, while the host portion of the address is limited to 8-bit positions.

The use of 21 bits for a network address enables approximately 2 million distinct networks to be supported by the Class C address class. Since 8 bits are used for the host portion of a Class C address, this means that each Class C address can theoretically support up to 256 hosts. Due to the subdivision of network and host portions of Class C addresses, they are primarily assigned for use by relatively small networks, such as organizational LANs. Since it is quite common for many organizations to have multiple LANs, it is also quite common for multiple Class C addresses to be assigned to organizations that require more than 256 host addresses but are not large enough to justify a Class B address. Although Class A through Class C addresses are commonly assigned by the InterNIC to Internet service providers for distribution to their customers, Class D and Class E addresses represent special types of IP addresses.

Class D.   A Class D IP address is defined by the assignment of the value 1110 to the first 4 bits in the address. The remaining bits are used to form what is referred to as a *multicast address*. Thus, the 28 bits used for that address enable approximately 268 million possible multicast addresses.

Multicast is an addressing technique that allows a source to send a single copy of a packet to a specific group through the use of a multicast address. Through a membership registration process, hosts can dynamically enroll in multicast groups. Thus, the use of a Class D address enables up to 268 million multicast sessions to simultaneously occur throughout the world.

Until recently, the use of multicast addresses was relatively limited; however, its use is increasing considerably, as it provides a mechanism to conserve bandwidth, which is becoming a precious commodity.

To understand how Class D addressing conserves bandwidth, consider a digitized audio or video presentation routed from the Internet onto a private network for which users working at 10 hosts on the network wish to receive the presentation. Without a multicast transmission capability, 10 separate audio or video streams containing audio would be transmitted onto the private network, with each stream consisting of packets containing 10 distinct host-destination addresses. In comparison, through the use of a multicast address, one data stream would be routed to the private network.

Since an audio or video stream can require a relatively large amount of bandwidth in comparison to interactive query-response client-server communications, the ability to eliminate multiple data streams via multicast transmission can prevent networks from being saturated. This capability can also result in the avoidance of session timeouts when client-server sessions are delayed due to high-LAN-utilization levels, providing another reason for the use of multicast transmission.

Class E.   The fifth address class defined by the IP address specification is a reserved address class known as Class E. A Class E address is defined by the first four bits in the 32-bit IP address having the value of 1111. This results in the remaining 28 bits being capable of supporting approximately 268.4 million addresses. Class E addresses are restricted for experimentation.

DOTTED-DECIMAL NOTATION

Recognizing that the direct use of 32-bit binary addresses is both cumbersome and unwieldy, a technique more acceptable for human use was developed. That technique is referred to as *dotted-decimal notation* in recognition of the fact that the technique developed to express IP addresses occurs via the use of four decimal numbers separated from one another by decimal points.

Dotted-decimal notation divides the 32-bit Internet Protocol address into four 8-bit (1-byte) fields, with the value of each field specified as a decimal number. That number can range from 0 to 255 in bytes 2, 3, and 4. In the first byte of an IP address, the setting of the first 4 bits in the byte that is used to denote the address class limits the range of decimal values that can be assigned to that byte. For example, from Figure 2-9, a Class A address is defined by the setting of the first bit position in the first byte to 0. Thus, the maximum value of the first byte in a Class A address is 127. Table 2-1 summarizes the numeric ranges for Class A through Class C IP addresses.

To illustrate the formation of a dotted-decimal number, let's first focus on the decimal relationship of the bit positions in a byte. Figure

TABLE 2-1

Class A Through
Class C Address
Characteristics

Class	Length of network address (bits)	First number range (decimal)
A	8	0—127
B	16	128—191
C	24	192—223

2-10 indicates the decimal values of the bit positions within an 8-bit byte. Note that the decimal value of each bit position corresponds to 2^n, where n is the bit position in the byte. Using the decimal values of the bit positions shown in Figure 2-10, let's assume the first byte in an IP address has its bit positions set to 01100000. Then the value of that byte expressed as a decimal number becomes 64 + 32, or 96. Now let's assume that the second byte in the IP address has the bit values 01101000. From Figure 2-10, the decimal value of that binary byte is 64 + 32 + 8, or 104. Let's further assume that the last 2 bytes in the IP address have the bit values 00111110 and 10000011. Then the third byte would have the decimal value 32 + 16 + 8 + 4 + 2, or 62, while the last byte would have the decimal value 128 + 2 + 1, or 131.

Based on the preceding, the dotted-decimal number 96.104.62.131 is equivalent to the binary number 01100000011010000011111010000011. Obviously, it is easier to work with (and remember) four decimal numbers separated by dots than a string of 32 bits.

RESERVED ADDRESSES

There were three blocks of IP addresses originally reserved for networks that would not be connected to the Internet. Those address blocks were defined in RFC 1918, Address Allocation for Private Internets, summarized in Table 2-2.

128	64	32	16	8	4	2	1

Figure 2-10

Decimal values of bit positions in a byte. The decimal value of the bit positions in a byte corresponds to 2n where n is the bit position that ranges from 0 to 7.

TABLE 2-2	Address Blocks
Reserved IP Addresses for Private Internet Use	10.0.0.0—10.255.255.255
	172.16.0.0—172.31.255.255
	192.168.0.0—192.168.255.255

Both security considerations as well as difficulty in obtaining large blocks of IP addresses resulted in many organizations using some of the addresses listed in Table 2-2 while connecting their networks to the Internet. Since the use of any private Internet address by two or more organizations connected to the Internet would result in addressing conflicts and the unreliable delivery of information, those addresses are not directly used. Instead, organizations commonly install a proxy firewall that provides address translation between a large number of private Internet addresses used on the internal network and a smaller number of assigned IP addresses. Not only does this technique allow organizations to connect large internal networks to the Internet without being able to obtain relatively scarce Class A or Class B addresses, but the proxy firewall hides internal addresses from the Internet community. This provides a degree of security, because any hacker who attempts to attack a host on your network actually has to attack your organization's proxy firewall.

APPLICATION NOTE   The translation of IP addresses by a router or firewall adds a slight delay to packets as they flow through the device. If your voice over IP application is stretched toward the maximum amount of tolerable delay, you may wish to consider placing stations that depend upon the application on their own network, which avoids the necessity of network address translation and its delay.

NETWORKING BASICS

As previously noted, each network has a distinct network prefix, and each host on a network has a distinct host address. When two networks are interconnected by the use of a router, each router port that represents an interface is assigned an IP address that reflects the network to which it is connected. Figure 2-11 illustrates the connection of two networks via a router, indicating possible address assignments. Note that the first decimal number (192) of the 4-byte dotted-decimal numbers associated with two hosts on the network on the left portion of Figure 2-11 denotes a Class C

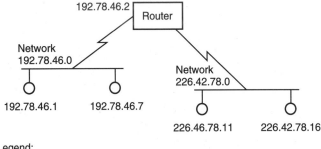

Figure 2-11
Router connections
to networks require
an IP address for each
connection.

address. This is because 192 decimal is equivalent to 11000000 binary. Since the first 2 bits are set to the bit value 11, Figure 2-11 indicates a Class C address. Also note that the first 3 bytes of a Class C address indicate the network, while the fourth byte indicates the host address. Thus, the network shown in the left portion of Figure 2-11 is denoted as 192.78.46.0, with device addresses that can range from 192.78.46.1 through 192.78.46.254.

In the lower right portion of Figure 2-11, two hosts are shown connected to another network. Note that the first byte for the 4-byte dotted-decimal number assigned to each host and the router port is decimal 226, which is equivalent to binary 11100010. Since the first 2 bits in the first byte are again set to 11, the second network also represents the use of a Class C address. Thus, the network address is 226.42.78.0, with device addresses on the network ranging from 226.42.78.01 to 226.42.78.254.

Although it would appear that 256 devices could be supported on a Class C network (0 through 255 used for the host address), in actuality the host-portion field of an IP address has two restrictions. First, the host-portion field cannot be set to all-0 bits. This is because an all-0 host number is used to identify a base network or subnetwork number. Concerning the latter, we will shortly discuss subnetworking. Second, an all-1 host number represents the broadcast address for a network or subnetwork. Due to these restrictions, a maximum of 254 devices can be defined for use on a Class C network. Similarly, other network classes have the previously discussed addressing restrictions, which reduces the number of distinct addressable devices that can be connected to each type of IP network by two. Since, as previously explained, an all-0 host number identifies a base network, the two networks shown in Figure 2-11 are shown as 192.78.46.0 and 226.42.78.0.

Subnetting. One of the problems associated with the use of IP addresses is the necessity to assign a distinct network address to each network. This can result in the waste of many addresses as well as a considerable expansion in the use of router tables. To appreciate these problems, let's return to Figure 2-11, which illustrates the connection of two Class C networks via a router.

Assume each Class C network supported 29 workstations and servers. Adding an address for the router port, each Class C network would use 30 out of 254 available addresses. Thus, the assignment of two Class C addresses to an organization that needs to support two networks with a total of 60 devices would result in 448 ($254 \times 2 - 60$) available IP addresses in effect being wasted. In addition, routers would have to recognize two network addresses instead of one. When this situation is multiplied by numerous organizations requiring multiple networks, the effect on routing tables becomes more pronounced, resulting in extended search times as routers sort through their routing tables to determine an appropriate route to a network. Because of these problems, RFC 950 became a standard in 1985. That standard defines a procedure to subnet or divide a single Class A, B, or C network into subnetworks.

Through the process of subnetting, the two-level hierarchy of Class A, B, and C networks shown in Figure 2-9 is turned into a three-level hierarchy. In doing so, the host portion of an IP address is divided into a subnet portion and a host portion. Figure 2-12 provides a comparison between the two-level hierarchy initially defined for Class A, B, and C networks and the three-level subnet hierarchy.

Through the process of subnetting, a Class A, B, or C network address can be divided into different subnet numbers, with each subnet used to identify a different network internal to an organization. Since the network portion of the address remains the same, the route from the Internet to any subnet of a given IP network address is the same. This means that routers within the organization must be able to differentiate between different subnets, but routers outside the organization consider all subnets as one network.

Figure 2-12
Comparing the three-level subnet hierarchy to the two-level network class hierarchy.

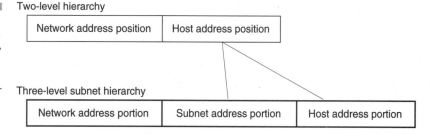

The subnet process facilitates the use of IP addresses by reducing waste and decreasing routing table entries. Let's examine the process. In doing so, we will discuss the concept of masking and the use of the subnet mask, both of which are essential to the extension of the network portion of an IP address.

To illustrate the concept of subnetting, let's return to the two networks illustrated in Figure 2-11: networks 192.78.46.0 and 226.42.78.0. Let's assume that instead of two networks geographically separated from one another at two distinct locations, we require the establishment of five networks at one location. Let's further assume that each of the five networks will support a maximum of 15 stations. Although your organization could apply for four additional Class C addresses, doing so would waste precious IP address space since each Class C address supports a maximum of 254 devices. In addition, if your internal network were connected to the Internet, entries for four additional networks would be required in a number of routers in the Internet in addition to your organization's internal routers. Instead of requesting four additional Class C addresses, let's use subnetting, dividing the host portion of the IP address into a subnet number and a host number. Since we need to support five networks at one location, we must use a minimum of 3 bits from the host portion of the IP address as the subnet number. Since a Class C address uses one 8-bit byte for the host identification, this means that a maximum of five bit positions can be used (8 – 3) for the host number. Assuming we intend to use the 192.78.46.0 network address for our subnetting effort, we would construct an extended network prefix based on combining the network portion of the IP address with its subnet number.

Figure 2-13 illustrates the creation of five subnets from the 192.78.46.0 network address. The top entry in Figure 2-13, labeled "Base network," represents the Class C network address with a host address byte field set to all 0s. Since we previously decided to use 3 bits from the host portion of the Class C IP address to develop an extended network prefix, the five entries in Figure 2-13 below the base network entry indicate the use of 3 bits from the host position in the address to create extended prefixes that identify

Figure 2-13
Creating extended network prefixes via subnetting.

Base network:	11000000.01010000.00101110.00000000 = 192.78.46.0
Subnet #0:	11000000.01010000.00101110.000_00000 = 192.78.46.0
Subnet #1:	11000000.01010000.00101110.001_00000 = 192.78.46.32
Subnet #2:	11000000.01010000.00101110.010_00000 = 192.78.46.64
Subnet #3:	11000000.01010000.00101110.011_00000 = 192.78.46.96
Subnet #4:	11000000.01010000.00101110.100_00000 = 192.78.46.128

five distinct subnets created from one IP Class C address. To the Internet, all five networks appear as the network address 192.78.46.0, with the router at an organization responsible for directing traffic to the appropriate subnet. It is important to note that externally (i.e., to the Internet) there is no knowledge that the dotted-decimal numbers shown in the right column represent distinct subnets. This is because the Internet views the first byte of each dotted-decimal number and notes that the first 2 bits are set. Doing so tells routers on the Internet that the address is a Class C address for which the first 3 bytes represent the network portion of the IP address and the fourth byte represents the host address. Thus, to the outside world, address 192.78.46.32 would not be recognized as subnet 1. Instead, a router would interpret the address as network 192.78.46.0, with host address 32. Similarly, subnet four would appear as network address 192.78.46.0, with host address 128. However, within an organization, each of the addresses listed in the right column in Figure 2-13 would be recognized as a subnet. To visualize this dual interpretation of network addresses, consider Figure 2-14, which illustrates the Internet versus the private network view of subnets.

As we might logically assume from our prior discussion of Class C addresses, any address with the network prefix 192.78.46.0 will be routed to the corporate router. However, although we noted how subnet addresses are formed, we have yet to discuss how we assign host addresses to devices connected to different subnets or how the router can break down a subnet address so it can correctly route traffic to an appropriate subnet. Thus, we need to expand our discussion of host addressing on subnets to include the role of the subnet mask.

Host Addresses on Subnets.   We previously subdivided the host portion of a Class C address into a 3-bit subnet field and a 5-bit host field. Since the host field of an IP address cannot contain all 0 bits or all 1 bits, the use of 5 bits in the host portion of each subnet address means that each subnet can support a maximum of $2^5 - 2$, or 30 addresses. Thus, we could use host

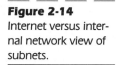

Figure 2-14
Internet versus internal network view of subnets.

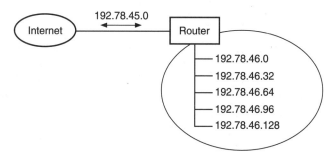

▬▬ ▬▬ ▬▬ ▬▬
Figure 2-15
Assigning host
addresses by subnet.

Subnet #3:	11000000.01010000.00101110.01100000 = 192.78.45.96
Host #1:	11000000.01010000.00101110.01100001 = 192.78.46.97
Host #2:	11000000.01010000.00101110.01100010 = 192.78.46.98
Host #3:	11000000.01010000.00101110.01100011 = 192.78.46.99
	• • • • • •
Host #30:	11000000.01010000.00101110.01111110 = 192.78.46.126

addresses 1 through 30 on each subnet. Figure 2-15 illustrates the assignment of host addresses for subnet 3, whose creation was previously indicated in Figure 2-13. In examining Figure 2-15, note that we start with the subnet address 192.78.46.96, for which the first 3 bits in the fourth byte of the address are used to indicate the subnet. We use the remaining 5 bits to define the host address on each subnet. Thus, the address 192.78.46.96 represents the third subnet, while addresses 192.78.46.97 through 192.78.46.126 represent hosts 1 through 30 that can reside on subnet 3.

Although we now have an appreciation for creating subnets and host addresses on subnets, we haven't yet discussed how devices on a private network recognize subnet addressing. For example, if a packet arrives at an organizational router with the destination address 192.78.46.97, how does the router know to route that packet onto subnet 3? The answer to this question involves what is known as the *subnet mask.*

THE SUBNET MASK

The subnet mask represents a mechanism that enables devices on a network to determine the separation of an IP address into its network, subnet, and host portions. To accomplish this, the subnet mask consists of a sequence set to 1 bit that denotes the length of the network and subnet portions of the IP network address associated with a network. For example, let's assume our network address is 192.78.46.96, and we want to develop a subnet mask that can be used to identify the extended network. Since we previously used 3 bits from the host portion of the IP address, the subnet mask would become 11111111.11111111.11111111.11100000.

Similar to the manner in which IP addresses can be expressed using dotted-decimal notation, we can also express subnet masks using that notation. Doing so, we can express the subnet mask as 255.255.255.224.

The subnet mask tells the device examining an IP address which bits in the address should be treated as the extended network address consisting of network and subnet addresses. Then the remaining bits that are not set in the mask indicate the host on the extended network address. However, how does a device determine the subnet of the destination address? Since the subnet mask indicates the length of the extended network, including the network and subnet fields, knowing the length of the network portion of the address provides a device with the ability to determine the number of bits in the subnet field. Once this is accomplished, the device can determine the value of those bits, which indicates the subnet. To illustrate this concept, let's use the IP address 192.78.46.97 and the subnet mask 255.255.255.224, with the latter used to define a 27-bit extended network. The relationship between the IP address and the subnet mask is shown in Figure 2-16.

Since the first 2 bits in the IP address are set, this indicates a Class C address. Since a Class C address consists of 3 bytes used for the network address and 1 byte for the host address, this means the subnet must be 3 bits in length (27 – 24). Thus, bits 25 through 27, which are set to 011 in the IP address, identify the subnet as subnet 3. Since the last 5 bits in the subnet mask are set to 0, this means that those bit positions in the IP address identify the host on subnet 3. Since those bits have the value 00001, this means the IP address references host 1 on subnet 3 on network 192.78.46.0.

APPLICATION NOTE Although modern routers are based on relatively fast microprocessor technology, it is important to remember that most networks include routers manufactured three, four, or even five years ago. Although they may provide a high level of support for traditional data transfer operations, if you are using subnetting, the extra cycles may add several milliseconds of delay that could represent the figurative straw that breaks the back of a real-time voice transport application. Instead of replacing the router, you might want to consider placing stations requiring real-time voice transport on their own network, thus avoiding the extra cycles associated with subnet processing.

CONFIGURATION EXAMPLES

When configuring a workstation or server to operate on a TCP/IP network, most network operating systems require you to enter a minimum of three IP addresses and an optional subnet mask or mask bit setting. The

Figure 2-16
The relationship between the IP address and the subnet mask.

IP address: 192.78.46.97   11000000.01010000.00101110.01100001
Subnet mask: 255.255.255.244   11111111.11111111.11111111.11100000

Extended network address

three IP addresses are as follows: (1) the IP address assigned to the workstation or server, (2) the IP address of the gateway or router responsible for relaying packets with a destination that is not on the local network to a different network, and (3) a name resolver that is referred to as the Domain Name Server (DNS). The latter is a computer responsible for translating near-English mnemonic names assigned to computers into IP addresses.

Figure 2-17 illustrates the first configuration screen in a series of screens displayed by the NetManage Chameleon Custom program. The IP Configuration screen illustrated in Figure 2-17, which is displayed by selecting an appropriate entry from the Setup menu, provides you with the ability to enter an IP address that is assigned to the workstation or server running the Chameleon TCP/IP protocol stack. The configuration screen also provides you with the ability to enter the number of subnet mask bits, which the program then converts into an appropriate decimal number. Table 2-3 compares the number of subnet bits to host bits and indicates the resulting decimal mask.

In examining the screen displayed in Figure 2-17, note that simply clicking on different tabs results in the display of new configuration screens. For example, Figure 2-18 illustrates the Name Resolution Configuration screen. Note that you would enter the address of one or more

Figure 2-17

The NetManage Chameleon IP Configuration screen enables you to set the IP address of the host running the program's TCP/IP protocol stack.

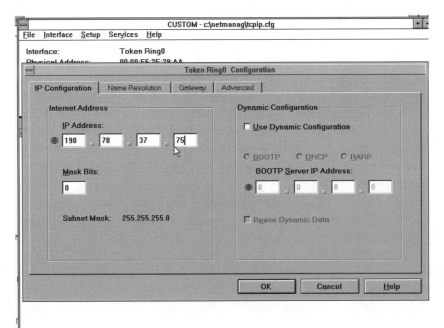

TABLE 2-3

Subnet Masks

Subnet Bits	Host Bits	Decimal Mask
0	8	0
1	7	28
2	6	192
3	5	224
4	4	240
5	3	248
6	2	252
7	1	254
8	0	255

domain servers as well as the name assigned to your host and its DNS domain name. In this example, the host name entered was "gil," while the DNS domain name entered was "feds.gov." This informs the domain server at the indicated address that requests to access the host with the near-English mnemonic gil.feds.gov should be routed to the IP address previ-

Figure 2-18
The Chameleon Name Resolution screen enables a host to be configured so that it can be identified by its near-English mnemonic name. The specification of the IP address of a domain server also enables the use of near-English mnemonic names to access other computers.

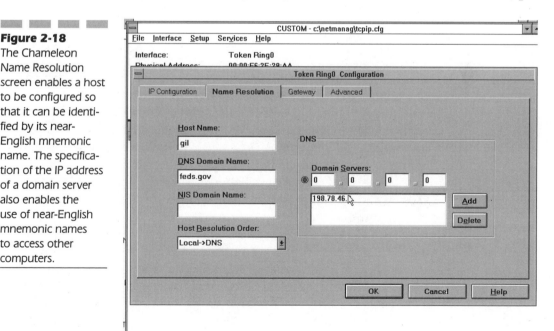

ously entered into the IP Configuration screen. Thus, this display screen provides network users with the ability to have their computers identified by a name rather than by a more cumbersome IP address. The specification of the IP address of at least one domain server also enables the use of near-English mnemonic names to access other computers. This is because the computer now knows to send the name-to-IP address resolution requests to the indicated domain server IP address.

CLASSLESS NETWORKING

As previously noted, the use of individual Class A, B, and C addresses can result in a significant amount of unused address space, which make them very inefficient to use. Recognizing the inefficiency associated with Class A, B, and C addressing, another method was developed to assign IP addresses to organizations. This method results in a more efficient assignment of IP addresses, because the number of distinct IP addresses is more closely tied to the requirements of an organization. Since the technique does away with network classes, it is commonly referred to as *classless networking.*

Under classless networking, an organization is assigned a number of bits to use as the local part of its addresses that best correspond to the number of addresses it needs. For example, if an organization requires 4000 IP addresses, it would be given 12 bits (4096 distinct addresses) to use as the local part of its address. The remaining 20 bits in the 32-bit address space are then used as a prefix to denote what is referred to as a *supernetwork.* To denote the network part of a classless network, the forward slash (/) is used, followed by the number of bits in the prefix. Thus, the previously mentioned classless network would be denoted as /20.

Currently, address allocations used for classless networking are taken from available Class C addresses. Thus, obtaining a 20-bit prefix is equivalent to obtaining 16 continuous Class C addresses. Table 2-4 lists the classless address blocks that can be assigned from available Class C address space.

In addition to providing a better method for allocating IP addresses, classless addressing enables a router to forward traffic to an organization using a single routing entry. Due to the tremendous growth of the Internet, classless addressing provides a more efficient mechanism for locating entries in router tables. This is because one classless entry can replace up to 129 Class C addresses, enabling a router to locate entries faster as it searches its routing tables. Thus, you can expect the use of classless addressing to increase as a mechanism to both extend the availability of IP addresses and enable routers to operate more efficiently as we wait for IPv6 to be deployed.

TABLE 2-4

Classless Network Address Assignments

Network Part	Local Bits	Equivalent Number of Class C Addresses	Distinct Addresses
124	8	1	256
123	9	2	512
122	10	4	1024
121	11	8	2048
120	12	16	4096
119	13	32	8192
118	14	64	16284
117	15	128	32768

IPv6

IPv6 was developed as a mechanism to simplify the operation of the Internet Protocol, provide a mechanism for adding new operations as they are developed through a header daisy chain capability, add built-in security and authentication, and extend source and destination addresses to an address space that could conceivably meet every possible addressing requirement for generations. The latter is accomplished through an expansion of source and destination addresses to 128 bits and is the focus of this section.

ADDRESS ARCHITECTURE

IPv6 is based on the same architecture used in IPv4, resulting in each network interface requiring a distinct IP address. The key differences between IPv6 and IPv4 with respect to addresses are the manner in which an interface can be identified and the size and composition of the address. Under IPv6, an interface can be identified by several addresses to facilitate routing and management. In comparison, under IPv4, an interface can be assigned only one address. Concerning address size, IPv6 uses 128 bits, or 96 more bits than an IPv4 address.

ADDRESS TYPES

IPv6 addresses include unicast and multicast, which were also included in IPv4. In addition, IPv6 adds a new address category known as *anycast*. Although an anycast address identifies a group of stations similarly to a multicast address, a packet with an anycast address is delivered to only one station, the nearest member of the group. The use of anycast addressing can be expected to facilitate network restructuring while minimizing the amount of configuration changes required to support a new network structure. This is because you can use an anycast address to reference a group of routers, and the alteration of a network by stations using anycast addressing would enable them to continue to access the nearest router without a user having to change the address configuration of his or her workstation.

ADDRESS NOTATION

Since IPv6 addresses consist of 128 bits, a mechanism is required to facilitate their entry as configuration data. The mechanism used is to replace those bits with eight 16-bit integers separated by colons, each integer being represented by four hexadecimal digits. For example,

6ACD:00001:00FC:B10C:0001:0000:0000:001A

To facilitate the entry of IPV6 addresses, you can skip the leading 0s in each hexadecimal component. That is, you can write 1 instead of 0001 and 0 instead of 0000. Thus, this ability to suppress 0s in each hexadecimal component would reduce the previous network address to the following:

6ACD:1:FC:B10C:1:0:0:1A

Under IPv6, a second method of address simplification was introduced: the double colon (::). Inside an address a set of consecutive null 16-bit numbers can be replaced by two colons. Thus, the previously reduced IP address could be further reduced as follows:

6ACD:1:FC:B10C:1::1A

It is important to note that the double colon can be used only once inside an address. This is because the reconstruction of the address requires the number of integer fields in the address to be subtracted from 8 to determine the number of consecutive fields of zero value the double colon represents. The use of two or more double colons would create ambiguity that would not allow the address to be correctly reconstructed.

ADDRESS ALLOCATION

The use of a 128-bit address space provides a high degree of address-assignment flexibility beyond that available under IPv4. IPv6 addressing enables Internet service providers to be identified and has the ability to identify local and global multicast addresses, private-site addresses for use within an organization, hierarchical geographical global unicast addresses, and other types of addresses. Table 2-5 lists the initial allocation of address space under IPv6.

The Internet Assigned Numbers Authority (IANA) was assigned the task of distributing portions of IPv6 address space to regional registries around the world, such as the InterNIC in North America, RIPE in Europe, and

TABLE 2-5

IPv6 Address Space Allocation

Allocation	Prefix (binary)	Fraction of address space
Reserved	0000 0000	$1/256$
Unassigned	0000 0001	$1/256$
Reserved for NSAP alloation	0000 001	$1/128$
Reserved for IPX allocation	0000 010	$1/128$
Unassigned	0000 011	$1/128$
Unassigned	0000 1	$1/32$
Unassigned	0001	$1/16$
Unassigned	001	$1/8$
Provider-based unicast address	010	$1/8$
Unassigned	011	$1/8$
Reserved for geographic-based unicast address	100	$1/8$
Unassigned	101	$1/8$
Unassigned	110	$1/8$
Unassigned	1110	$1/16$
Unassigned	1111 0	$1/32$
Unassigned	1111 10	$1/64$
Unassigned	1111 110	$1/128$
Unassigned	1111 1110 0	$1/512$
Link-local use addresses	1111 1110 10	$1/1024$
Site-local use addresses	1111 1110 11	$1/1024$
Multicast addresses	1111 1111	$1/256$

APNIC in Asia. To illustrate the planned use of IPv6 addresses, let's turn our attention to what will probably be the most common type of IPv6 address—the provider-based address.

Provider-based Addresses.   The first official distribution of IPv6 addresses will be accomplished through the use of provider-based addresses. Based on the initial allocation of IPv6 addresses as shown in Table 2.5, each provider-based address will have the 3-bit prefix 010. That prefix will be followed by fields identifying the registry that allocated the address, the service provider, and the subscriber. The latter field actually consists of three subfields: a subscriber ID that can represent an organization and variable network and interface identification fields used in a similar manner to IPv4 network and host fields. Figure 2-19 illustrates the initial structure for a provider-based address.

Special Addresses.   Under IPv6, there are five special types of unicast addresses that were defined, of which one deserves special attention. That address is the version 4 address, which was developed to provide a migration capability from IPv4 to IPv6.

In a mixed IPv4 and IPv6 environment, devices that do not support IPv6 will be mapped to version 6 addresses using the following form:

0:0:0:0:0:FFFF:w.x.y.z

Here w.x.y.z represents the original IPv4 address. Thus, IPv4 addresses will be transported as IPv6 addresses through the use of the IPv6 version 4 address format. This means that an organization with a large number of workstations and servers connected to the Internet has only to upgrade its router to support IPv6 addressing when IPv6 is deployed. Then it can gradually upgrade its network on a device-by-device basis to obtain an orderly migration to IPv6. Now that we have an appreciation for IPv4 and IPv6 addressing, let's turn our attention to the address resolution process

Figure 2-19
Provider-based
address structure.

Prefix	Registry ID	Provider ID	Subscriber ID	Subnet ID	Station ID

Legend:

Prefix	= 3 bits set to 010
Registry	= 5 bits identifies organization that allocated the address
Provider	= 24 bits with 16 used to identify ISP and 8 used for future extensions
Subscriber	= 32 bits with 24 used to identify the subscriber and 8 for extension
Subnet	= 16 bits to identify the subnetwork
Station	= 48 bits to identify the station

prior to exploring the TCP and UDP headers and the relatively recently developed Real-Time Transport Protocol.

ADDRESS RESOLUTION

The physical address associated with a local area network workstation is often referred to as its *hardware* or *media access control* (MAC) *address.* In actuality, that address can be formed via software to override the burned-in address on the network adapter card, a technique referred to as *locally administrated addressing.* When the built-in hardware address is used, this addressing technique is referred to as *universally administrated* addressing, as it represents a universally unique address whose creation we will shortly discuss. For both techniques, frames that flow at the data link layer use 6-byte source and destination addresses formed either via software or obtained from the network adapter.

Figure 2-20 illustrates the formats for both Ethernet and Token Ring frames. Both networks were standardized by the IEEE and use 6-byte source and destination addresses. The IEEE assigns blocks of addresses six hex characters in length to vendors that represent the first 24 bits of the 48-bit field used to uniquely identify a network adapter card. The vendor then encodes the remaining 24 bits, or six hex character positions, to identify the adapter manufactured by the vendor. Thus, each Ethernet and Token Ring adapter has a unique hardware of burned-in identifiers that denote the manufacturer and the adapter number. If an organization

Figure 2-20
Ethernet and Token Ring frame formats.

Ethernet frame format

Preamble (1)	Start of frame delimiter (7)	Destination address (6)	Source address (6)	Type/ length (2)	Information (46 to 1500)	FCS (4)

Token Ring frame format

Starting delimiter (1)	Access control (1)	Frame control (1)	Destination address (1)	Source address (6)	Routing information (optional)

Variable information	FCS (4)	Ending delimiter (1)	Frame status (1)

Legend:
FCS = Frame check sequence
(*n*) = *n* bytes represents field length

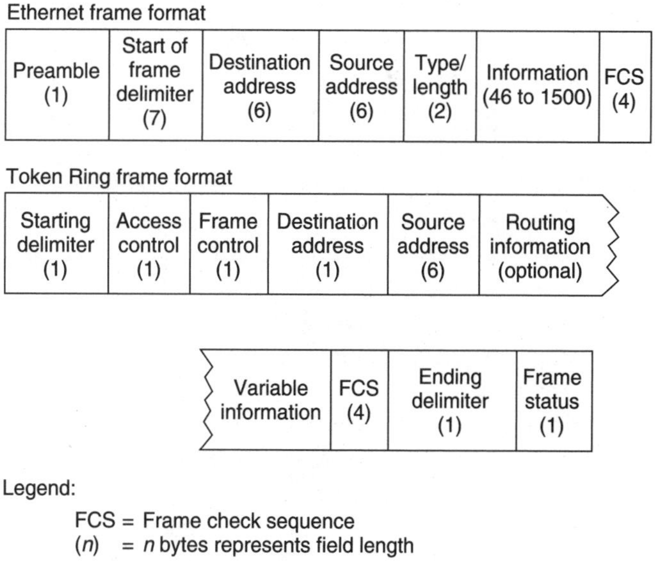

decides to override the hardware address, it can do so via software; however, a 48-bit address must still be specified for each station address.

When an Ethernet or Token Ring station has data to transmit, it encodes the destination address and source address fields with 48-bit numbers that identify the layer 2 locations on the network to receive the frame and the layer 2 device that is transmitting the frame. In comparison, at the network layer, IP uses a 32-bit address that has no relation to the MAC or layer 2 address. Thus, a common problem associated with the routing of an IP datagram to a particular workstation on a local area network involves the delivery of the datagram to its correct destination. This delivery process requires an IP device that needs to transmit a packet via a layer 2 delivery service to obtain the correct MAC or layer 2 address so it can take a packet and convert it into a frame for delivery. In the opposite direction, a workstation must be able to convert a MAC address into an IP address. Both of these address-translation problems are handled by protocols developed to provide an address resolution capability. One protocol, known as the Address Resolution Protocol (ARP), translates an IP address into a hardware address. The Reverse Address Resolution Protocol (RARP), as its name implies, performs a reverse translation, or mapping, converting a hardware layer 2 address into an IP address.

Operation.   To obtain a general appreciation for the operation of ARP, let's assume one computer user located on an Ethernet network wants to transmit a datagram to another computer located on the same network. The first computer would transmit an ARP packet that would be carried as an Ethernet broadcast frame to all stations on the network. Thus the packet would be transported to all devices on the Ethernet LAN. The packet would contain the destination IP address, which is known because the computer is transmitting the IP address to a known location. Another field in the ARP packet used for the hardware address would be set to all 0s, as the transmitting station does not know the destination hardware address. Each device on the Ethernet LAN will read the ARP packet as it is transmitted as a broadcast frame. However, only the station that recognizes that it has the destination field's IP address will copy the frame off the network and respond to the ARP request. When it does, it will transmit an ARP reply in which its physical address is inserted in the ARP address field that was previously set to 0.

To illustrate the necessity to constantly transmit ARP packets as well as to lower the utilization level of the LAN, the originator will record received information in a table known as an ARP *cache*, allowing subsequent datagrams with previously learned correspondences between IP addresses and MAC addresses to be quickly transmitted to the appropriate hardware address on the network. Thus, ARP provides a well-thought-out methodology for equating physical hardware addresses to IP's logical addresses and allows IP addressing at layer 3 to occur independently from LAN addressing at layer 2.

APPLICATION NOTE   Many routers and workstations run operating systems that dynamically update the ARP cache. This means that old entries are purged to make space available for new entries. This also means that if an entry for a voice gateway is purged, and then the layer 2 address requires resolution for an inbound packet transporting digitized voice, there will be a delay as a router attempts to resolve the layer 3 address to a layer 2 address so it can transmit the packet to the gateway.

To avoid ARP delays to devices that operate on digitized voice packets, consider configuring permanent ARP entries in your router that support communications to such devices. Doing so will eliminate the delay associated with the address resolution protocol and may shave a few additional milliseconds off end-to-end communications.

Now that we have an appreciation for IP addressing and the method by which IP addresses are equated to hardware layer 2 addresses, let's again focus our attention on layer 4 of the TCP/IP protocol suite. This time we will focus on the headers used by TCP and UDP and discuss the benefits and problems associated with their use as a transport protocol for time-sensitive information.

2.3   TCP and UDP Headers

Both TCP and UDP represent layer 4 transport protocols. As discussed in the first section in this chapter, there are significant differences between the functionality of each transport protocol. TCP is a connection-oriented, reliable transport protocol that creates a virtual circuit for the transfer of information. In comparison, UDP is a connectionless, unreliable transport protocol that results in routers forwarding datagrams without requiring setup of a session between originator and recipient. This method of transmission represents a best-effort forwarding method and does not require the handshaking process used by TCP to establish and maintain a communications session. This means that you can consider TCP versus UDP as a trade-off between reliability and performance. Now that we've reviewed the general differences between TCP and UDP, let's turn our attention to the format of their headers to include their port number field, which is used in conjunction with IP address fields by routers and firewalls as a mechanism to filter packets.

The TCP Header

At the transport layer, TCP accepts application data in chunks of up to 64 Kbytes in length. Those chunks are fragmented into a series of smaller pieces that are transmitted as separate IP datagrams, typically 512 or 1024 bytes in length. Since IP provides no mechanism that guarantees datagrams will be correctly received as to both content and sequence, it is up to the TCP header to provide the mechanism for reliable and orderly delivery of data. To do so, the TCP header includes a field that is used for the sequencing of datagrams and a checksum field for reliability. Because traffic from different applications, such as FTP and HTTP, can flow from or to a common host, a mechanism is required to differentiate the type of data carried by each datagram. This data differentiation is accomplished by the use of a destination port field containing a numeric that identifies the process or application in the datagram. In actuality, the TCP header plus data is referred to as a *segment,* so the port number identifies the type of data in the segment, and the IP header is added to the TCP header to form the datagram that will contain the source and destination IP address. Now that we have a general appreciation for the TCP header and its relationship to the application process and IP header, let's turn our attention to the fields in the TCP header whose structure is illustrated in Figure 2-21.

Source and Destination Port Fields

The source and destination port fields are each 16 bits in length. Each field identifies a user process or application, with the first 1024 out of 65,536 available port numbers standardized with respect to the type of

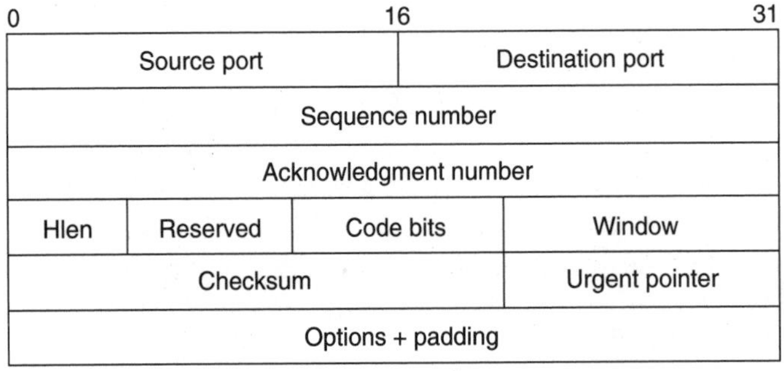

Figure 2-21
The TCP header.

0			16		31
Source port			Destination port		
Sequence number					
Acknowledgment number					
Hlen	Reserved	Code bits		Window	
Checksum				Urgent pointer	
Options + padding					

traffic transported via the use of a specific numeric value. The source port field is optional and, when not used, is set to a value of 0. The term *well-known port,* which is commonly used to denote an application layer protocol or process, actually refers to a port address at or below 1023. Both TCP and UDP headers contain fields for identifying source and destination ports. For example, Telnet, which is transported by TCP, uses the well-known port number 23, while SNMP, which is transported by UDP, uses the well-known port number 161.

Sequence and Acknowledgment Number Fields

The sequence number field is 32 bits in length and provides the mechanism for ensuring the sequentiality of the data stream. The acknowledgment number field, which is also 32 bits in length, is used to verify the receipt of data.

Hlen Field

The Hlen field is 4 bits in length. This field contains a value that indicates where the TCP header ends and the data field starts. This field is required because the inclusion of options can result in a variable-length header.

Code Bits Field

The code bits field is also referred to as a *flags field,* as it contains 6 bits, each of which is used as a flag to indicate whether a function is enabled or disabled. Two bit positions indicate whether or not the acknowledgment and urgent pointer fields are significant. The purpose of the urgent bit or flag is to recognize an urgent or a priority activity, such as when a user presses the CTRL-BREAK key combination. Then the application will set the Urgent flag, which results in TCP immediately transmitting everything it has for the connection. The setting of the urgent bit or flag also indicates that the urgent pointer field is in use. Here, the urgent pointer field indicates the offset in bytes from the current sequence number where the urgent data is located. Other bits or flags include a PSH (push) bit, which requests the receiver to immediately deliver data to the application and forgo any buffering, an RST (reset) bit to reset a connection, a SYN (synchronization) bit used to establish connections, and a FIN (finish) bit, which signifies the sender has no more data and the connection should be released.

Window Field

The window field is 2 octets in length. This field is used to indicate the maximum number of blocks of data the receiving device can accept. A large value can significantly improve TCP performance, as it permits the originator to transmit a number of blocks without having to wait for an acknowledgment and permits the receiver to acknowledge the receipt of multiple blocks with one acknowledgment. Although each field in the TCP header is important, the goal of this chapter is to provide an understanding of the operation of voice over IP and the configuration of equipment required to support it, so we will not probe deeper into the TCP header. Instead, we will examine the UDP header and conclude the chapter by discussing the Real-Time Transport Protocol, the Resource ReSerVation Protocol (RSVP), and the H.323 standard.

The UDP Header

Through the use of UDP, an application can transport data in the form of IP datagrams without having to first establish a connection to the destination. This also means that when transmission occurs via UDP, there is no need to release a connection, which simplifies the communications process. This in turn results in a header that is greatly simplified and much smaller than TCP's header.

Figure 2-22 illustrates the composition of the UDP header, which consists of 16 bytes followed by actual user data. Similarly to TCP, an IP header will prefix the UDP header. The resulting message, consisting of the IP header, the UDP header, and user data, is referred to as a UDP *datagram*.

Source and Destination Port Fields

The source and destination port fields are each 2 octets in length and function in a similar manner to their counterparts in the TCP header. That is, the source port field is optional and filled with 0s when not in use, while the destination port contains a numeric that identifies the application or process. Since UDP is commonly used by several Internet telephony products, you must determine the port a specific product uses. Then you will probably have to reprogram your organization's router access list and modify the configuration of your organization's firewalls to enable UDP datagrams using ports previously blocked to transport Internet telephony data onto your private network via the Internet.

Figure 2-22
The UDP header.

0	16	31
Source port	Destination port	
Length	Checksum	

APPLICATION NOTE There are currently no standards concerning the use of different UDP port numbers for the transmission of digitized voice. This means that there exists a high degree of probability that different applications will use different UDP ports. This also means that if you use a router access list or firewall to enable certain applications to flow into and out of your private network, you will have multiple statements that require checking, adding a delay to delay-sensitive digitized voice packets. The best way to minimize this delay is to standardize on one or two products instead of having your router or firewall administrator enter literally dozens of statements to support a large number of products. Another technique is to move your UDP checking statements toward the top of your access list statements, positioning them directly below any antispoofing address statements to minimize delay.

Length Field

The length field indicates the length of the UDP datagram to include header and user data. This 2-octet field has a minimum value of 8, which represents a UDP header without data.

Checksum Field

The checksum field is 2 octets in length. The use of this field is optional and is filled with 0s if the application does not require a checksum. If a checksum is required, it is calculated on what is referred to as a *pseudo header*. This new logically formed header consists of the source and destination addresses and the protocol field from the IP header. By verifying the contents of the two address fields through its checksum computation, the pseudo header ensures that the UDP datagram is delivered to the correct destination network and host. However, it does not verify the contents of the datagram.

Firewall and Router Considerations

Since an IP header will prefix TCP and UDP headers, there are four addresses that can be used for enabling or disabling the flow of datagrams. Those addresses are the Source and Destination IP addresses contained in the IP header and the Source and Destination port numbers contained in the TCP and UDP headers. Both firewalls and routers include a packet-filtering capability that enables users to program access lists to permit or deny the flow of packets from the Internet onto a private network or the reverse. Although most firewalls are very flexible and permit a high degree of user configuration capability, some firewalls are limited to supporting only a subset of all possible source and destination port values. This can create problems when running certain voice processes over IP if the application uses a high-value port number not supported by the firewall.

2.4 RTP, RSVP, and H.323

In concluding this chapter, we will briefly focus our attention on the Real-Time Transport Protocol (RTP), the Resource ReSerVation Protocol (RSVP), and the International Telecommunications Union (ITU) H.323 standard. Although the latter is not part of the TCP/IP protocol suite, it is being used in conjunction with the protocol suite as a mechanism to deliver voice onto a LAN. RTP provides the mechanism to time-stamp packets so that random delays resulting from other network traffic loads placed on network switches and routers can be compensated for by the use of buffers at a destination location. That is, by time-stamping packets, they can be buffered and removed from the buffer in a correct sequence by time to minimize the potential distortion that would be more pronounced if video or audio arrived with random time delays between packets. In comparison, RSVP provides the mechanism to reserve network resources that are necessary to transport real-time traffic carried by RTP, while H.323 represents an umbrella recommendation from the ITU for multimedia transmission over LANs that do not provide a quality of service (QoS).

RTP

RTP was approved as an Internet standard in late 1995 and is defined in RFCs 1889 and 1890. RFC 1889 is titled "RTP: A Transport Protocol for Real-Time Applications." RFC 1890 is titled "RTP Profile for Audio and Video Conferences with Minimal Control." RTP was developed to provide several desirable features for applications with real-time properties, including the ability to reconstruct timing, loss detection, security, and the identification of the content of packets. Several major vendors, including

Intel, Microsoft, and Netscape, have signaled their intention to construct their voice and video products by including RTP in existing standards. Although most current Internet audio applications use a protocol known as VAT, that protocol uses the audio-encoding method specified in RTP. Thus, we can expect a gradual migration to RTP to occur, which will facilitate the interoperability of products currently based on proprietary technology.

Overview

RTP was developed as an end-to-end delivery service for data with real-time characteristics, such as interactive audio and video. Those services include time stamping, sequence numbering, delivery monitoring, and identification of the type of data transported. The actual monitoring of the quality of service is performed by the RTP Control Protocol (RTCP).

RTP can be considered an application service. Applications such as Internet telephony will usually run RTP on top of UDP, with RTP and UDP forming distinct portions of the transport functionality required to support real-time data transfer. Instead of functioning as a distinct layer 4 protocol, RTP was designed to be embedded into an application process. Thus, the RTP specification provides a mechanism for denoting a common set of functions for applications that require the use of a Real-Time Transport Protocol. Although RTP provides a considerable degree of flexibility, readers should note that it does not contain any mechanism that guarantees the timely delivery of data, nor does it provide any other quality of service guarantees. Instead, RTP relies on lower-layer services, such as the evolving ReSerVation Protocol (RSVP), to provide this capability.

When RTP is transported by UDP or similar protocols, the specification requires the use of an even port number, with a corresponding RTCP stream functioning as a control mechanism using the next higher odd port number. If an application provides an odd number for use as the RTP port, the specification requires its replacement with the next lower or even-numbered port.

The RTP Protocol

Similar to any data transfer protocol, RTP consists of a header followed by data to form a packet. Unlike other transport protocols that use the contents of fields within the protocol header for control purposes, RTP uses a separate control mechanism in the form of RTCP packets for control purposes.

The RTP Header

Figure 2-23 illustrates the format of the RTP header. This header contains 10 fields, of which the last field is optional and is included when audio packets are resynchronized to reconstruct a constant 20-ms spacing. The resynchronization is performed by an RTP-level relay, referred to as a mixer, that enables an audio stream to be varied based on the available bandwidth of different circuits. The mixer is an important part of the RTP protocol. In conjunction with translators, it enables stations with different capabilities to participate in real-time conferencing without requiring all stations to set themselves to operate at the lowest common denominator in terms of speech encoding and other characteristics that govern a real-time data stream. Mixers can be used to reconstruct audio and other media streams into lower-bandwidth, and usually lower-quality, data streams. Thus, they enable other stations to receive a de-graded version of a multicast transmission instead of forcing all stations to receive the degraded version or excluding some stations from receiving the transmission due to their inability to service a higher-quality data stream.

A mixer receives a sequence of RTP packets from one or more sources and combines them into a new data stream. That data stream can be directed to a single or to multiple destinations, with the format of data either left as is or changed. A translator represents a simpler device, as it operates on one packet at a time, generating one outbound packet for each inbound packet received. The translator can change the format of data in the packet as well as initiate the use of a different protocol for the transfer of data. Together, mixers and translators provide a mechanism that

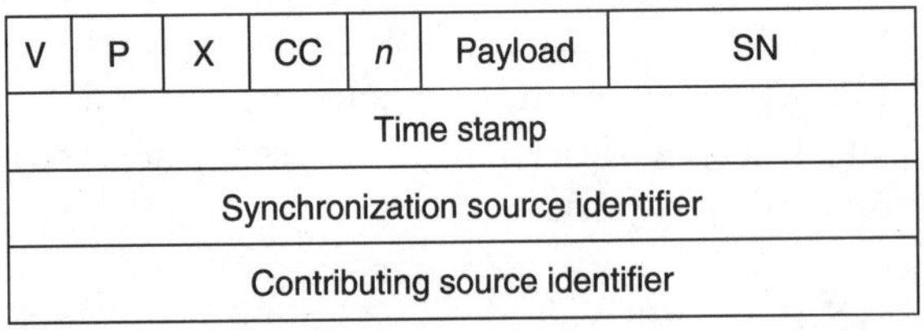

Figure 2-23
The RTP Header

V	P	X	CC	n	Payload	SN
Time stamp						
Synchronization source identifier						
Contributing source identifier						

Legend:

V	= Version field (2 bits)
P	= Padding field (1 bit)
X	= Extension field (1 bit)
CC	= Contributing source identifier count (4 bits)
M	= Marker field (1 bit)
Payload	= Payload type field (7 bits)
SN	= Sequence number field (16 bits)

enables stations with different capabilities to independently receive real-time data streams without adversely affecting the capability of other stations to do so. To obtain an appreciation for the capability of RTP, let's turn our attention to the fields in its header.

VERSION FIELD

The version field is 2 bits in length and identifies the version of RTP. The current version of RTP is 2, with a value of 1 used by the first-draft version and the value of 0 used by RTP as initially implemented in the VAT audio protocol.

PADDING FIELD

The padding field is a 1-bit flag that indicates whether the packet contains padding octets that are not part of the actual payload but are appended into the payload field. The setting of this bit flag is designed to accommodate the use of encryption that requires a fixed block length or for transporting several RTP packets in a lower-layer protocol data unit.

EXTENSION FIELD

The extension field is also 1 bit in length and can be considered as a flag that indicates whether or not the fixed header is followed by a header extension. The header extension provides a mechanism that enables developers to experiment by adding payload-format-independent functions that require additional header information while allowing other interoperating implementations to ignore the extension.

CSRC COUNT FIELD

The contributing source (CSRC) count field is 4 bits in length. This field indicates the number of CSRC identifiers that follow the fixed header—*contributing source* being a term used for the source of a stream of RTP packets that contributed to the combined stream produced by an RTP mixer. The mixer will insert a list, called the CSRC list, of the synchronization source identifiers of the sources that contributed to the generation of the packet into the RTP header. An example of the generation of a CSRC list would be an audio conference where a mixer would indicate all the talkers whose speech was combined to generate the transmitted packet.

MARKER FIELD

The 1-bit marker field functions as a flag; however, its interpretation is governed by the payload type. When set, the marker bit will indicate that the payload type field carries specific information defined to suit different requirements. For example, when video is transported, the marker field would indicate the end of a frame. In comparison, for audio it would mark the beginning of the speech occurring between two silent periods.

PAYLOAD TYPE FIELD

This 7-bit field identifies the format of the RTP payload and determines the interpretation of its contents by the application. The code for the payload type identifies both the audio and video encoding schemes, the clock or sampling rate, and, if appropriate, the number of audio channels carried. For example, a payload type value of 2 indicates the ITU G.721 audio coding technique in which a clock rate of 800 Hz is used to provide a single audio channel.

Table 2-6 contains a list of a few of the defined RTP payload types and RTCP control packet types. By examining the entries in Table 2-6, it becomes obvious that RTP was developed as an all-encompassing multimedia time-stamping mechanism that may not represent the best method

TABLE 2-6

Representative RTP Payload Types and RTCP Control Packets

Payload Type	Encoding Name	Audio/Video	Clock Rate (Hz)
2	G.721	A	8000
4	G.723	A	8000
7	LPC	A	8000
9	G.722	A	8000
15	G.728	A	8000
26	JPEG	V	90000
31	H.261	V	90000
34	H.263	V	90000

RTCP Control Packet Types	
Value	Report Type
200	Sender report
201	Receiver report
202	Source description
203	Goodbye
204	Application defined

for time stamping and sequencing digitized voice for two-way communications. This is because more than 99 percent of all telephone calls are nonconference calls. Thus, forcing such calls to use RTP where 32-bit fields are unnecessary adds additional delay that could be removed by a streamlined version of RTP for two-way voice. Perhaps developers reading this book will initiate action on an RFC to provide a streamlined version of RTP for two-way communications, shaving another millisecond or more when a shortened header flows over a low-speed link.

SEQUENCE NUMBER FIELD

The 16-bit sequence number field provides a mechanism that allows a receiver to detect the loss of a packet. However, the method used to compensate for the loss of a packet is up to the application.

TIME-STAMP FIELD

The 32-bit time-stamp field notes the sampling instant of the first octet in the RTP data packet. This field enables a receiver to determine if the arrival of a packet was adversely affected by a delay known as *jitter.* However, the actual method by which an application compensates for jitter is up to the application.

Through the use of a uniform time-stamp field, developers can receive packets with random spacing and buffer them prior to reconstructing speech. Then each packet can be removed from the buffer based upon the value of the time-stamp field to provide a uniform method of reconstructed speech that eliminates what would otherwise appear as random delays that would make portions of speech sound awkward.

SYNCHRONIZATION SOURCE IDENTIFIER FIELD

This 32-bit field identifies the synchronization source. In actuality, an algorithm generates a random identifier so that no two synchronization sources within the same RTP session will have the same identifier.

CONTRIBUTING SOURCE IDENTIFIER FIELD

As previously discussed, this 32-bit field identifies the contributing sources for the payload contained in the packet. Up to 15 sources can be inserted by mixers into this field.

Summary

Although the use of RTP provides a standardized mechanism to transport audio, the manner in which it is operated depends on the application.

Although this fact will differentiate applications from one another, the support of the different RTP payloads will provide a high degree of interoperability between applications.

RSVP

The Resource ReSerVation Protocol (RSVP) represents a signaling protocol that was an Internet Engineering Task Force (IETF) draft standard when this book was prepared. The goal of RSVP is to provide a mechanism whereby applications that require guaranteed bandwidth for successful operation, such as real-time audio and video, can request such bandwidth. Thus, RSVP addresses the quality of service (QoS) issues associated with transmitting real-time data streams on a TCP/IP network.

Overview

Unlike TCP and other protocols that initiate operations from the sender, RSVP requests are made by the receiver. While at first glance this may appear a bit awkward, there is a valid reason for this approach. That reason is the fact that the support of multicasting can result in different members of a multicast group having different resource requirements. If multicast traffic can be divided into subflows, some members of a multicast group may require the receipt of only one or a few subflows instead of the cumulative multicast traffic. Similarly, if multiple sources are generating traffic into a multicast group, some receivers may need to receive only a portion of the multicast traffic in the form of a subset of resources. Due to the preceding as well as the likelihood that the QoS of receivers will differ from one another, it makes more sense to provide receivers, rather than senders, with the ability to reserve resources.

As a signaling protocol, RSVP is used by receivers to request a specific quality of service from the network. To do so, its primary task is to establish and maintain resource reservations. Thus, a discussion of RSVP operations requires us to examine how the protocol operates with RSVP-compliant devices such as routers, which enable bandwidth to be reserved.

Operation

RSVP operations are based on tailoring the method in which a defined sequence of packets is handled as an entity. A set of packets will be treated as a flow, and the manner in which its treatment is specified is referred to as a *flow specification,* or simply a *flowspec.* That is, the flowspec describes the traffic transmitted as well as the service requirements of an application, which results in a request for a desired QoS. We use the term *desired* QoS since the flowspec does not have to be honored. Thus, a flowspec can be considered to represent a reservation request.

FLOWSPEC AND FILTERSPEC

The actual reservation request consists of a flowspec and a filterspec. As previously discussed, the flowspec defines the desired QoS. The *filterspec* specifies those packets that will be serviced by the flowspec. Thus, the filterspec enables specific traffic to be provided with a QoS, while the flowspec defines the QoS provided. Figure 2-24 illustrates the relationship between the filterspec and flowspec at an RSVP-compliant router.

CLASSIFIERS AND SCHEDULERS

In examining Figure 2-24, note that the packet schedule is used on a router to make QoS decisions concerning packets that flow into one or more priority queues. Each RSVP-compliant router has both a packet classifier and packet scheduler. The packet classifier is responsible for determining the route of packets, while the scheduler is responsible for servicing and forwarding decisions required to achieve the requested QoS.

Returning to the flowspec, it can consist of up to three components—a service class, an Rspec, and a Tspec. The service class is defined by the application. The QoS is defined by the Rspec where *R* represents *reserve*. The Tspec describes the traffic flow. The Tspec can be considered to form one side of a "contract" between the data flow and the service. That is, once a router accepts a specified QoS, it must continue to provide that level of service as long as the flow is within the Tspec. However, if traffic should exceed the expected level, the router can then drop packets, revert to servicing the flow on a best-effort basis, or employ another service mechanism.

Figure 2-24

Relationship between filterspec and flowspec.

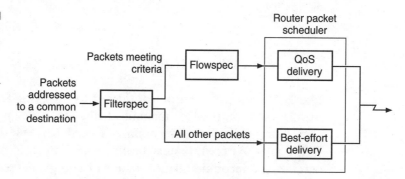

MESSAGE TYPES

RSVP supports two basic message types: Resv and Path. The Path message is originated by the sender and includes information concerning the traffic characteristics of the data stream that will be generated. Path messages are forwarded through the network to provide downstream routing information. The Resv message is sent by each receiver in the opposite direction toward the sender by reversing the paths of the path messages. Thus, the Path message will indirectly provide upstream routing information. To maintain an RSVP session, a sender will periodically issue Path messages.

Both Path and Resv messages include a time-out value. Those values are used by switches and routers with a path to set their own internal timers. If those timers expire, the reservation and routing information associated with the reservation will be tiered down. In this manner, the seizure of resources resulting from the failure of a receiver to terminate an RSVP session is limited to a short duration.

Status

During 1997, the IETF cautioned the Internet community concerning the implementation of RSVP. RSVP is a complex technology that requires all equipment between source and destination to support it. Thus, it could be many years before RSVP becomes practical for use on the Internet, and even the billing issues of how to charge users for reserving bandwidth remains to be tackled. Recognizing these problems, it was suggested that organizations should consider experimenting with RSVP on internal intranets for the foreseeable future. Thus, it is this author's opinion that the use of RSVP on the Internet will probably not occur in the near future. This in turn will result in the use of the Internet as a mechanism to transport digitized speech primarily for Internet telephony and not for the full-use corporate communications that require a very high degree of predictability.

The H.323 Standard

The H.323 standard can be considered to represent an umbrella recommendation from the ITU for multimedia transmission on LANs and via packet networks that have nonguaranteed bandwidth, such as IP and frame relay. As an umbrella recommendation, this means that not all parts of the recommendation have to be implemented. In addition, the standard does not define how different parts should be implemented, resulting in interoperability problems between equipment from different vendors that are H.323-compliant. Due to this problem several vendors formed iNOW! to develop interoperability among H.323 products.

Components

The H.323 standard defines four major components: terminals, gateways, gatekeepers, and multipoint control units. It should be noted that not all components are required and that the functions of two or more components can be implemented on a common platform.

An H.323 terminal represents an endpoint on a LAN that supports real-time, two-way communications. Thus, a workstation running an Internet telephony operation that is H.323-compliant would represent an H.323 terminal.

A gateway provides a translation service between H.323 conference endpoints and other H.323-compliant terminals. The presence of a gateway is optional and, when required, is commonly implemented on the same platform as a gatekeeper.

The gatekeeper controls access to the network for H.323 endpoints. Thus, it provides a control mechanism that prevents a LAN from being overloaded with too many voice and video calls. For example, if you set a threshold for the maximum number of simultaneous conferences, the gatekeeper will refuse to allow more conversations once the threshold is reached.

Another key function performed by the gatekeeper is address translation. Here the gatekeeper translates addresses from LAN aliases for terminals and gateways to IP addresses. The actual translation process is governed by the Registration, Admission and Status (RAS) protocol, which conveys the registration of terminals and gatekeepers, admissions, bandwidth changes, and status messages between IP telephony devices and gatekeepers.

The fourth component of the H.323 standard is the multipoint control unit (MCU). The MCU supports conferences between three or more endpoints by functioning as a bridge.

The H.323 Protocol Stack

To obtain an appreciation for the operation of the H.323 protocol, let's first turn our attention to its protocol stack. Figure 2-25 illustrates the H.323 protocol stack and indicates various components of the protocol and their relationship to the TCP/IP protocol stack.

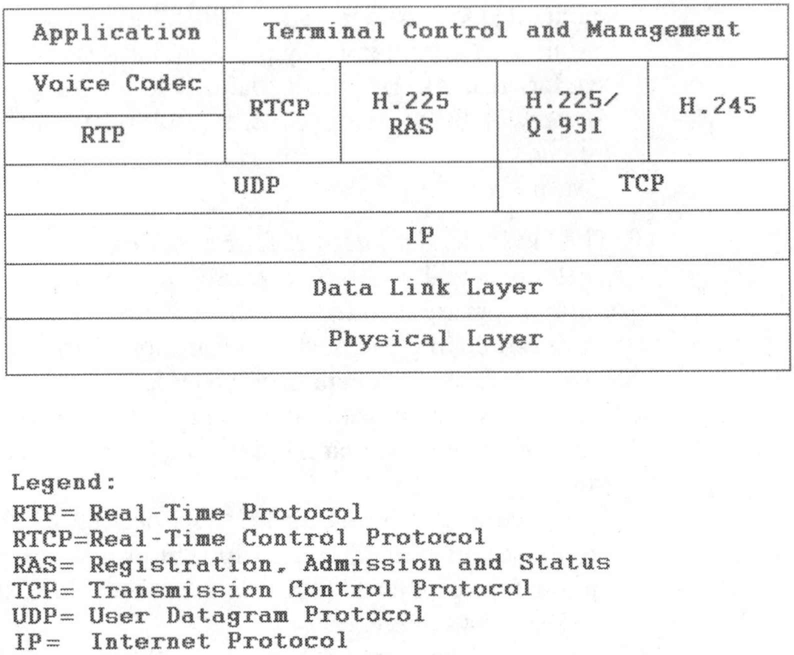

Figure 2-25
The H.323 protocol
stack

Application	Terminal Control and Management			
Voice Codec	RTCP	H.225 RAS	H.225/ Q.931	H.245
RTP				
UDP			TCP	
IP				
Data Link Layer				
Physical Layer				

Legend:
RTP= Real-Time Protocol
RTCP=Real-Time Control Protocol
RAS= Registration, Admission and Status
TCP= Transmission Control Protocol
UDP= User Datagram Protocol
IP= Internet Protocol

In examining Figure 2-25, note that H.225 represents a call signaling protocol that is required for establishing and terminating calls and is based upon the ISDN Q.931 standard. The H.245 protocol, in comparison, provides the negotiation capability between endpoints, allowing, for example, two devices to select the use of a commonly supported voice-compression method.

Operation

The H.323 standard defines several protocol exchanges between terminals, gateways, and gatekeepers that must occur prior to establishing an audio connection between two terminals. Table 2-7 summarizes the required protocol exchanges.

The explanation for the first exchange listed in Table 2-7 is as follows: When a gateway connects to a network it needs to register its presence with a gatekeeper and join the gatekeeper zone. To do so, it informs the gatekeeper of its IP address and related alias address, such as telephone number and host name. The fourth exchange in the table represents end-to-end control messages exchanged after a connection is established. For

Protocol Exchange	Description
H.225—RAS	Gatekeeper discovery and terminal registration
H.225—RAS	Routed call setup between the terminals through the gatekeeper
H.225—Q931	Can represent a terminal-to-gatekeeper-to-gateway-to-terminal channel or directly between gateways after gatekeeper allows admission
H.245	Initial communications and capability exchange
H.245	Establishes audio communication via opened logical channel
RTP/RTCP	Audio communications with packets time-stamped

each call using H.225, one H.245 control channel is used. Once initial communications results in a capability exchange and a codec is selected, audio communications are established through the use of a logical channel. This is then followed by the use of RTP and TRCP to ensure packets are time-stamped.

Because the H.323 standard includes the ability to negotiate the capabilities of different terminals, it functions as a mechanism to provide common denominator support. In addition, because it also provides a mechanism to control voice aned video activity, it represents a standard being supported by many vendors developing voice over IP products.

While H.323 provides different vendors with a mechanism to develop interoperable products, several caveats deserve mention. First, it is important to note that H.323 compliance is not sufficient for compatibility. As previously mentioned, H.323 represents an umbrella standard, which means that a vendor does not have to implement the full standard. In addition, the manner of implementation is not standardized. In fact, by the time the new edition of this book is published, there will be three versions of H.323: the original version introduced a few years ago; version 2, which added options for encryption; and version 3, which is expected to be published before the new millennium. With three versions, and no standard for implementation, it is highly doubtful that two H.323-compliant products from different vendors will interoperate. This is the reason for the iNOW! initiative being launched by vendors of Internet telephony products in an attempt to define options manufacturers may use with H.323 products and to designate how the use of such options is negotiated.

Interoperability

In concluding this section on the H.323 standard we will turn our attention to three methods commonly used to obtain equipment interoperability. Those methods include gateway-to-gateway, combined gateway-to-gateway, and gatekeeper-to-gatekeeper interoperability.

GATEWAY-TO-GATEWAY

Gateway-to-gateway interoperability provides a mechanism to enable different brands of gateway products to exchange calls. Because you must operate a matching gatekeeper for each brand of gateway, this method of interoperability can result in an extra degree of administrative burden on the network manager.

GATEWAY-TO-GATEWAY PLUS GATEKEEPER-TO-GATEKEEPER

Although this method of interoperability requires a matching gatekeeper for each brand of gateway, each gatekeeper needs to know information only about its own brand of gateway. Thus, this method of interoperability is easier to administrate.

GATEKEEPER-TO-GATEWAY

This third method of H.323 interoperability enables gatekeepers of one brand of products to directly communicate and control gateways developed by a different vendor. However, to obtain this method of interoperability, the gatekeeper must truly interoperate with gateways produced by other vendors.

Frame Relay

The ability to appreciate many of the issues associated with transporting voice over frame relay requires knowledge of the basic operation of the technology associated with this packet switching network. The purpose of this chapter is to provide readers with information concerning the development, operation, and utilization of frame relay as well as the basic cost components associated with the use of public frame relay networks. In doing so, we will examine the fields in the frame relay frame and their use, the flow of data through a frame relay network, and the use of parameters that define the operation and throughput associated with a connection to a frame relay network.

3-1   Overview

The rationale for the development of frame relay can be traced to the operation of its predecessor, X.25, as well as to advances in the acceptance of local area networks and the requirement of organizations for interconnecting LANs with a minimum amount of latency or transmission delay. X.25 was developed when most long-distance transmission occurred over relatively poor-quality microwave and copper transmission facilities. To compensate for the poor-quality transmission facilities, each switch at an X.25 network node performs an error check on each received packet. To do so, the switch must first buffer the packet in order to compute a cyclic redundancy check on the contents of the received packet, transmit a negative acknowledgment to the sender, and discard the packet if the locally generated CRC does not match the CRC appended to the end of the packet.

X.25 Network Delay Constraints

Although the delay associated with error checking at any individual X.25 node may be only between 100 and 200 ms, since error checking occurs at each X.25 node the cumulative effect of error checking becomes significant. This significance results from the fact that an average session requires routing through three or four network nodes. This means that the typical latency or delay associated with the routing of data through an X.25 data network can range between 300 and 800 ms and commonly averages 400 ms, which makes this type of network unsuitable for low-delay data transfer applications such as transporting real-time audio and video data streams and supporting interactive query response between geographically separated local area networks interconnected via an X.25 network.

Fiber-optic-based Backbones

The development of X.25 data networks primarily occurred during the 1970s and 1980s. During the latter part of the 1980s, communications carriers began to significantly improve the transmission capability of their networks via the installation of tens of thousands of miles of fiber-optic cable. In addition to greatly increasing the transmission capability in comparison to the existing microwave and copper infrastructure, the use of fiber-optic cable greatly lowered the error rate, in many cases by several orders of magnitude. This new communications-carrier infrastructure facilitated the development of a new type of transmission facility that placed responsibility for error detection and correction in the higher layers of the protocol instead of in each node and the endpoints in an X.25 network. Not only does this shift in the responsibility for error detection and correction provide for greater throughput, but it results in a lower amount of protocol overhead. This in turn allows frame relay to make more efficient use of transmission lines.

Comparison to X.25

Other significant differences between frame relay and X.25 include the layer in which they operate in the protocol stack, their network access rates, and how they handle network congestion.

Protocol Stack Operation

Frame relay is a layer 2 protocol that uses some of the core aspects of that layer. That is, a frame relay network will check the validity of a frame but will not request retransmission if an error is found. Instead, the frame is simply dropped, and the higher layers in the protocol become responsible for noting and correcting this situation. In comparison, X.25 is a fully featured protocol that operates at layer 3 in the OSI Reference Model. As a layer 3 protocol, X.25 includes responsibility for error detection and correction, flow control, and extensive support for controlling the delivery of packets and sending supervisory information between network nodes.

These functions are, to a large degree, removed from frame relay, which reduces its overhead, enhances its throughput, and results in its name as frames are relayed from node to node through the network from source to destination, thus minimizing delay.

Network Access

Frame relay design was based on the use of more modern digital circuits as opposed to the analog infrastructure commonly available when X.25 networks were developed. This difference enabled frame relay designers to construct their networks to support higher data access rates, because the fiber backbone permits high-speed transmission between network nodes. Thus, while access to an X.25 network is limited to 56 Kbps, access to a frame relay network is supported at data rates of up to the 1.544-Mbps T1 and 2.048-Mbps E1 circuit operating rates, and T3 access offerings at approximately 45 Mbps recently became available and are offered by several vendors.

Network Congestion

The third area of difference between frame relay and X.25 networks lies in the manner in which they handle network congestion. In an X.25 network, congestion is handled by flow control, a process that regulates the flow of data through the network. Although flow control ensures that packets are not lost, this technique both delays the flow of packets through the network and adds a considerable amount of supervisory overhead that adversely affects the packet processing capability of switches in the network. In addition, since X.25 switches may be required to temporarily buffer a large number of packets during network flow control conditions, those switches include a relatively large amount of buffer memory. Since the processing of packets occurs on a first-in, first-out (FIFO) basis, flow control conditions can result in a considerable degree of packet latency. In comparison, frame relay uses a very simple procedure for dealing with periods of network congestion: packet dropping. That is, a frame relay network is constructed with sufficient capacity to service a baseline of traffic from each network subscriber that is technically referred to as the *committed information rate* (CIR), which we will describe and discuss in detail later in this chapter. When congestion occurs in a frame relay network, switches used by the frame relay communications carrier will simply drop or discard certain packets. Those packets, which are referred to as *frames* since frame relay is a layer 2 protocol, are examined for the setting of a discard eligibility (DE) bit that designates the frame can be dropped. Thus, a frame relay network compensates for network congestion by simply dropping certain frames, leaving it to higher layers at endpoints to recognize the fact that frames were dropped and to take corrective action by retransmitting those frames.

Feature Comparison

Table 3-1 provides a general comparison of frame relay and X.25 features. In examining the entries in Table 3-1, note that statistical multiplexing refers to the ability of each network to interleave by time packets and frames from different sources routed to the same or different destinations, enabling high-speed circuits linking network nodes to be used more efficiently. Figure 3-1 illustrates an example of statistical multiplexing. In this example, it is assumed that device X transmits a packet to device Z. Next, device Y transmits a packet to Z, followed by device Y again transmitting a packet to Z. Although the path between nodes B and A are shared by time, the multiplexing is statistical since packets are transmitted only when a device has data to send.

Returning to Table 3-1, port sharing refers to the ability of both X.25 and frame relay to support the establishment of multiple virtual circuits via the connection of one port from an X.25 packet assembler/disassembler (PAD) or frame relay access device (FRAD) to an X.25 or a frame relay network. This concept is also illustrated in Figure 3-1 since device X, which

TABLE 3-1

Comparing Frame Relay and X.25

Feature	Frame relay	X.25
Statistical multiplexing	Yes	Yes
Port sharing	Yes	Yes
OSI layer operation	2	3
Maximum access rate	1.544/45 Mbps	56 Kbps
Throughput delay	Low	High
Flow control	None	Built-in
Packet/frame discard	Yes	No
Service-level agreement	Yes	No
Priority queuing	Yes	No

Figure 3-1

Statistical multiplexing permits both X.25 and frame relay networks to share communications circuits among many users by time.

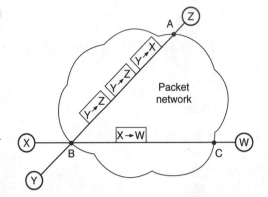

is connected to node B on the packet network, is shown transmitting data to device Z on node A and device W on node C. Thus, two virtual circuits representing temporary connections from node B to nodes A and C are established to enable device X to communicate with devices W and Z.

For those not familiar with the term *virtual circuit,* it represents a path between endpoints in a network that is established based on information in a packet or frame header. There are two types of virtual circuits supported by most packet networks: permanent and switched. A permanent virtual circuit (PVC) is assigned by the network operator. Depending on the network operator, the actual path of a PVC can vary and PVCs can have alternate routing. In addition, as illustrated in Figure 3-1, multiple PVCs can be established over a single connection to a packet network.

In comparison to a PVC, which represents a fixed connection through a network set by the network operator, a switched virtual circuit (SVC) represents a temporary path through a network. The destination endpoint of an SVC call is set by the user and requires the use of a call setup procedure. Until recently, most frame relay networks were limited to supporting PVCs.

Returning to Table 3-1, the last two entries represent recent additions to offerings of many frame relay service providers that are related to one another and that can be essential for success when transmitting voice over frame relay. A service-level agreement (SLA) is a contract between a customer and the frame relay operator that guarantees a defined level of performance. That level of performance can be expressed in a variety of ways, ranging from a mean time to repair a network failure to the percentage of frames that are delivered with and without their discard eligibility (DE) bit set. Perhaps the most important SLA with respect to voice over frame relay is an agreement that defines maximum latency. To provide a maximum latency guarantee, frame relay providers typically divide traffic into classes and assign classes to different queues in their network switches. By favoring the extraction of frames from high-priority queues over lower-priority queues, a maximum latency time can be guaranteed.

APPLICATION NOTE When considering voice over frame relay, the ability to initiate a service-level agreement (SLA) that guarantees a maximum end-to-end latency through the network enables you to develop a predictable voice transport mechanism.

Although frame relay builds on the port and bandwidth sharing of X.25 technology, its design was based on the use of a digital circuit infrastructure that permits higher-speed access and lower delays through the network. This in turn makes frame relay more suitable for transporting relatively bursty traffic associated with interconnecting local area networks, while the low latency makes it suitable for carrying digitized voice, even though the network was originally designed as a data transport facility. Although frame relay has many advantages over X.25, the use of the latter is probably several orders of magnitude higher than the former, even though frame relay utilization is increasing at a rate probably twice that of X.25. The key reason for this is the fact that a large percentage of credit card and other financial transactions are carried via X.25 networks, a trend expected to continue. Credit card and bank transactions are transported in relatively short packets, and the error checking performed at each node does not sufficiently delay the authorization in comparison to the willingness of customers at supermarket checkout counters, gas stations, or bank teller windows to wait a few seconds for the transaction to be completed.

Now that we have an appreciation for the general characteristics of frame relay in comparison to X.25, let's turn our attention to a few specifics and examine the technology in detail.

3-2 Evolution and Standardization

Frame relay, while considered by many persons to represent a recently developed transmission method, actually has its roots in the efforts of the Consultative Committee for International Telephone and Telegraph (CCITT) during 1988. In that year, the CCITT, which is now known as the

International Telecommunications Union (ITU), approved its Recommendation I.122, titled "Framework for additional packet mode bearer series," which was a part of a series of ISDN-related specifications.

LAP-D

An important part of the I.122 recommendation is known as Link Access Protocol—D channel (LAP-D), which is used to transmit signaling information on the ISDN D channel. ISDN developers noted that LAP-D had several characteristics that made it useful for other applications. One such characteristic was the multiplexing of virtual circuits at layer 2 of the ISO Reference Model instead of at layer 3, which was used by X.25 networks. Recognizing the additional capabilities of LAP-D, the I.122 Recommendation was written to provide a general framework to indicate how the protocol could be used to support applications other than ISDN signaling.

Bell Labs and ANSI Standards

Building on the CCITT Recommendation I.122, the research arm of AT&T, which at that time was Bell Laboratories, performed a significant amount of work to develop a fast-packet technology. The American National Standards Institute (ANSI) provided a significant focal point for the development of a series of frame relay standards that were approved beginning in 1990. Those standards, while forming an important foundation, were just a beginning. Recognizing the potential afforded by this evolving technology, a group of equipment manufacturers, including Cisco Systems, Digital Equipment Corporation, Stratacom, and Northern Telecom, formed a consortium known as the Frame Relay Forum during 1990.

The Frame Relay Forum

The goal of the Frame Relay Forum is to focus on the development of frame relay technology and to facilitate the interoperability of equipment by developing appropriate standards. In addition to developing a specification that conforms to the basic protocol standardized by ANSI and the CCITT, the Frame Relay Forum has led the way in developing *implementation agreements* (IAs), which define the methods for using frame relay with other technologies and for other applications. An example of the former is the IA for frame relay being carried over ATM, while an example of the latter is the recently approved IA for voice over frame relay. Table 3-2 lists the 14 Frame Relay Forum Implementation Agreements that were completed as of late 1999. As noted in the table, FRF.11 is the IA for Voice over Frame Relay. In Chapter 7, when we discuss voice over frame relay in detail, we will also examine the FRF.11 IA. Due to the effort of the Frame Relay Forum, developers have the ability to promote the interoperability of equipment and to standardize the use of new technology that enhances frame relay service.

Although FRF.11 IA is very important for obtaining network equipment interoperability, another important IA is FRF.13, which covers service-level agreements. The focus of FRF.13 is in the definition of parameters that address frame transfer rate, frame delivery ratio, data delivery ratio, and service availability, all of which make it easier to compare and contrast SLAs from different service providers.

TABLE 3-2

Frame Relay Forum
Implementation
Agreements (IAs)

FRF.1.1	User-to-Network Implementation Agreement
FRF.2.1	Network-to-Network Implementation Agreement
FRF.3.1	Multiprotocol Encapsulation Implementation Agreement
FRF.4	Switched Virtual Circuit Implementation Agreement
FRF.5	Frame Relay/ATM Network Internetworking Implementation Agreement
FRF.6	Frame Relay Customer Network Management Implementation Agreement
FRF.7	Frame Relay PVC Multicast Service and Protocol Description Implementation Agreement
FRF.8	Frame Relay ATM/PVC Service Interworking Implementation Agreement
FRF.9	Data Compression over Frame Relay Implementation Agreement
FRF.10	Frame Relay Network-to-Network Interface Switched Virtual Connections Implementation Agreement
FRF.11	Voice over Frame Relay
FRF.12	Frame Relay Fragmentation Implementation Agreement
FRF.13	Service-Level Definitions Implementation Agreement
FRF.14	Physical Layer Interface Implementation Agreement

Under the FRF.13 IA, a representative network structure is defined for both intranetwork and internetwork communications, with the latter representing the flow of data on an end-to-end basis between two or more frame relay networks. Perhaps one of the more important aspects of the FRF.13 IA with respect to the transmission of voice over a frame relay network is a formal definition of frame transfer delay. Under the FRF.13 IA, the frame transfer delay is as follows:

$$FTD = t_2 - t_1$$

where t_1 is the time in milliseconds a frame leaves its source and t_2 is the time a frame arrives at its destination. It is important to note that this definition can be structured to produce end-to-end, edge-to-edge interface, or edge-to-edge egress parameters. Because it is important to understand the full effect of delay upon voice on an end-to-end basis, you should normally request any SLA delay to be specified on an end-to-end basis.

APPLICATION NOTE When considering a service-level agreement covering delay, make sure the agreement covers latency on an end-to-end basis.

Currently the Frame Relay Forum has three working groups: (1) Market, Development, and Education, (2) Technical, and (3) Interoperability and Testing. In addition to facilitating the development of frame relay—related standards and promoting interoperability of vendor equipment, the Forum provides a conduit for end users to obtain information concerning the latest developments in frame relay technology as well as access to developing and finalized IAs. The Market, Development, and Education working group is similar to corporate PR and marketing departments.

The Technical working group is responsible for developing and modifying standards as well as providing guidance on technically related issues. One important example of the work of the Technical working group is an extension to the core frame relay specification known as the Local Management Interface (LMI). LMI addresses such issues as global addressing, multicasting, and the manner in which status updates can be transmitted as unsolicited messages by a frame relay network. Here the term multicast refers to the ability of a frame relay network to transmit messages for users that belong to a predefined group. Instead of transmitting one message per member of the group, only one message is transmitted, which significantly reduces the use of network bandwidth.

The third working group of the Frame Relay Forum is the Interoperability and Testing working group. As its name implies, this group is responsible for structuring tests to ensure interoperability issues can be resolved and equipment from different vendors can work with one another.

3-3   Frame Relay Operations

In this section, we will focus on the basic operation of frame relay. In doing so, we will first examine the format or composition of a frame relay frame. Using that information as a foundation will enable us to discuss the operation of frame relay to include the manner in which a connection is established through a frame relay network.

Frame Formats

Frame relay is a synchronous higher-level data link control (HDLC) type of protocol that traces its roots to LAP-D. The key difference between the frame relay protocol and LAP-D is the absence of a control field, since the passing of supervisory and control information, which is extensive and pervasive in X.25 and true HDLC, is conspicuous by its absence in frame relay. In actuality, the absence of control and supervisory information required through the use of a control field is by design, since frame relay does not directly support flow control and error detection and connection, and it uses higher-layer software on a separate channel for setting up and tearing down connections. In comparison, X.25 data networks use the control field to perform the preceding and more, placing a heavy administrative burden on the network.

Figure 3-2 illustrates the three basic formats of the frame relay frame. In actuality there is only one basic frame relay frame format, which has three address field variations, indicated in the lower portion of Figure 3-2. To help understand the operation of frame relay, let's focus on the fields in the frame.

Flag Fields

The flag fields are used to delimit the beginning and end of each frame. Each flag has the bit composition 01111110, and any sequence of 5 set bits in natural data is automatically modified by the insertion of a 0, a process

Figure 3-2

The frame relay frame.

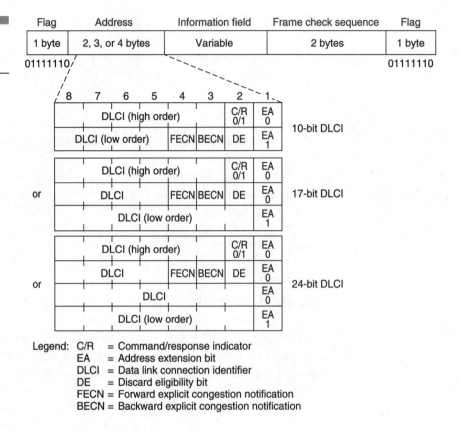

Flag	Address	Information field	Frame check sequence	Flag
1 byte	2, 3, or 4 bytes	Variable	2 bytes	1 byte

01111110

01111110

Legend:
C/R = Command/response indicator
EA = Address extension bit
DLCI = Data link connection identifier
DE = Discard eligibility bit
FECN = Forward explicit congestion notification
BECN = Backward explicit congestion notification

referred to as zero insertion, to prevent the possibility of a false flag formed from natural data being misinterpreted as a flag. Thus, the flag fields function in the same manner in frame relay as their counterparts in HDLC.

Header Field

The frame relay header provides addressing, congestion control, link management, and routing information through the use of six subfields:

1. Data link control identifier (DLCI)

2. Command/response (C/R) bit

3. Address extension (EA) bits

4. Forward explicit congestion notification (FECN)

5. Backward explicit congestion notification (BECN)

6. Discard eligibility (DE) bits

To obtain an appreciation for their role, let's examine each of the six sub-fields in the header field.

DLCI SUBFIELD

The DLCI is either 10, 17, or 24 bits in length, based on the setting of the extended address (EA) bits. The purpose of this field is to identify the logical connection that is multiplexed onto the physical channel. The DLCI identifies both directions of a virtual connection through a frame relay network and not an actual destination address.

To illustrate the use of DLCI addressing, consider Figure 3-3, which shows a four-node frame relay network with FRADs or routers supporting frame relays located in New York, Chicago, Atlanta, and Miami. If the router or FRAD in New York and Chicago establish a virtual circuit between them, they would both specify DLCIs that could be mapped to one another by the network. In this example DLCI = 20 in Chicago would be mapped to DLCI = 37 in New York. Thus, the DLCI can be considered to have local instead of network significance.

A second term that may require a degree of explanation for some readers is the FRAD. In addition, since many routers are frame relay—compliant, a brief discussion of the difference between the use of a FRAD and a router to access a frame relay network may be in order.

A frame relay access device (FRAD) directly converts a data source, such as IBM's SNA or an Ethernet LAN frame, into the frame relay frame illustrated in Figure 3-2. In examining Figure 3-2, you will note that the header is relatively short. When a router is used to provide a connection

Figure 3-3

Using data link connection identifiers (DLCIs) to establish connections through a frame relay network.

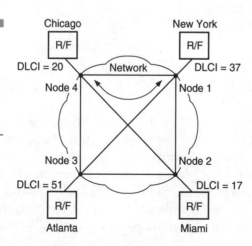

to a frame relay network, it uses IP encapsulation, resulting in the frame relay frame being transported within an IP packet. This action results in a much larger overhead; however, there are certain functions a router can perform that are not commonly included in a FRAD. Some of those functions include dial backup support and load balancing when operating dual access lines. Most frame relay network operators support both FRAD and router connectivity, leaving the choice of the access device to the subscriber.

APPLICATION NOTE If you have a choice between using a FRAD and a router to access a frame relay network and intend to transmit voice, use a FRAD. Doing so will eliminate IP encapsulation, which results in a significant degree of overhead that especially adds to latency when access to the network occurs over relatively low-speed fractional T1 lines.

To illustrate the mapping of DLCIs, consider node 1 in Figure 3-3. Let's assume it is a four-port router or FRAD, with one port connected to the circuit routed to the customer in New York. Let's further assume that the customer in New York is connected to the node via port 1, and ports 2, 3, and 4 are connected to nodes 2, 3, and 4 in the frame relay network. The routing table for node 1 showing the relationship between ports and DLCIs known to the network would be as follows:

Port	DLCI
1	37
2	20
3	51
4	17

There are certain DLCIs that have predefined significance. For example, DLCI = 0 and DLCI = 1023 are used for Local Management Interface (LMI) management control identification. Through the use of DLCI = 0, call control messages are placed in the information field and are used to request the establishment and clearing of a logical connection. Each side can request the establishment of a logical connection via the use of a SETUP message, with the other party responding with a CONNECT message if it accepts the connection, or a RELEASE COMPLETE message if it elects not to accept the connection request. The side sending the SETUP message can assign the DLCI by including it in its SETUP message; however, the other party can respond with a different DLCI in its CONNECT message. Once data is exchanged, either party can issue a RELEASE message to clear the logical connection, with the other party responding with a RELEASE COMPLETE message.

FECN, BECN, AND DE SUBFIELDS

The forward explicit congestion notification (FECN), backward explicit congestion notification (BECN), and discard eligibility (DE) subfields each consist of a single bit. The setting of each bit to a value of 1 provides the network with the ability to perform congestion control.

When a frame relay switch begins to experience congestion, it can inform its upstream and downstream nodes of the problem by setting either or both FECN and BECN bits to a binary 1. The BECN bit is set in frames transmitted downstream to notify the source of the traffic that congestion exists at a switch in the virtual connection path. On receipt of this notification, the traffic source will ideally control the flow of its traffic until the congestion problem is cleared and the switch no longer sets the BECN bit in each frame transmitted downstream. When congestion is occurring downstream, a switch can also set the FECN bit in frames transmitted to upstream nodes that act as receivers in the virtual path.

Figure 3-4 illustrates the direction of FECN and BECN set bits in transmitted frames by a switch experiencing congestion—in this example,

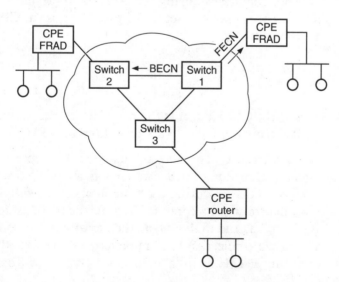

Figure 3-4

The direction of FECN and BECN set bits generated by a congested switch.

switch number 1. Although the setting of the FECN bit may appear illogical when congestion is caused from the other direction, it provides the possibility for the opposite party to take action to correct a congestion problem caused by the other party. For example, the status of the FECN bit could be passed to an upper-layer protocol that might slow down acknowledgments, which in turn reduces the flow of data to the destination via the congested switch.

In the event network congestion continues, the frame relay network will invoke a frame-discard strategy that will provide a degree of fairness among network users. To accomplish this, the network will use the discard eligibility (DE) bit in the frame header to determine which frames to send to the great bit bucket in the sky. This is because the DE bit is set to identify frames from users who exceed their negotiated throughput rates. The negotiated throughput rate represents a user's estimate of his or her normal traffic during a busy period and is technically referred to as a *committed information rate* (CIR).

The CIR Each PVC has an associated CIR; however, the CIR represents a guaranteed transmission rate and not a cap on the transmission rate. That is, a PVC can burst transmission above its CIR, with the ability to do so and the data rate above the CIR that's achievable dependent on several variables, including the *committed burst size* (B_c), the *excess burst size* (B_e), and the *network time interval* (T_c).

Committed Burst Size The committed burst size (B_c) represents the amount of data in bits that a frame relay network agrees to transfer under normal network conditions during a predefined time interval (T_c). Most frame relay network operators set T_c at 1 second. Thus, the CIR can be redefined as follows:

$$CIR = \frac{B_c}{T_c} = B_c$$

That is, the CIR represents the rate at which the network agrees to transfer B_c during normal network conditions on a PVC.

Excess Burst Size The excess burst size (B_e) represents the maximum amount of uncommitted data in bits above B_c that the network will attempt to deliver during the time interval T_c, with T_c normally set by most networks to 1 second. To illustrate the relationship between the CIR, B_c, B_e, and T_c and to show how the network alters the DE bit, let's assume you have a connection to a frame relay network via the use of a T1 line operating at 1.544 Mbps and have negotiated a 64-Kbps CIR. This means that when you are transmitting data at less than or equal to 64 Kbps, the network will not alter the DE bit. While a transmission rate of 64 Kbps may be sufficient for many networking activities, such as short query/responses, suppose you just initiated a file transfer. Since the operating rate of the frame relay access line connection exceeds the CIR, you can burst your transmission above the CIR. In this example, the B_e for a long file transfer would become 1.536 Mbps—64 Kbps, or 1.472 Mbps, since the T1 line uses 8 Kbps for framing that cannot be used for information transfer. Thus, you obtain the ability to burst your transmission above the CIR; however, when this occurs, the network will set the DE bit to 1.

Figure 3-5 graphically illustrates the relationship between the line access rate, excess burst size, and committed burst size. Note that as user activity exceeds the CIR, the DE bit in frames entering the network are set.

Using the DE Bit   When the DE bit is set to 0, this tells each network switch that the frame should not be discarded unless there is absolutely no alternative. For most networks, the setting of the DE bit to a value of 0 essentially guarantees that the frame will reach its destination. In comparison, the setting of the DE bit to a value of 1 indicates to each switch in the frame relay network that the frame is eligible for the great bit bucket in the sky if the switch is experiencing network congestion. However, just because the DE bit is set to a value of 1 does not mean it will be discarded. In fact, the vast majority of frames with a DE bit set to a value of 1 reach their destination; however, there is no guarantee that they will do so, and they will be discarded much more frequently than frames whose DE bit is set to a value of 0. In fact, many frame relay network operators guarantee that 99 percent of all frames with a DE bit set to a value of 1 will reach

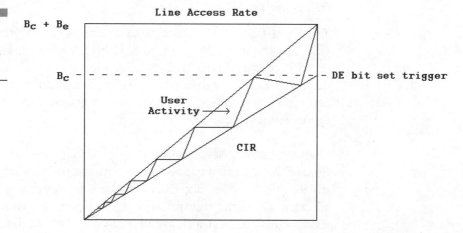

Figure 3-5
The relationship between frame relay metrics.

their destination. In addition to the examination of the DE bit as a criteria for discarding frames, there are several other criteria that will result in a frame being discarded. These criteria include a frame not being bound by opening and closing flags, the absence of an information field, an FCS error, and the use of an invalid DLCI value in a frame.

COMMAND/RESPONSE SUBFIELD

The command/response (C/R) subfield represents another 1-bit flag included in the header field. The C/R bit was included in the header to facilitate the support of polled protocols, such as IBM's SNA. Through the use of the C/R field, the direction of a poll can be designated. That is, a command frame would set the C/R bit to a value of 0, while a response frame would set the C/R bit to a value of 1. Thus, the C/R subfield can be considered to represent an application-specific subfield whose values are set and processed only by end stations.

EXTENDED ADDRESS SUBFIELD

The extended address (EA) subfield provides the mechanism by which the boundary of the address field is defined. This means that an additional header byte follows that contains additional address information. When the EA subfield is set to a value of 1, this means the header field has terminated and no additional addressing information follows.

When the first EA subfield has a value of 1, the DLCI is represented by 10 bits. This is the most common type of DLCI address and provides 1024 possible PVC numbers or identifiers. In actuality, 32 DLCIs are reserved for use by the frame relay network, resulting in 992 being available for assignment as PVC numbers.

Information Field

The third field in the frame relay frame is the information field. This field can theoretically be up to 8192 bytes in length and transports the payload or data being routed from source to destination. In actuality, there is no defined information field maximum length. However, most equipment is commonly set to transport frames using a 512- or 1024-byte information field.

VARIABLE-LENGTH FIELD PROBLEMS

One of the key problems associated with the use of a variable-length information field is the fact that a frame transporting a file transfer can adversely affect the transmission or reception of a frame carrying time-sensitive information such as audio or video data. To illustrate this concept, assume a FRAD has two internal private-network connections and one frame relay network connection as illustrated in Figure 3-6. Let's further assume that the frame relay network connection operates at 128 Kbps and that each internal network connection to the frame relay network has a PVC whose CIR is 64 Kbps, which enables a burst of up to 128 Kbps when the other PVC is inoperative. Assume at time $t = 0$ both internal private-network connections are not used. At $t = 1$, a LAN device initiates a file transfer and fills each frame so that the information field transports 8192 bytes of data, resulting in a frame length of 8198 when a 2-byte address field is used. If the file transfer bursts up to 128 Kbps, the delay introduced by the frame carrying the file transfer is 8198 bytes × 8 bits/byte/128 bits/ second, or approximately 0.512 second. If the PBX sends a voice signal to the FRAD, which digitizes the signal and places it into a frame, each time the LAN station is serviced it will generate a frame that will delay the subsequent digitized voice frame by approximately 1/2 second without considering any network delay. This means that the ability to transport voice over a frame relay network along with data will require some type of priority scheme, an adjustment of the maximum frame length, or a quality of service mechanism. Otherwise, lengthy frames transporting data that are

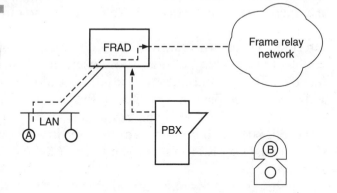

Figure 3-6
Without a priority or frame length–limiting mechanism, a frame with a lengthy information field transporting data can adversely affect the transmission or reception of frames carrying time-sensitive information. If workstation A initiates a file transfer a fraction of a second before the user on telephone B has its conversation sampled, a lengthy information field can delay the voice sample by approximately 0.5 seconds.

serviced ahead of digitized voice frames can induce an amount of delay or latency sufficient to produce awkward-sounding reconstructed voice.

QUALITY OF SERVICE

Until 1997, the only way a frame relay subscriber could enhance the ability of frames to flow end to end with a minimum amount of latency or delay was to increase their committed information rate. Although doing so can improve performance through a frame relay network, it adds to your monthly bill and still does not provide a quality of service (QoS). Recognizing the need for subscribers to obtain a better guarantee that frames will reach their destination with a minimal delay, frame relay network providers introduced several techniques to enhance the flow of data through their networks. Two of the more interesting methods are MCI Communications Corporation's Priority Permanent Virtual Circuit (PPVC) and LCI International's guarantee concerning the delivery of frames.

The MCI Priority PVC enables subscribers to assign their PVCs high, medium, or low priority. The MCI network then uses a round-robin sampling scheme that samples high-priority PVCs more often than lower-priority PVCs. Although this technique does not provide subscribers with a mechanism to obtain priority over other MCI subscribers, it does enable subscribers to prioritize their traffic. Doing so can result in the partial avoidance of the previously described situation where a data packet can adversely delay the transmission of a frame carrying a digitized voice sample. Thus, although a priority mechanism is a significant improvement over nonprioritized traffic, it does not directly provide a QoS. In addition, MCI implements its Priority PVC through the use of Bay Network switches and software and can be considered to represent a proprietary technique. This means you cannot obtain a priority for your traffic if it is routed via MCI to a subscriber that uses a different frame relay network operator.

Another frame relay technique to prioritize the flow of frames, which provides a better approach to a true QoS, is a technique introduced by LCI International, Inc., in March 1997. LCI guarantees the arrival of frames at their destination based on their length. Frames of up to 1600 bytes in length are guaranteed to arrive in less than 0.25 seconds. Frames of less than 500 bytes are guaranteed to arrive in less than 95 milliseconds, or just under $1/10$ second. Finally, frames of less than 100 bytes in length are guaranteed to arrive in less than 35 milliseconds. Although the LCI International frame arrival guarantee would minimize latency problems if subscribers could ensure that their voice-digitized frames were minimized with respect to their length, it is the function of the equipment and not the network that controls the length of the information field in the frame.

Since the introduction of MCI's Priority PVC and LCI International's latency delay guarantee, other service providers have added a variety of service-level agreement parameters to their frame relay offerings. Today you can readily select guaranteed latency based on frame length from several service providers.

When we discuss voice over frame relay in Chapter 7, we will also discuss several methods used by equipment vendors to ensure that frames transporting digitized voice are provided to the frame relay network with an information field length that facilitates the transportation of the frame through the network.

Frame Check Sequence Field

The frame check sequence (FCS) field is used as a mechanism to detect bit errors in the frame header and information fields. However, unlike X.25 and other protocols that generate a negative acknowledgment and wait for a retransmission on detection of an FCS error, a frame relay network simply discards the frame. Thus, error recovery is left up to the higher layers at end-user devices.

Management

As briefly discussed earlier in this chapter, the Local Management Interface (LMI) specification provides a mechanism for network management functions to be performed. LMI is an extension to frame relay. Unfortunately, there are three LMI types: (1) ANSI, which is equivalent to the LMI extensions developed by the Frame Relay Forum, (2) an ITU version, and (3) a variation used by Cisco Systems. To further compound an interesting situation, some LMI extensions are referred to as *common* and are expected to be adopted by vendors that comply with a specific specification, while other LMI functions are referred to as *optional* and may or may not be supported by a vendor that supports a particular specification. Some FRADs and frame relay—compliant routers support all specifications using an automatic sensing feature to determine the specific LMI version used by the network. To do so, the device transmits a status request in each LMI version, listing on DLCI 0 and DLCI 1023 to the network response to configure the hardware of the version of LMI supported by the network. The device listens on both DLCI 0 and DLCI 1023 because the LMI protocol can operate on either data link control identifier.

FRAME TYPES

The use of LMI is optional and requires the subscriber to originate all exchanges of information. By forcing subscribers to initiate the exchange of LMI frames, the network is precluded from transmitting unwanted information to subscribers whose FRADs or routers do not support the LMI protocol. Thus, LMI represents a polling scheme, with subscriber status requests answered by network reports. Once a device indicates it supports LMI, a third type of LMI frame can be transmitted. That frame is an unsolicited status update generated by the network for a subscriber.

LMI frames are identified by their DLCI values. In the original LMI specification, it was defined to be DLCI 1023; however, it can now be either DLCI 0 or DLCI 1023. The basic LMI protocol supports three types of information elements (IE): report type, keep-alive, and PVC status. The keep-alive frame is used to establish an interval at which the far-end FRAD or router will be polled by the network. Its use enables the network and distant FRAD or router to note that the interface and the circuit used to connect the subscriber to the network are alive. The default value for the keep-alive interval is 10 seconds, and this value must be set to a value less than a polling verification timer value, which is used by LMI to denote the maximum number of seconds that can transpire before a polling error is logged. Each LMI message contains one report type element and one keep-alive element. A full status message from the network to the user also contains one PVC status element for each PVC on the circuit connecting the subscriber to the network.

Figure 3-7 shows the general format for each type of LMI message. In examining the three formats shown in Figure 3-7, note that the LMI header is 6 bytes in length. The first 2 bytes contain the DLCI as well as the C/R, EA, FECN, BECN, and DE frame relay control bits. With the exception of the EA bit, the other control bits are not used. The first 2 bytes then define the DLCI. The third byte identifies each LMI frame as an unnumbered information frame, as specified by the LAP-D standard. The fourth byte contains a value that identifies the frame as one containing LMI information and is technically referred to as a *protocol discriminator.* Although it may appear redundant to use a DLCI value and protocol discriminator to define an LMI frame, the intention of the protocol discriminator is to allow other signaling protocols to be transported instead of, or along with, LMI. The fifth byte contains an LAP-D parameter referred to as a *call reference,* which is a dummy field in LMI frames and is always set to 0. The last byte in the header identifies the LMI message type as either a status enquiry transmitted from the subscriber or status transmitted from the network or an update status transmitted from the network.

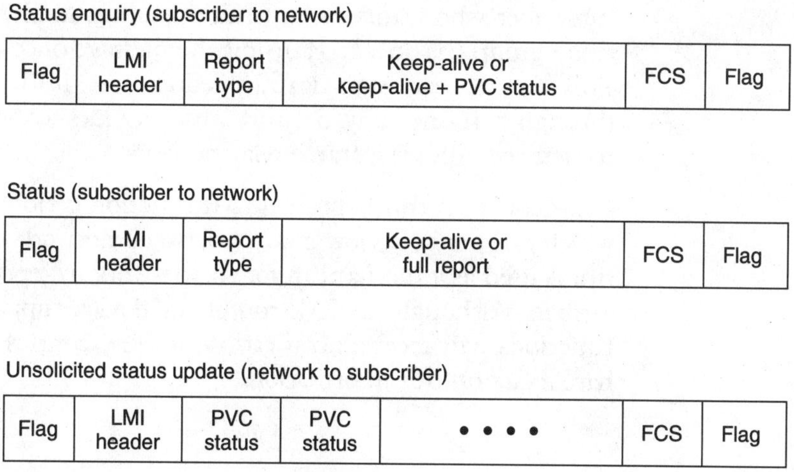

Figure 3-7
LMI message formats.

Status enquiry (subscriber to network)

Flag	LMI header	Report type	Keep-alive or keep-alive + PVC status	FCS	Flag

Status (subscriber to network)

Flag	LMI header	Report type	Keep-alive or full report	FCS	Flag

Unsolicited status update (network to subscriber)

Flag	LMI header	PVC status	PVC status	• • • •	FCS	Flag

One of the more important functions of common LMIs is the exchange of PVC status information between a subscriber and the network. Through the exchange of PVC status information, PVCs can be synchronized and can prevent the situation in which a subscriber transmits data into a nonexistent PVC, a situation referred to as a *black hole*. Thus, PVC status exchanges can be used to report the existence of new PVCs and the deletion of old PVCs.

OPTIONAL LMI FUNCTIONS

Although common LMI functions are important, some of the optional LMI functions provide the capability to significantly enhance the utility of frame relay. Three very interesting optional LMI functions are global addressing, multicasting, and flow control.

Global Addressing Global addressing provides a mechanism for each DLCI to uniquely identify a subscriber. To provide this capability, both the network and subscriber equipment must support the extension of the DLCI field, and the network operator must support unique DLCIs. Through the use of global addressing, subscribers can enhance the interconnection of LANs, because the process requiring the observation of DLCIs in use and an appropriate selection of an available DLCI is eliminated.

Multicasting Multicasting enables frame relay to function similarly to LANs. That is, multicasting allows a subscriber to transmit a single frame and have it delivered to all members of the multicast group. LMI multicasting is accomplished by the use of DLCIs between 1019 and 1022. A subscriber who wants to transmit a message to all members of a predefined group has only to transmit the message once on a multicast DLCI. This feature can significantly reduce the utilization of bandwidth through a frame relay network and provides a mechanism to support conference calls via a frame relay network.

Flow Control   A third optional LMI function is flow control. Unlike X.25, which can perform flow control between network nodes, LMI flow control is used as a mechanism for the network to report congestion to subscribers. Although an LMI-compliant device supporting optional LMI functions will receive notification of flow control, the device does not have to act on this information.

3-4   Cost of Use

In concluding this chapter on frame relay, we will turn our attention to a topic near and dear to network managers and administrators as well as to the bean counters located in many organizations. That topic is the cost associated with the use of a frame relay network. Since there are several components associated with the use of a commercial frame relay network, perhaps the best place to commence an examination of the cost of using this type of packet network is by reviewing how we normally connect an organization's data facility to a frame relay network.

Cost Components

Figure 3-8 illustrates the connection of an organization's FRAD or router to a public frame relay network. From a physical perspective, you will need (1) an access line routed from your organization or customer site to the frame relay network operator's point of presence (POP) and (2) a dedicated port on the frame relay network operator's frame relay switch. Let's first concentrate on the cost of these two physical entities; then we'll turn to other cost elements that can be associated with the use of a public frame relay network.

Local Access Line

In examining Figure 3-8, note that unless a bypass network operator is used, the local access line that connects the subscriber's site to the frame

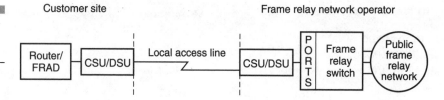

Figure 3-8
Accessing a public
frame relay network.

relay network is furnished by the local telephone company. Most frame relay network providers will acquire the local access line and bundle the cost of the circuit into the price of their service. Most frame relay network providers simply pass the cost of the access line to the subscriber, which precludes excess charges, but it also precludes the potential savings of using a bypass operator to obtain a connection to the frame relay provider's point of presence (POP).

Switch Port Cost

Each access line routed from a customer site to a frame relay network operator will terminate into a serial port on a frame relay switch located at the network operator's node. As you might expect, many frame relay network operators charge their subscribers for the use of the port on their switch, basing the monthly fee on the operating rate of the line connected to the port.

PVC Charge

Most frame relay network operators base PVC prices on their CIR in a manner analogous to the cost of digital leased lines. That is, the cost of the PVC depends on the CIR. The higher the CIR, the higher the monthly cost. However, unlike leased lines, where the monthly cost depends on both the operating rate of the line and interexchange mileage, frame relay is not distance-sensitive. This means you can access Tulsa or Tampa for the same fee!

Other Cost Considerations

The actual manner in which frame relay network providers bill subscribers can be quite complex. Although some frame relay providers may simply bill subscribers based on the local access, port charge, and CIR, there are additional charges you may have to consider. Those charges can include the number of PVCs used on a frame relay connection and a monthly fee for the use of a vendor's switch port. In addition, some frame

TABLE 3-3

Common Frame
Relay Network
Usage Cost Com-
ponents

Cost component	Requirement	Vendor A	Vendor B
Access line	____Kbps/Mbps	_____	_____
Network port	____Kbps/Mbps	_____	_____
Network connection	____PVC/CIR	_____	_____
	____PVC usage	_____	_____

relay network operators include a usage fee per PVC, which is based on the quantity of data transmitted on each PVC during the billing period.

Table 3-3 lists the common cost components that can be associated with the use of a public frame relay network. In examining the entries in Table 3-3, it is important to note that there can be significant differences in the method by which different network operators bill subscribers. In addition, it should also be noted that it is important to perform a complete analysis of the cost components associated with the use of a frame relay network to be able to compare the estimated cost associated with the use of different vendor networks. This means you should not jump to conclusions about the economic merits associated with the use of one network over another just because one network operator appears to have a simplified billing structure in comparison to the billing structure of other frame relay network operators.

Returning to Table 3-3, note that it is structured to enable readers to enter their specific requirements, which can then be used as a mechanism to compare pricing from two or more vendors. Although Table 3-3 only lists two vendors, you can easily extend the columns to include a cost comparison for additional vendors. For example, to compare the cost of an access line, you would first enter the operating rate of the circuit under the requirements column. Then you would use that operating rate to compare the cost of this frame relay network cost component among different network operators.

Although the costs associated with access lines, network ports, and the number of PVCs and their CIRs are relatively straightforward and easy to determine, if a vendor also charges a fee based on PVC usage, this fee can only be estimated. Thus, it becomes important to obtain a reasonable estimate of the potential use of a frame relay network due to the addition of the transmission of digitized voice over the network when a billing component includes a charge based on Mbytes of data. Concerning that charge, it should be noted that many "efficient" voice digitization methods result in the transmission of a voice conversation at a data rate of 8 Kbps. At that data rate, 1 minute of voice results in a data transfer of 8000 bps × 60 sec/min/8 bit/byte, or 60,000 bytes. Thus, a full hour of voice activity (ignoring the fact that some schemes do not transmit data during periods of silence) would result in the transmission of 3.6 Mbytes of data. If the vendor charges $.10 per Mbyte, the transmission of each hour of digitized voice over frame relay network would add $.36 to your organization's monthly bill and be equivalent to running voice at a cost of $.36/60 seconds, or $.006 per minute, not including the cost associated with establishing a PVC and associated CIR for the PVC that is used to transport voice. Since an 8-Kbps PVC might cost $10 per month, you can easily see that the use of digitized voice over a common local access line also used for data can provide a voice transmission facility for under a penny a minute. Thus, this little exercise illustrates that voice transported via frame relay can result in long-distance calls costing a penny a minute for the use of the network. Now that we understand the basic cost components of using a public frame relay network, let's look at an example of pricing so we can appreciate the cost of adding a PVC and its associated CIR to support digitized voice over an existing frame relay network connection. We will defer until Chapter 7 a more detailed economic analysis. In that chapter, we will turn our attention to voice over frame relay.

Pricing Example

To illustrate the potential cost of adding voice to an existing frame relay network connection requires a series of reasonable assumptions to be made. The first assumption is that the organization is using a T1 line operating at 1.544 Mbps for its connection to the frame relay network provider, and that sufficient bandwidth is available to add a PVC with an 8-Kbps CIR to the T1 line to support one voice conversation between two locations. Since the access line and switch port remain the same, there is no additional cost associated with those two frame relay pricing components. Thus, the additional cost associated with transporting voice will depend on the vendor pricing for a PVC at a given CIR. Based on a series of telephone calls made during the fall of 1997 to several frame relay network operators, this author determined that the average monthly cost of a 16-Kbps PVC/CIR is $10. Since two locations must set up PVCs to communicate with one another, this would result in an additional monthly cost of $20 to the frame relay network operator to support one voice conversation between two locations, assuming sufficient bandwidth was available on each access line. If a provider does not add a PVC usage component to its price, this is probably a bargain, as it allows you to make as many calls as you wish for one low monthly fee—regardless of usage. If you connect a PBX at each location to a FRAD or router and encourage personnel to use this new interoffice communications method, you might be able to replace several hours of long-distance PSTN traffic each day with the use of frame relay. Assuming just 2 hours per day can be moved onto a frame relay network that costs $.15 per minute on the PSTN, your savings can rapidly build up. For example, 120 minutes per day at $.15 per minute would eliminate $18 per day of public telephone usage. On a monthly basis, assuming 22 working days per month, this would eliminate $396 ($18/day × 22 working days) of toll charges in exchange for paying your frame relay network operator an additional $20 per month. Although this example does not consider the cost of equipment necessary to obtain the capability to transmit voice over frame relay, by comparing PSTN and frame relay network charges, it clearly shows that you can obtain a reasonable level of savings by moving toll calls onto an existing frame relay network. In fact, when you consider the cost of international calls, the savings become even more pronounced. In Chapter 7, we'll examine voice over frame relay in detail to *include* the cost associated with equipment that permits this capability, and we'll also discuss its use as a mechanism to interconnect national and international organizational locations for both voice and data transmission.

Understanding Voice

You must first understand voice to select appropriate equipment for transmitting voice over data networks by weighing the advantages and disadvantages of different transmission methods. You'll need a knowledge of the basic properties of speech, including its production, how we comprehend it, and different techniques used to digitize a voice conversation—all topics covered in this chapter.

First, we'll focus on the basic properties of speech to learn how sounds are produced. Next, we will examine three distinct coding categories used to digitize voice and the different techniques within each category. From information presented in this chapter, we will understand the advantages and disadvantages associated with different voice-digitization techniques, which will in turn enable us to understand the advantages and disadvantages of using different products, or options supported by different products, to transmit voice over data networks.

One of the key parameters we will discuss at appropriate points in this chapter is the *latency,* or *delay* inherent in different voice coding methods. If this book were titled *Wall Street Voice* and this author were the mythical character Gordon Gecko, we would not be able to say, "Greed is good." This is because there are certain trade-offs between the operating rates of different voice-digitization techniques and the delay in encoding voice using those techniques. Unfortunately, as we get greedier and attempt to use a lower bit rate voice coder, the delay or latency associated with the voice coding technique normally increases. Thus, the key trade-off we must consider is between the operating rate of different voice coding methods and their voice coding delay. If we remember the so-called Rosetta stone introduced in Chapter 1, we have a maximum delay of approximately 250 milliseconds before voice reconstruction sounds awkward—perhaps intolerably so. Thus, to Gordon Gecko of *Wall Street Voice,* we can say, "Greed may be bad for the health of your voice over data network application."

4-1   Basic Properties of Speech

Human speech is produced when air is forced from our lungs through our vocal cords and along our vocal tract. The vocal cords are formed from two pairs of folds of mucous membrane that project into the cavity of the larynx, while the vocal tract extends from the opening in the vocal cords, referred to as the *glottis,* to the mouth. As air is forced from our lungs through our vocal cords and along the vocal tract, the vocal folds open and close, resulting in sound produced by the reverberation of the folds. This reverberation, which is more formally referred to as *sound resonances, or formants,* concentrates audio energy that represents the frequency spectrum of a speech sound. As the shape of the vocal tract is varied—by moving your tongue, for example—the frequencies of the formants are controlled. The resulting sound heard by another person as you talk is also controlled by factors such as the size of the opening of your mouth, your lips, and even the size and spacing of your teeth. Figure 4-1 illustrates the human vocal tract and several parts of the body that effect the production of speech.

In examining Figure 4-1, note that the nasal cavity is an auxiliary path for the creation of sound. The nasal cavity, which begins at the velum or soft palate at the root of the mouth, separates the oral cavity from the nasal cavity. When the velum is lowered, the nasal tract becomes acoustically coupled with the rest of the vocal tract and changes the nature of the sound we produce.

Classes of Speech

A majority of normal speech sounds can be categorized into one of three classes based upon their mode of excitation. Those three classes of speech include voiced sounds, unvoiced sounds, and plosive sounds.

Figure 4-1
The human vocal
tract.

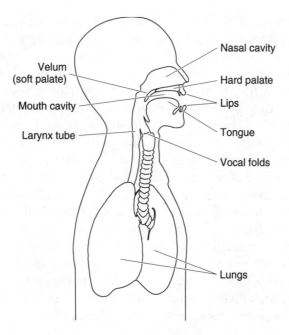

Voiced Sounds

Voiced sounds are produced when our vocal cords vibrate as a result of our lungs generating sufficient pressure to open our vocal folds. As air flows from our lungs, our vocal folds vibrate, with the frequency of vibration based on the length of our folds and their tension. For most persons, the vibration frequency of their folds is within the 50- to 400-Hz range and is referred to as the *pitch frequency* component of voice. Voiced sounds have a high degree of recurrence at regular intervals throughout the pitch period, which is commonly between 2 and 20 ms, while the amplitude of the sound attenuates during that time period.

Unvoiced Sounds

Unvoiced sounds refer to the period of time when our vocal folds are normally open, allowing air to pass from our lungs freely into the rest of our vocal tract. During this time, the frequency spectrum of the unvoiced sounds is relatively flat. Examples of unvoiced sounds include *s, f,* and *sh,* generated by constricting the vocal tract by slightly closing our lips.

Plosive Sounds

A third classification of sound is represented by plosive sounds. Plosive sounds result from the complete closure of our vocal tract, resulting in air pressure becoming extremely high behind the closure. Once the vocal tract opens, the result is a sound that contains a high degree of low-frequency energy. Examples of plosive sounds are *p* and *b,* which are formed by the closure and sudden release of the vocal tract.

In addition to voiced, unvoiced, and plosive sounds, there are some sounds that do not fall into a distinct class and are better categorized as a mixture of classes. One example results from the occurrence of a vocal cord vibration and a constriction in the vocal tract, causing speech produced with friction, referred to as a *fricative consonant.*

Figure 4-2 illustrates the repetitive or periodic nature of a voiced sound over a small increment of time, which typically ranges between 2 and 20 ms. Figure 4-3 shows an example of the power of a voiced sound, which, after resonating between nearly similar limits, alternates at its higher-frequency components. If we were to chart an unvoiced sound, we would note a different set of characteristics, with a flatter amplitude-versus-time plot and a higher power level across the frequency spectrum up to approximately 2500 Hz, after which we usually encounter a more significant drop in power than is associated with voiced sounds.

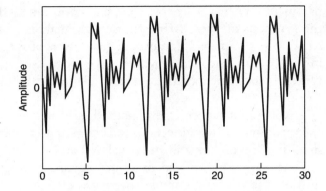

Figure 4-2
The repetitive or periodic nature of a voiced sound is observed by plotting its amplitude over time.

When engineers examined the composition of human speech, they made two observations that resulted in different methods being used to digitize and transmit voice. First, they noted that if the composition of human speech could be sampled at appropriate intervals, it could be digitized and reconstructed into a sound that would be difficult to distinguish from the original. All that was required was the ability to take an appropriate number of samples and encode the value of each sample so its reconstructed amplitude did not significantly differ from its original amplitude. This type of encoding is referred to as *waveform encoding*.

A second aspect of speech properties noted by engineers was that in terms of milliseconds, sound did not significantly vary. This means that, to a degree, sound is sort of predictable and can be synthesized. Thus, a second method of digital encoding could be based upon modeling speech, a technique referred to as *vocoding*. In vocoding, the synthesis that reconstructs voice results from analyzing speech and determining its key

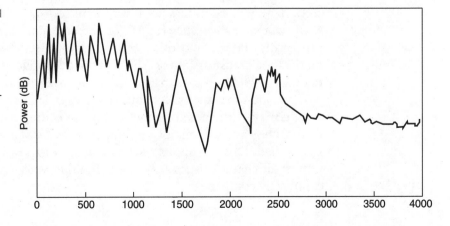

Figure 4-3
The power of a voiced sound attenuates at high frequencies.

parameters, such as its energy, tone, pitch, and other characteristics. Thus, the synthesis of speech first requires an analysis of a waveform to determine its parameters. Because the parameters of speech are transmitted instead of an encoded waveform, the operating rate of an analysis-synthesis vocoding technique is generally lower than that of a waveform encoding technique.

As you might expect, a third method was developed based on waveform *and* vocoding—a hybrid technique. In a hybrid voice coding technique, a small portion of a waveform is analyzed and key speech parameters are extracted. However, instead of simply passing the parameters for transmission, the hybrid coder uses the parameters to synthesize the speech sample and compare it to the original waveform. Then the coder uses the difference between the actual sample and the synthesized sample to adjust the parameters.

Prior to the development of low-cost high-processing-capability digital signal processors (DSPs), the ability to perform effective hybrid coding was more a figment of one's imagination than a reality. However, the development of low-cost high-processing-capability DSPs resulted in the potential use of a family of Code Excited Linear Predictor voice coding techniques commonly referred to as the CELP (pronounced *kelp*) family of voice coders. Now that we have an appreciation for the basic properties of speech, let's look at speech-coding methods.

4-2   Waveform Coding

Waveform coding is a process whereby an analog signal is digitized without requiring any knowledge of how the signal was produced. In this section, we will examine several waveform coding techniques, beginning with *pulse code modulation* (PCM) for three reasons: First, PCM is nearly universally the method of voice digitization used by communications carriers for transmission on the worldwide public switched telephone network. Second, an explanation of the manner in which PCM operates will provide a foundation for comparing its efficiency and reconstructed voice clarity with those of other waveform coding methods. Third, and for business applications of key importance, PCM is referred to as *toll-quality voice*. Due to this, its clarity, delay, and bandwidth utilization are important characteristics against which other voice coding methods are commonly compared.

Pulse Code Modulation

Pulse code modulation (PCM) is a waveform coding technique based on a three-step process: sampling, quantization, and coding. Thus, an understanding of the operation of PCM requires an understanding of each step in the PCM process.

Sampling

Under PCM, an analog signal is sampled 8000 times per second, or once every 125 μs. The selection of the sampling rate is based on the Nyquist theorem, which requires the number of sample points to be at least equal to twice the maximum frequency of the signal for the signal to be faithfully reconstructed.

Although a standard voice channel is filtered to produce a passband of frequency from 300 Hz to approximately 3300 Hz or a bandwidth of 3000 Hz, in actuality the filters do not work instantaneously and allow some lower-power speech to pass below 300 Hz and beyond 3300 Hz, as illustrated in Figure 4-4. As a result, the passband can extend to near 4000 Hz, resulting in the selection of a sampling rate of 8000 samples per second.

The sampling process results in a series of amplitude segments that form a pulse amplitude modulation (PAM) wave. Figure 4-5 illustrates the creation of a PAM wave resulting from the sampling of a single sine wave. In actuality, communications carriers use equipment to sample a group of voice channels at one time. In North America, the most common sys-

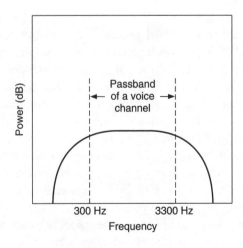

Figure 4-4
Construction of a voice channel. Through the use of filters, a passband between 300 and 3300 Hz is established for use as a voice channel.

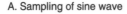

Figure 4-5

Creating a pulse
amplitude modula-
tion (PAM) signal via
sampling of a sine
wave.

A. Sampling of sine wave

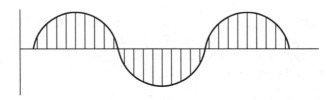

B. Resulting PAM signal

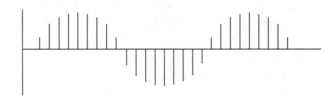

tem samples 24 voice channels in sequence, while in Europe an equivalent system samples 32 channels.

In examining Figure 4-5, note that the PAM signal represents a series of samples that can have an infinite number of voltages. The reason those voltage samples can be infinite is because the samples represent analog heights and not discrete digitally encoded signal values. Thus, the second step in the PCM process, called *quantization*, reduces the PAM signal to a limited number of discrete amplitude values.

Quantization

The second step in the PCM process requires the coding of each PAM sample. When PCM was being developed, it was recognized that it was important to limit the number of coding values for each sample while maintaining the ability to faithfully reproduce the sample. This need to limit the number of coding values for a sample was necessary to limit the transmission rate of an encoded signal. For example, a four-level binary code would provide 2^4, or 16, possible values, requiring a transmission rate of 8000 samples per second $\times$ 4 bits/sample or 32,000 bps. Similarly, an eight-level binary code would provide 2^8, or 256, possible values and would require a transmission rate of 8000 samples per second $\times$ 8 bits/sample, or 64,000 bps.

When examining the range of intensities of voice over an analog telephone channel, its approximately 60-dB power range would require 12 bits per sample if linear quantization was used. This would result in a bit rate of 96,000 bps, which, while feasible, represents an excess amount of bandwidth that could be reduced by using nonlinear quantization. A second method that can be used to reduce the number of bits required per sample is to compress or compand the signal prior to quantization, followed by uniform quantization.

NONUNIFORM QUANTIZATION

Nonuniform quantization is based on the fact that there is a higher probability of occurrence of lower-intensity signals than of higher-power signals. Larger quantum steps are used for encoding larger amplitude portions of a signal. Conversely, finer steps are used to encode signals that have a lower amplitude. Figure 4-6 illustrates the assignment of larger steps for higher-intensity signals and finer steps for lower-intensity signals.

COMPANDING

Most PCM systems today use companding followed by uniform quantization to reduce the number of bits necessary to encode each PCM sample to 8. To do so, the *compandor* (a term derived from *com*pressor-ex*pandor*) raises the power of weak signals so they can be transmitted above the noise and crosstalk level associated with a typical communications channel while attenuating very high signals to minimize the possibility of crosstalk affecting other communications channels.

Figure 4-7 illustrates the typical operation of a compandor. The compression portion of the compandor accepts a 60-dB-input power range, typically between 20 and 80 dB. The compressor raises the weakest sounds in power from 20 to 40 dB, while the strongest sounds are decreased in power from 80 to 70 dB, minimizing the power range to 30 dB.

The expandor portion of the compandor works in an opposite manner. That is, it expands the reduced power range back to its original form. To do so, the weakest sounds are decreased in power from 40 to 20 dB,

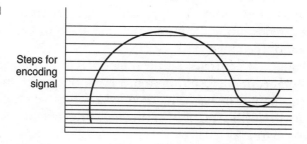

Figure 4-6
Nonuniform quantization results in the assignment of larger steps to higher-intensity signals and finer steps for lower-intensity signals.

Steps for encoding signal

Figure 4-7
A compandor com-
presses a transmitted
voice signal to reduce
its power range and
expands a received
signal to reconstruct
its original power
range.

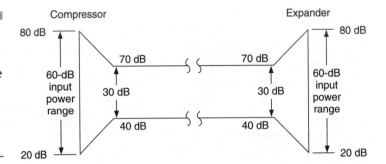

while the strongest sounds are increased in power from 70 dB up to 80 dB, resulting in a 60-dB-output power range that is the same as the input power range.

The compression and expansion functions of the receiving compandor are logarithmic and follow one of two laws: the A-law, which is employed primarily in Europe, and the μ-law, used in North America. The curve for the A-law can be plotted from the following formula, where A is set to a value of 87.56.

$$Y = \frac{Ax}{(1+\log A)} \quad 0 \le \frac{V}{A}$$

$$Y = \frac{1+\log (Ax)}{(1+\log A)} \quad \frac{V}{A} \le v \le V$$

where v represents the instantaneous input voltage and V represents the maximum input voltage. The curve for the μ-law can be plotted from the following formula:

$$\mu = \frac{\log (1+\mu x)}{\log (1+\mu)}$$

where μ has a value of 255. In the preceding formulas x has the value v/V and varies between −1 and 1, Y has the value i/B, with i representing the number of quantization steps commencing from the center of the range and B representing the number of quantization steps on each side of the center of the range.

Figure 4-8 illustrates a general plot of a μ-law compandor, showing the compressed input resulting from a range of input signals. This curve represents a value of 100 being used for μ, which was the value used for the original North American μ-law encoding system. Later, that value was changed to 255.

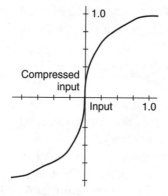

Figure 4-8
The logarithmic curve for the μ-law.

Both the A- and μ-laws define the number of quantizing levels used to describe a sample and how those levels are arranged. Under the μ-law, the quantization scale is divided into 255 discrete units of two different sizes, called *chords* and *steps*. Chords are spaced logarithmically, with each succeeding chord larger than the preceding one. Within each chord are 16 steps spaced linearly. Thus, steps are larger in larger chords. Figure 4-9 illustrates an example of the spacing of two chords and the steps within each chord. In actuality, the μ-law uses 16 chords, 8 for the positive portion of a signal and 8 for the negative portion of a signal. Since there are 16 steps in each chord and the zero level is shared, the number of levels used becomes $16 \times 16 - 1$, or 255.

Coding

Instead of directly encoding a step representing the power level of a sample, each PCM word is segmented into three parts: a polarity bit, 3 bits for

Figure 4-9
Chords are spaced logarithmically, with steps in the chord spaced linearly.

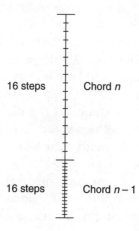

16 steps   Chord n

16 steps   Chord $n-1$

the chord value, and 4 bits to represent one of the 16 possible steps within a chord. The format of the PCM word is as follows:

P	C	C	C	S	S	S	S

where P is the polarity bit and indicates whether the sample is above or below the origin, C represents the chord value bits, and S represents the value of a step within the indicated chord.

In comparison to the use of 16 chords under the μ-law, the A-law uses 13 segments. Six are used to represent the positive portion of a signal, while a zero chord results in the 13th segment. For both the A-law and the μ-law, coding results in each sample being encoded in 8 bits. Since there are 8000 samples per second, the encoding process results in a digital data stream of 64 Kbps transporting one PCM analog voice conversation.

APPLICATION NOTE   Although PCM has the highest bandwidth of all voice coding techniques, its encoding latency is practically negligible, with an encoding delay under 1 microsecond, which for comparison purposes is several thousand times lower than low-delay hybrid coders.

PCM Multiplexing

As mentioned earlier in this section, PCM is commonly performed by communications carriers through the use of equipment at their central offices that encodes groups of either 24 or 30 voice conversations. The encoding of groups of voice conversations dates to the 1960s, when PCM systems were installed to relieve cable congestion in urban areas. At that time, communications carriers installed equipment referred to as *channel banks* in their central offices. Each channel bank consisted of a codec, a time division multiplexer (TDM), and a line drive as illustrated in Figure 4-10.

The codec (a term derived from *coder-decoder*) accepts a group of 24 analog voice signals in North America and samples each of those signals 8000 times per second, producing a series of PAM signals that are quantized and coded into 8-bit bytes. The TDM combines the digital bit stream from each of the 24 data sources into one high-speed serial bit stream, adding a framing bit to every sequence of twenty-four 8-bit groups. This framing bit, which occurs 8000 times per second, provides for the synchronization of transmission and results in each multiplexing frame consisting of $24 \times 8 + 1$, or 193 bits. As frames are transmitted 8000 times per second, the multiplexer produces a serial bit rate of 193 bits/frame × 8000 frames/second,

Figure 4-10
The channel bank
system.

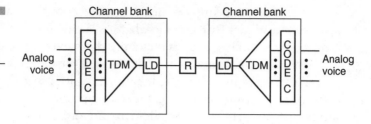

Legend: CODEC = Coder-decoder
LD = Line driver
R = Repeater

or 1.544 Mbps, which results in the operating rate of a T1 circuit. In fact, the channel bank system illustrated in Figure 4-10 can be considered a forerunner of the T-carrier transmission system.

The line driver in the channel bank converts the electrical characteristics of the serial bit stream for transmission on the digital transmission facility. This device converts unipolar signals into bipolar signals, and its modern equivalent is the *channel service unit/data service unit* (CSU/DSU). The repeater shown in Figure 4-10 actually represents a series of devices installed approximately 6000 feet from one another on span lines consisting of copper cables. Each repeater examines the digital pulses flowing on the span line linking channel banks and regenerates a new pulse, removing any prior distortion to the pulse. In comparison, amplifiers used with analog transmission systems boost the strength of the analog signal to include increasing any prior distortion of the signal. Thus, in addition to relieving cable congestion, digital channel bank systems also provide a higher level of signal quality than analog transmission. When T1 circuits became available for transmitting data, users were able to obtain a lower error rate than with analog transmissions.

PCM System Operation

PCM was standardized by the International Telecommunications Union (ITU) as Recommendation G.711 and represents by far the most commonly used method of waveform encoding on a worldwide basis. Both North American μ-law companding and European A-law companding result in a high quality of reproduced speech, and the differences between the two methods are so slight that a call between two locations results in a reconstructed signal that, to the human ear, is essentially indistinguishable from the original. Although used worldwide, the technology was developed during the 1960s, and improvements in voice encoding methods resulted in other techniques that provide what is referred to as *near-toll quality* reproduced voice at far lower data rates per digitized conversation.

Since communications carriers invested hundreds of billions of dollars over the years in PCM-based technology, it is reasonable to expect the PSTN to continue to use that technology for the foreseeable future. In fact, the popular .au audio files that are often used to transport sound over the World Wide Web are PCM files. However, there are expensive international communications facilities as well as private networks that can more practically employ other coding techniques, which has resulted in the development of both standardized and nonstandardized methods of lower-bit-rate voice encoding methods. One of those standardized methods is ADPCM, which we will now examine.

Adaptive Differential PCM

As discussed in the first section of this chapter, speech has a degree of repeating waveforms due to the vibration of the vocal cords. This degree of correlation between speech samples makes it possible to design a waveform coding scheme based on the prediction of samples if the error between the predicted samples and actual speech samples have a lower variance than the original speech samples. If so, the difference between the actual sample and the predicted sample could be quantized using fewer bits than the original speech sample. This technique forms the basis for a series of differential PCM methods, including *adaptive differential PCM* (ADPCM), in which the predictor and quantizer adaptively adjust to the characteristics of speech being coded. ADPCM was standardized by the ITU in the mid-1980s as Recommendation G.721.

OPERATION

ADPCM uses a sampling rate of 8000 samples per second, which is the same as that used in PCM. Instead of quantizing the actual signal sample, ADPCM uses a transcoder that includes an adaptive predictor and compressor, with the compressor subtracting the predicted value from the actual value of the sample and encoding the difference as a 4-bit word. At the receiver, another transcoder provides a reverse operation, using summation circuitry and the value generated by a predictor to subtract the predicted value from the received 4-bit difference, regenerating the actual value of the sample. In the event that successive samples vary widely, the predictive algorithm adapts by increasing the range represented by the 4 bits. However, the adaption process reduces somewhat the accuracy of

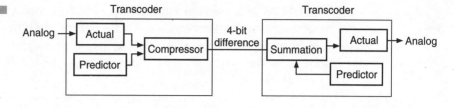

Figure 4-11
ADPCM operation.
The transmitting
transcoder subtracts
the predicted value
from the actual sam-
pled value, quantiz-
ing the difference as
a 4-bit word. The
receiving transcoder
subtracts the pre-
dicted value from the
4-bit difference to
generate a near
"actual" value.

voice-frequency reproduction. Figure 4-11 illustrates the basic operation of an ADPCM system.

Through the use of ADPCM, the data rate of a digitized voice conversation becomes:

8000 samples/second × 4 bits/sample = 32,000 bps

Thus, the use of ADPCM results in a transmission rate that's one-half the PCM rate of 64 Kbps.

The first standardized operating rate of ADPCM was the 32-Kbps rate just described. Later, the development of additional predictive techniques resulted in operating rates of 16, 24, and 40 Kbps being standardized.

IMPLEMENTATION

The most popular implementation of ADPCM is by communications carriers on long-distance international circuits at a data rate of 32 Kbps. Since ADPCM is based on the transmission of the difference between the actual sample and the predicted sample, it is not suitable for use by high-speed modems. This explains why an international modem connection often results in transmission occurring at a modem's lower fallback operating rate.

Using ADPCM is also popular with organizations that have established their own internal voice communications networks. Through the use of ADPCM adapter cards in T1 multiplexers, they can double the voice-carrying capability of T1 circuits between organizational locations when using ADPCM at 32 Kbps.

ADPCM is a popular option supported by many voice over IP and voice over frame relay products. This is because ADPCM can operate at as low as one-quarter the rate of PCM while providing toll-quality reconstructed voice.

APPLICATION NOTE The predictor and summation operations performed by ADPCM increase its latency over PCM by approximately 25 percent. However, this results in only a 125 μs delay, which is relatively insignificant when compared to the delay associated with many hybrid coding techniques.

Continuously Variable Slope Delta Modulation

In the continuously variable slope delta (CVSD) modulation technique, the analog input voltage is compared to a reference voltage. If the input is greater than the reference, a binary 1 is encoded, while a binary 0 is encoded if the input voltage is less than the reference level. This method of voice encoding permits a 1-bit data word to be used to represent the digitized voice signal.

OPERATION

The use of CVSD is based on a succession of 0 or 1 bits being used to indicate the change in the slope of the analog curve representing a voice conversation. Thus, the key to the fidelity of the reproduced signal is a sampling rate fast enough so that the sequence of 1-bit words can faithfully reproduce the analog signal.

Most CVSD systems sample the input at 32,000 or 16,000 times per second, resulting in a bit rate of 32 or 16 Kbps representing a digitized voice signal. Another popular CVSD rate is 24 Kbps, which results from a sampling rate of 24,000 times per second.

UTILIZATION

The original use of CVSD dates to military systems, as the generation of a digital data stream was much easier to encrypt than using of filters to move segments of frequencies of an analog signal. Today, CVSD is primarily offered as an option on some T1 multiplexer voice-compression modules that can be set for sampling rates of 8, 16, 24, or 32 thousand times per second. Although a sampling rate of 8000 times per second enables 192 voice channels to be carried on a T1 circuit, the quality of voice is so poor that this level of compression is rarely used. Instead, organizations using CVSD on their private internal networks commonly use operating rates of 24,000 or 32,000 bps for their voice channels. Similar to ADPCM, the use of CVSD presents a barrier to the use of high-speed modems. In addition, ADPCM commonly delivers a higher voice quality of speech than CVSD, which will probably result in the gradual elimination of the use of this waveform encoding method.

Digital Speech Interpolation

Digital Speech Interpolation (DSI) is a technique that enhances the ability of a trunk circuit to transport additional voice conversations instead of using a voice-compression method. Although technically it does not belong in a section covering waveform coding methods, it is frequently used by equipment supporting different waveform coding methods and thus deserves coverage.

DSI recognizes the fact that human speech is half-duplex—unless we are rude and talk at the same time as the other party. In addition, because humans periodically pause when speaking, it becomes possible to take advantage of periods of silence in one conversation by placing a portion of another conversation in a trunk slot routed between two multiplexers or similar equipment. For example, a DSI system might be configured to support 36 PCM voice conversations over a T1 circuit that has 24 time slots and normally is limited to supporting 24 voice conversations. While DSI configured for a 36:24 ratio normally works very well due to the half-duplex nature of voice and the periods of silence in conversations, suppose 25 persons begin to talk. Because there are only 24 time slots, one sample must be dropped. This dropping occurs randomly in small segments over all 24 slots and is referred to as *clipping*. Although DSI properly configured at a ratio of 3:2 or less is normally imperceivable to the human ear, it will cause havoc to modem transmission. Thus, DSI and modem transmission are mutually exclusive.

4-3   Vocoding

As discussed in the first section of this chapter, a second method used to digitally encode speech is based on the characteristics of the human voice. This method is called *vocoding*, which is an acronym for *voice coding*, and is based on the modeling of speech production.

Operation

Vocoding is based on the assumption that speech is produced by exciting a linear system through a series of periodic pulses for voiced sounds or random noise for unvoiced sounds. Figure 4-12 illustrates the general speech production model employed by vocoders.

The general vocoder speech production model illustrated in Figure 4-12 assumes that when voiced sound occurs, the distance between the periodic series of impulses represents the pitch period. The model also assumes that unvoiced speech resulting from the air pressure of our lungs blowing through a constriction in our vocal tract can be modeled via a sequence of random noise.

The vocoding process results in the transmitter analyzing the various properties of speech to select appropriate parameters and the excitation or power level that best corresponds to the source voice input. Instead of digitizing the analog signal, the vocoder digitizes the voice model parameters and excitation level, which are then transmitted to the receiving vocoder. At the receiving vocoder, the model parameters and excitation level are used to synthesize speech.

The primary advantage associated with the use of vocoders is their ability to produce intelligent speech at very low bit rates. Depending on the model used, the resulting synthesized sounds can seem unnatural and awkward. The reason that vocoders generate less than toll-quality voice results from the fact that the human ear is very sensitive to pitch and human vocal tract characteristics vary widely, which makes modeling accuracy difficult. Another problem associated with the use of vocoders results from the fact that the speech modeling used assumes either voiced or unvoiced sound and does not include any intermediate states. In spite of these problems, there are several popular types of vocoders, and their development has resulted in the knowledge used to build hybrid encoding devices that produce a more natural sound while maintaining a relatively low bit rate.

Figure 4-12
The general speech production model employed by vocoders.

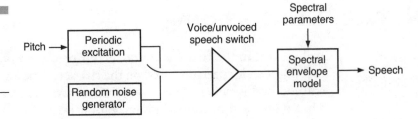

Types of Vocoders

Over the past 50 years, a number of different types of vocoders have been developed. Two of the more popular types are homomorphic vocoders and linear predictive vocoders.

Homomorphic Vocoders

Homomorphic vocoders are based on the use of nonlinear signal processing techniques that provide a better model of human speech. A homomorphic vocoder assumes that speech represents a convolution in time of the vocal tract's impulse response and excitation functions. Since the impulse response of the human vocal tract varies slowly in comparison to the variation of the excitation level, it becomes possible to separate the two components via the use of a low-pass filter. This enables a more accurate modeling of pitch information, which is transmitted along with certain coefficients of the signal generated by applying an inverse Fourier transformation of the frequency components of the signal. The resulting coefficients, which describe the vocal tract along with a more accurate representation of pitch information, can be transmitted at a data rate of approximately 4 Kbps.

Linear Predictive Vocoder

The linear predictive vocoder is the most popular type of vocoder and one of the most useful methods for encoding good-quality speech at a very low bit rate. Although it uses the same speech production model as other vocoders, a linear predictive vocoder employs a different model of the vocal tract. That model assumes that each voice sample represents a linear combination of previous samples, enabling an infinite impulse response filter to be used to model speech. The linear predictive vocoder computes the coefficients of the filter to minimize the error between the prediction and the sample.

Linear predictive vocoders operate on blocks of speech of approximately 20-ms duration. Each block is stored and analyzed so the vocoder can determine the appropriate set of predictor coefficients that minimize the error between the sample and the predictor. Once the coefficients are determined, they are quantized and transmitted to the receiving vocoder. That vocoder uses the received coefficients to generate 20 ms of predicted speech, which is then passed through an inverse of the vocal tract filter, allowing the prediction error to be generated. This technique enables the predictor to remove the correlation between adjacent voice samples and allows the pitch period of speech to be more accurately reconstructed. The resulting effect results in a more natural-sounding synthesized voice.

The first generation of linear predictive vocoders was actually limited to generating synthesized human speech. During the 1970s, Texas Instruments marketed an "educational" calculator. Pressing a button on the calculator generated a word such as *dog* or *cat* through a miniature speaker. A child using the calculator would then enter the characters necessary to spell the pronounced word. A green light would indicate that the spelling was correct. Today, linear predictive vocoders can be used to provide a transmission mechanism for synthesized speech at bit rates as low as 2.4 to 4.8 Kbps, which results in a reasonable quality of reconstructed speech. Unfortunately, certain speech sounds are not very well reproduced, so certain portions of speech appear better than others. One version of LPC, referred to as LPC-10e, is described in Federal Standard (FS) 1015.

4-4   Hybrid Coding

In examining the operation of waveform coders, we noted that they provide a mechanism to reconstruct the signal based on samples taken from the original waveform. This technique, which is the key to the operation of PCM, ADPCM, and CVSDM, can produce very high quality reproduced speech at data rates ranging from PCM's 64 Kbps to ADPCM's 32 Kbps, and even at a CVSDM data rate of 24 Kbps. Unfortunately, none of these techniques are capable of being used to code speech at a very low data rate. In comparison, vocoders attempt to extract parameters of speech that can be used to synthesize its reproductions. Although vocoders can be used to transmit speech at very low bit rates, down to 2.4 Kbps, the resulting speech, while being highly intelligible, tends to have periods that sound very synthetic. In an attempt to fill the gap between waveform and vocoders, a series of hybrid coding methods were developed. Such methods combine portions of waveform and vocoding with the most successful hybrid coders using an analysis-by-synthesis method. Such coders use the same or a very similar linear prediction filter model of the vocal tract that is used in linear predictive coding—based vocoders.

The key difference between LPC vocoders and hybrid coders is in the method of modeling speech. LPC-based vocoders use a model that concentrates on voiced and unvoiced portions of speech. In doing so, the isolation of the predictable portion of speech requires the removal of other components, referred to as *speech residue*, containing information that can be important for the effective reconstruction of sound. Since the goal of LPC is to minimize the data rate of encoded speech, the transmission of the residue would defeat the purpose of the encoding technique. In an analysis-by-synthesis hybrid coder, the selection of an excitation signal compensates for the residue problem by attempting to match the analysis parameters via synthesis as closely as possible to the original speech waveform. As you might expect, the ability to perform this analysis-by-synthesis process is highly computation-intensive, and although some hybrid coders were introduced during the early 1980s, it wasn't until the availability of powerful digital signal processors (DSPs) at reasonable prices during the late 1980s and early 1990s that it became practical to implement different hybrid coding methods. Two of the more popular types of hybrid encoders are the Regular Pulse Excited (RPE) coder and the Code Excited Linear Prediction (CELP) coder, with the latter using a code book in its operation.

Regular Pulse Excited Coding

The Regular Pulse Excited (RPE) hybrid coding method forms the basis for speech encoding used by the Global System for Mobile Communications (GSM), a digital mobile radio system used extensively throughout Europe. Under the RPE process, input speech is subdivided into 20-ms frame segments. For each frame, a set of eight short-term predictor coefficients are computed, after which the frame is further subdivided into four 5-ms subframes. For each subframe, the encoder computes a delay and a gain for its long-term predictor. Next, the coder uses 40 residual signal samples (eight per subframe) and converts those samples into three groups of excitation samples, each 13 samples in length. The computation of excitation samples can be considered an interactive process, with the selected coefficients used by a synthesis filter to reconstruct a waveform that is matched against the original waveform. After the difference between waveforms is noted, the process is repeated using a new set of coefficients until the error between synthesized speech and the original waveform reaches a minimal level. Three samples that, when synthesized, produce a minimal difference between the original and synthesized waveform are then selected. The sequence that has the highest energy level is then selected as the best representation of the excitation sequence, and the amplitude of each pulse in the sequence is quantized using 3 bits. This technique results in the generation of a 13-Kbps data rate. At the decoder, the received signal is fed through long- and short-term synthesis filters to reconstruct speech.

Finally, a postfilter is used to improve the perceived quality of the reconstructed sound.

The RPE coder provides a good quality of reconstructed speech and does not require a very high level of processing to implement. While RPE represents a viable hybrid coding method, a higher quality of reproduced speech can be obtained by using several versions of a series of hybrid coders known as Code Excited Linear Predictor (CELP) hybrid coders. Thus, let's turn our attention to CELP.

Code Excited Linear Predictor Coders

The Code Excited Linear Predictor (CELP) speech coders were first proposed in 1985, and they represent a relatively recent addition to the various methods used to encode speech. CELP also represents a hybrid coding technique that employs both waveform and vocoding techniques, resulting in an analysis-by-synthesis process to code speech.

CELP differs from RPE in that the excitation signal is vector-quantized after speech is passed through a vocal tract and pitch predictor, and an index from a code book is used in place of the actual quantization of the excitation signal. This technique allows a code book of 1024 entries to use a 10-bit index, which can substantially reduce the data rate required to transmit the excitation signal that best represents the original waveform. That is, an analysis-by-synthesis approach minimizes the difference between the original waveform sample and a synthesized waveform by using an index selected from the code book.

As a result of using a code book index, CELP coders operate at data rates between 4.8 and 16 Kbps. The key difference between various CELP coders is in the adaptability of code book entries and the delay associated with selecting and transmitting a code book index that represents the excitation signal.

FS 1016

The U.S. Department of Defense standardized a version of CELP, FS 1016, that operates at 4.8 Kbps. This version of CELP uses a code book in which one portion is adaptively changed, while the other portion is fixed. The fixed portion of the code book contains entries that represent one pitch of speech residue, while the adaptive portion is filled in during operation with copies of the previous residue delayed by variable amounts of time.

Although the FS 1016 CELP method is widely used by the U.S. Department of Defense for secure telephone communications via the encryption of its digitized data stream, it introduces an end-to-end transmission delay that at times during a normal voice conversation may appear slightly awkward. This is caused by delays associated with processing a block of sampled voice and searching the code book for a suitable index, during which time the analyzed sample is synthesized until an entry that produces a minimum amount of error is selected. The delay associated with the FS 1016 CELP system can range up to approximately 100 ms.

The G.728 Recommendation

Recognizing the delay problem associated with previously developed versions of CELP, the ITU released a set of requirements for a 16-Kbps voice digitization method in 1988 to provide toll-quality speech comparable to the 32-Kbps ADPCM standardized under its G.721 Recommendation. The ITU requirements were satisfied by the development of a backward-adaptive CELP coder that was developed at AT&T Bell Laboratories and standardized in 1992 as Recommendation G.728.

The G.728 CELP Recommendation uses a backward-adaptive process to calculate short-term filter coefficients. This enables the computation of filter coefficients from past reconstructed speech instead of from 20 to 30 ms of buffered input and allows a much shorter frame length than that used by other CELP coding techniques. Under the G.728 Recommendation, a frame length of five samples is used, which results in a delay of approximately 20 ms. The algorithm delay of the G.728 coder is approximately 0.625 ms, resulting in an achievable end-to-end delay of approximately 2.5 ms. This represents the lowest latency of all CELP coding techniques.

APPLICATION NOTE G.728-compatible coders are referred to as *Low Delay* CELP (LD-CELP) because their 2.5-ms latency is the lowest of all members of the CELP family of coders.

Another interesting aspect of the G.728 Recommendation is its use of a high-order short-term predictor, thus eliminating the need for a long-term predictor. This technique allows 10 bits to be used per sample, with 7 representing a fixed code book index and 3 representing an excitation gain, resulting in a data rate of 16 Kbps. Two additional CELP-related standards warrant attention: the G.729 Recommendation and the G.723.1 Recommendation. Let's turn to these now.

The G.729 Recommendation

The G.729 Recommendation and a reduced-complexity alternative specified in Annex A to that standard represent two voice coding methods that produce both high-quality voice and a high compression ratio that result in a low data rate for the transmission of digitized speech. The G.729 Recommendation is based on the CELP algorithm, but it uses a speech frame length of 10 ms. The more formal name of the G.729 Recommendation is Conjugate-Structure Algebraic Code Excited Linear Prediction (CS-ACELP), and the original standard was approved by the ITU in November 1995.

CS-ACELP uses a 10-ms frame size plus a 5-ms lookahead, which results in a total of a 15-ms algorithmic delay, slightly exceeding the G.728 low-delay coding method. However, instead of requiring a 16-Kbps data rate, CS-ACELP uses a data rate of 8 Kbps to encode a voice conversation. The G.729 Annex A CS-ACELP speech-compression algorithm represents a reduced-complexity version of the G.729 coder. The G.729 Annex A speech coder was developed for use in simultaneous voice and data multimedia applications and is primarily employed in modems that provide simultaneous voice and data transmission capability.

Due to the fact that voice digitization based on the G.729 Recommendation provides a near-toll quality roughly compatible to the ADPCM G.721 standard but at one-quarter of its bandwidth, another popular use of G.729 is in adapter cards for multiplexers, frame relay access devices (FRADs), and similar products. Its use enables voice to be transported at a very low data rate. In fact, some vendors have added a proprietary silence-suppression capability to the G.729 coding mechanism that reduces the average amount of bandwidth required to transport a voice conversation to approximately 4 Kbps.

APPLICATION NOTE Although the use of a CS-ACELP coder results in half the bandwidth of LD-CELP, the coding delay increases from approximately 2.5 ms to 15.0 ms.

The G.723.1 Recommendation

When transporting voice-encoded packets over public packet networks, there exists a probability that packets will be lost. This is especially true for transmission occurring on frame relay networks since the design of this network was based on certain frames being discarded during periods of high utilization. When transmission occurs on other types of packet networks, such as an IP network, the occurrence of an error condition could result in the retransmission of a packet. If the packet contains digitized voice, the delay associated with retransmission would alter the ability to receive the packet at the time it was needed for the correct reconstruction of the portion of a voice conversation carried in the packet, and it might just as well be dropped. Thus, the transmission of packets containing digitized voice requires a coding method with a degree of robustness to handle lost packets.

This robustness, also referred to as frame erasure ability, became an important consideration when the ITU was examining several competing methods to standardize the audio portion of videoconferencing and public telephony. As a result, the ITU selected a dual-rate coding technique now known as Recommendation G.723.1.

A G.723.1 coder supports both 5.3- and 6.3-Kbps coding rates, with the higher bit rate providing a higher quality of reproduced voice. Support for both rates is a mandatory part of the specification, and an option exists to enable implementers to suppress periods of silence using a voice activity detection (VAD) technique, which when used provides a variable operating rate that can result in an average data rate of between 2.65 and 3.15 Kbps.

The G.723.1 Recommendation was approved by the ITU in March 1996 and, during 1997, was recommended by the International Multimedia Teleconferencing Consortium's Voice over IP Forum as the default low bit rate audio coder for the ITU H.323 standard. The ITU H.323 standard defines the method for voice and video communications over packet-based networks, which makes the G.723.1 standard suitable for Internet videoconferencing, Internet telephony, voice over frame relay, and other applications.

The quality of reproduced voice encoded and decoded based on the G.723.1 Recommendation is best judged by the results of a quality test known as Mean Opinion Score (MOS). MOS is a test used to rate the quality of different speech-coding techniques. On the MOS scale, a score of 4.0 is considered to represent toll quality, the quality of speech you would hear on a call routed through a typical PSTN call. Based on several MOS tests, G.723.1 coders were rated at 3.98, which is a variation of only 0.02 point from full toll quality while requiring approximately 1/17th the bandwidth of PSTN toll-quality communications. Due to this capability, it is very reasonable to expect that, although only recently standardized, the use of G.723.1 coding will be quickly adopted by a large number of hardware and software developers.

However, like Gordon Gecko's greed, the low bandwidth of the G.723.1 Recommendation can get you into trouble. This is because the multi-rate

TABLE 4-1

Voice Coding Algorithm Selection Criteria to Consider

■ What coding bandwidth does the algorithm require?

■ Is the algorithm standardized?

■ Do other vendor products support interoperability based on the algorithm being considered?

■ Does the algorithm generate high-quality voice or just intelligent speech?

■ What is the end-to-end delay associated with the algorithm?

■ Is the algorithm suitable for use on packet networks?

■ Does the algorithm pass fax and/or modem modulation and call progress or similar signaling tones?

CELP coding technique has the longest delay of all CELP coding techniques, resulting in a delay of approximately 30 ms! Due to this extended delay, the anticipated migration to the G.723.1 Recommendation has not reached its apparent level of original interest.

4.5   Algorithm Selection

Although your first impression might be to select a voice coding algorithm that uses the least amount of bandwidth, the use of that metric might not result in the selection of an appropriate algorithm. While bandwidth is an important selection criteria, there are additional areas you should investigate. Table 4-1 lists seven algorithm selection criteria ques-

TABLE 4-2

G-Series Voice Coding Comparison

Standard	Description	Bandwidth (Kbps)	Coding delay
G.711	PCM	64	1 μs
G.721	ADPCM	32, 16, 24, 40	1.25 μs
G.728	LD-CELP	16	2.5 ms
G.729	CS-ACELP	8	15.0 ms
G.723.1	Multi-rate CELP	6.3/5.3	30.0 ms

tions you may wish to answer. To facilitate answers to the fifth question, Table 4-2 provides a comparison of five popular G-series voice coding recommendations. By carefully comparing the answer to each question contained in Table 4-1 with the information contained in Table 4-2 against the requirements of your application, you can select an appropriate voice coding algorithm to satisfy your requirements.

Telephone Operations

In Chapter 4, we focused on various methods used to digitize human speech. In this chapter, we turn our attention to the manner in which digitized voice is conveyed between source and destination over the telephone company infrastructure or a private network formed by the use of leased lines to interconnect corporate PBXs. To do so, we will examine the operation of the telephone and PBX and learn how signal information is passed between telephone instruments. This will provide the foundation necessary to understand how to configure different types of voice over data network products so they can correctly interoperate with existing and planned voice and data communications equipment.

5-1 Signaling

The purpose of signaling in a voice network is twofold. First, signaling is necessary to convey information about a potential connection. Second, signaling enables a connection to be established through a voice network.

Types

There are two primary types or categories of signaling that are necessary to establish a telephone call. When you pick up a telephone handset, your action must be recognized by a central office or PBX serving your instrument. This type of signaling is commonly referred to as *subscriber loop* or *station loop signaling,* as it occurs on the loop connecting the telephone subscriber to the central office or PBX.

A second type of signaling occurs at the central office or PBX when the destination telephone number is not serviced by the central office switch or a corporate PBX. In such situations the call must be forwarded to another switch or PBX via a trunk line linking central office switches or company PBXs. The ability to access the trunk involves trunk signaling and represents a second type of signaling required to establish a voice call.

In this chapter, we will examine both types of signaling. Because all manual calls commence with a telephone instrument, let's turn our attention to the manner in which it is used to initiate a telephone call.

5-2 Initiating a Telephone Call

When you pick up a telephone handset in your home or office, a sequence of predefined operations occurs that provides you with the ability to receive a dial tone and initiate a telephone call. The ability to make a telephone call begins when you remove the handset from the telephone. Thus, let's examine the manner by which a telephone is connected to a communications carrier's central office switch or a corporate PBX, as both devices function in a similar manner by directly interoperating with the connected telephone instrument.

The Telephone Connection

A telephone is connected via a pair of wires, called the *ring* and the *tip*, to a connector on a communications carrier's central office switch or a similar connection on a corporate PBX. An example of this connection is illustrated in Figure 5-1.

Each local telephone number consists of a prefix and extension. The prefix, such as 477, identifies an exchange served by the central office switch or PBX. The four-digit extension identifies a unique device in the exchange. Originally, most central office switches and PBXs were limited to supporting a single exchange; however, the rapid growth in the installation of telephones resulted in the development of switches and PBXs capable of handling multiple exchanges. In the example illustrated in Figure 5-1, we will assume for simplicity that the switch or PBX serves one exchange whose prefix is 477, while the extension assigned to the telephone is 0293.

Figure 5-1

Directly connecting a telephone to a central office switch or corporate PBX.

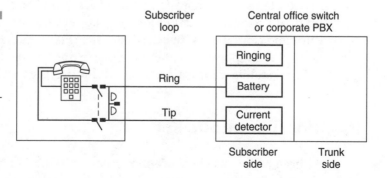

The Subscriber Loop

The wire pair routed from the switch or PBX to the telephone is referred to as a *subscriber loop*. A 48-volt direct current (VDC) potential is placed across the loop by the switch or PBX to power the telephone instrument as well as to provide a mechanism for monitoring telephone activity. Concerning the latter, when you lift the telephone handset to initiate a call, this action results in the closure of a switch hook in the telephone, enabling current to flow through the local loop. The flow of current signals to the switch or PBX that the instrument has gone off-hook and the user wants to initiate a call.

Dial Registers and Dial Tones

On detecting the presence of loop current, a switch or PBX performs two associated actions. First, it searches for an available buffer area to store dialed digits as they are received, an area more formally referred to as a *dial register*. Once an available dial register is associated with the local loop, the switch or PBX transmits a dial tone to the subscriber, enabling the telephone user to dial the desired number.

Intraswitch Communications

If the dialed exchange is served by the switch or PBX, the device will attempt to make a cross-connection through the switch. To do so, the switch or PBX first checks the line associated with the dialed number to ascertain if it is in use. Assuming it isn't, the switch or PBX transmits a ringing voltage down a different local loop, which causes the bell in the telephone attached to that loop to ring. If the called party is in, he or she lifts the handset, which causes current to flow in the loop. This action informs the switch or PBX that the ringing voltage should cease and the audio connection between calling and called parties should be established. Now that we have a basic appreciation for the method in which a call is established through a central office switch or corporate PBX, let's examine in additional detail the components of the telephone infrastructure and the manner in which signaling information is passed through the telephone network.

The Telephone Set

Although the switched telephone network is a two-wire network, the connection between switches and PBXs as well as the operation of the telephone are based on the use of four wires representing a pair of wire pairs. To understand why the telephone requires a pair of wire pairs requires a brief examination of the telephone handset. Then we can briefly discuss how the four-wire to two-wire conversion is accomplished.

The Handset

The telephone handset has a *transmitter* and a *receiver* better known as its *mouth* and *ear pieces*. Two wires are connected to the mouth piece and two to the ear piece, as each operates independently of the other and requires two wires to form a circuit. Those four wires are routed into the base of the telephone where they are connected to a conversion device known as a *hybrid*. The hybrid converts the four-wire interface into a two-wire interface, which enables the telephone to operate via a two-wire connection to the telephone company switch or corporate PBX. Other components of the telephone that warrant a degree of discussion include its switch hook, side tone, dialer, and ringer.

The Switch Hook

The switch hook is placed in an open position by pressure from the handset. Thus, when the handset is lifted, the switch hook closes, enabling current to flow through the telephone and local loop and signaling the telephone company switch or corporate PBX.

The Side Tone

The side tone represents a design of the hybrid within the telephone that enables a portion of speech to "bleed" over the ear piece or receiver. The purpose of the side tone is to enable a person to hear themselves talk so they have a better ability to adjust the tone of their conversation.

The Dialer

There are two types of telephone dialers: rotary and push button or tone. In rotary dialing you rotate a circular dial to the digit position to generate the dialed digit. In comparison, push button dialing results in the generation of a unique combination of frequencies or tones when a button is pushed, hence the name *tone dialing*. When we discuss signaling later in this chapter, we will include both pulse and tone dialing in that discussion.

The Local Loop

As previously discussed, the connection between the telephone instrument and the switch or PBX is the subscriber loop, more commonly known as the local loop. This connection is a two-wire circuit, with one wire known as the *tip* and the other referred to as the *ring*. This nomenclature dates to the use of switchboards, in which two wires terminated in a plug that was inserted into a circular tube in the switchboard to make a connection. One wire in the plug is attached to the top of the connector, while the other wire is electrically connected to the ring on the connector, resulting in the terminology "tip" and "ring." In the more modern communications environment, the tip wire is connected to the ground side of the battery at the central office switch or corporate PBX, while the ring side is connected to the negative terminal.

The Switch Hybrid

The use of a two-wire circuit to connect a telephone instrument to a serving telephone company switch or corporate PBX was primarily based on economics. A two-wire circuit is less expensive than a four-wire circuit and provides a full-duplex transmission path suitable for a variable distance based on the wire gauge of the conductor. Usually, two-wire circuits can be used at distances of up to approximately 1 to 2 miles.

When the telephone network was established, the routing of calls between exchanges required the transmission of voice over much longer distances than those used in local loops. Since a signal attenuates as it traverses a circuit, the telephone company inserted amplifiers within long-distance circuits to rebuild attenuated signals. However, since amplifiers are unidirectional, voice had to be separated into two different paths for transmission between central office switches, with one path used for transmission and the other used for reception. This signal splitting resulted in the use of a four-wire circuit for transmitting voice between central offices, with the circuit commonly referred to as a *trunk*. This four-wire circuit requirement is also applicable when leased lines are used to create a private voice network by interconnecting corporate PBXs.

The conversion of the two-wire local loop to a four-wire trunk is accomplished by a hybrid in a manner similar to the hybrid in a telephone. However, unlike the telephone-set hybrid that is lightly imbalanced to generate side tones, the switch hybrid must be balanced. Otherwise, it

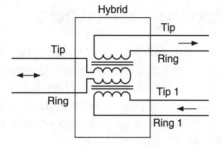

Figure 5-2
The central office hybrid converts the two-wire local loop to the four-wire trunk and vice versa.

would reflect energy that would result in an echo. On a four-wire circuit connecting PBXs or central office switches, the transmit path conductors are referred to as tip and ring, while the receive path conductors are referred to as tip 1 and ring 1 to differentiate them from the transmit path. Figure 5-2 illustrates the operation of a central office hybrid. To alleviate the echo that results from a portion of speech energy being reflected back toward the talker, communications carriers use echo suppressors or echo cancelers. Both devices are designed to minimize the effect of reflected speech energy.

When transmitting voice over IP or frame relay, it is important to note that the telephone system normally does not perform echo cancellation on local calls, even when a call is routed between two switches and results in a two-wire to four-wire conversion and a reconversion from a four-wire to a two-wire circuit. For relatively short transmission distance, typically less than 50 miles, latency is not long enough for the echo to return as a separate transmission. Because local connections are used for voice over IP and voice over frame relay, the telephone system will not perform echo cancellation. However, because long-distance calls are being made, the echo from two-wire to four-wire hybrids will propagate through the network back to the speaker and would become very disruptive unless canceled. Thus, voice-compliant routers, FRADS, and gateways should provide an echo-cancellation capability when used for transmission beyond a 50-mile range.

APPLICATION NOTE To prevent disruptive echo from being returned to the speaker, voice-compliant routers, FRADs, and gateways should perform echo cancellation when used to establish a voice over IP or voice over frame relay transmission path that exceeds 50 miles in length.

5-3   Signaling Methods

In this section, we turn our attention to the types of signaling used to establish a telephone call and the manner in which those signals are routed via subscriber or local loops onto trunks. This information builds on the prior section, and the goal of both sections is to provide you with the information necessary to acquire and configure equipment to transmit voice over data networks.

Types of Signaling

There are three types of signaling that must be conveyed to establish a telephone call: supervisory, address, and call progress. In this section, we will examine each type of signaling; however, due to key differences between local loop and trunk supervisory signaling, we will discuss each separately.

Supervisory Signaling

Supervisory signaling is used to inform the telephone instrument and ports on the telephone company switch or corporate PBX of the status of the local loop and any connected trunks between switches and PBXs. There are several methods used for supervisory signaling, with the loop-start signaling method representing the most common method used on the local loop.

LOOP-START SIGNALING
Under the loop-start signaling method, the lifting of the telephone handset, a condition referred to as *off-hook,* results in the switch hook closing. This action results in a current flowing through the local loop, which the switch or PBX detects and responds to with a dial tone. When the switch or PBX generates the dial tone, it also places its port connected to the telephone via the local loop in an off-hook indication mode. This action results in the local loop becoming active. When a call is terminated by a subscriber placing the headset back into its cradle, the switch hook opens, stopping the flow of current, and the local loop returns to its *on-hook* state. Regardless of the type of signaling used, the terms "on-hook" and "off-hook" are universally used to describe the state of the local loop with respect to the presence or absence of a current caused by the state of the

switch hook. When loop-start signaling is used, the terminating end of the loop in the form of a central office switch or corporate PBX supplies the battery and current-detection circuitry. In comparison, the originating end provides only a DC path via the positioning of the switch hook.

Address Signaling

A second type of signaling used in a telephone system is address signaling. Address signaling provides the telephone number that enables a call to be routed to its appropriate destination. There are two commonly used methods of address signaling: dial pulse and dual-tone multifrequency (DTMF) signaling.

DIAL PULSE

Under dial-pulse signaling, digits are transmitted from the originating telephone instrument by the opening and closing of the local loop. In actuality, as you turn the rotary dial, your action winds up a spring. When you release the dial to select a digit, the spring rotates back to its originating position and opens and closes the loop a number of times, which corresponds to the value of the dialed digit. Figure 5-3 illustrates the generation of three digits via a rotary dial.

In examining Figure 5-3, note that each dialed digit must be generated at a specific rate and must be within a predefined tolerance for it to be recognized. To accomplish this, each pulse consists of two parts referred to as *make* and *break*. The make segment represents the period when the circuit is closed, while the break segment represents the period of time that the circuit is placed in the open condition during a dialed-digit period.

In North America the make/break ratio is 39 percent make to 61 percent break, while in the United Kingdom the ratio used is 33 percent make to 67 percent break. A second metric that governs the operation of pulse dialing is pulse rate. In North America, digits are pulsed at a constant rate of 10 pulses per second (PPS). The rate may vary in other locations.

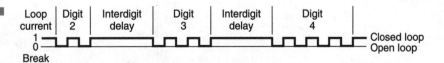

Figure 5-3
Pulse dialing a series of digits.

APPLICATION NOTE When planning to interconnect a voice gateway to the switched telephone network in a foreign country, you should determine the make/break ratio and pulses-per-second rate required for pulse dialing.

TONE DIALING

A second type of address signaling results from the transmission of tones instead of pulses. Tone dialing, more formally known as *dual-tone multi-frequency* (DTMF) signaling, results in the use of a 12-key keypad that has two frequencies associated with each key. Each row and column of keys on a tone-generation instrument is associated with a predefined frequency, as illustrated in Figure 5-4. Pressing a key on the keypad results in the generation of a low- and high-frequency sine wave tone pair. For example, pressing the 8 key shown in Figure 5-4 would result in the generation of the frequency pair 852 and 1336 Hz, which informs the connected switch or PBX port that the digit 8 was dialed. This also explains the *dual* in DTMF.

Informational Signaling

A third type of signaling can be categorized as informational, as it informs the originator of the status of a dialed call and rings the called party to alert him or her to the presence of the call. This type of signaling is also commonly referred to as *call-progress signaling*, since most of the signaling is used to inform the originator of the call's progress. Common types of informational signaling include busy and fast busy signals, a dial tone signal, a ring signal, and a ringback signal.

DIAL TONE

In North America, certain predefined frequency pairs are used to convey informational signaling. For example, a dial tone results from the genera-

Figure 5-4

Tone assignments for the DTMF keypad.

	1209 Hz	1336 Hz	1477 Hz
697 Hz	1	2	3
770 Hz	4	5	6
852 Hz	7	8	9
941 Hz	*	0	#

tion of a continuous 350- and 440-Hz frequency pair by the telephone company switch or the corporate PBX.

RINGING SIGNAL

When a call is routed to its destination, the serving switch or PBX sends a 20-Hz 86-VAC ringing signal that cycles for 2 seconds ON followed by 4 seconds OFF.

RINGBACK SIGNAL

To inform the originator that the call is in a ringing state, a ringback tone is generated by the local switch or PBX. This ringback tone consists of a 400- and 480-Hz frequency pair, also cycled at 2 seconds ON followed by 4 seconds OFF.

BUSY SIGNAL

If the called party is using the telephone, the local switch or PBX will generate a busy signal to the call originator. This signal consists of the frequency pair 480 and 620 Hz cycled for 0.5 second ON followed by 0.5 second OFF. If the call cannot be completed because of trunks between switches being busy (for example, on Mother's Day), the local switch or PBX will generate a fast busy signal.

FAST BUSY SIGNAL

The fast busy signal consists of the frequency pair 480 to 620 Hz cycled for 0.2 seconds ON followed by 0.3 seconds OFF. As previously noted, this signal is generated immediately by the local switch when it cannot find a trunk through which to route a call whose destination is beyond the local switch. All of the preceding informational signaling tones represent frequencies and cycling periods used in North America. These will vary in other locations throughout the world.

APPLICATION NOTE Prior to connecting equipment to a PBX or the switched network in a foreign location, it is important to verify the compatibility of the equipment with call-progress signaling frequencies. Doing so ahead of time can alleviate a considerable amount of potential frustration.

Trunk Signaling

The composition of a telephone number is used by a switch as a decision metric to determine if the destination is local or requires the establishment of a path to a distant switch. For example, if you enter the numeric 1 followed by other digits when making a call over the PSTN, the 1 indicates that the called party is not local to the switch serving the subscriber. If you are connected to a corporate PBX, the entry of a 9 is commonly used to inform the PBX you need an outside line, and the digits that follow are then routed to a telephone company switch. Similarly, entering a 7 might be used by the PBX to identify local PBX calls and allow you to enter a four-digit extension, resulting in the PBX making a cross-connection directly between the caller and called party without routing the call beyond the PBX.

The ability to program a PBX by assigning prefix numbers to predefined trunk groups or PBX ports that function as a rotary group enables organizations to connect their PBXs to different communications devices and even different communications carriers. For example, you could connect a group of PBX ports to voice card ports on a frame relay access device and configure the group as a hunt or rotary group. This means that multiple users connected to the PBX could each dial a prefix, such as 5, and have the PBX establish a cross-connection to the first available port in the group of ports designed to function as an entity.

As previously discussed, the path between two central office switches is referred to as a *trunk*. When corporate PBXs are interconnected to form a voice network, those connections are also referred to as trunks. Unlike the local loop, both central office and PBX trunks are shared by transmissions from different subscribers, although only one subscriber can use a trunk at any point in time.

Originally, trunks represented individual physical lines, with each trunk carrying one conversation at a time. The development of the T1 circuit as a mechanism to reduce cable congestion in urban areas resulted in multiple logical trunks occurring on one physical trunk. That is, the T1 circuit was developed to convey 24 voice-digitized conversations between switches via the assignment of one voice conversation to each of 24 channels derived by time. Thus, the T1 circuit is a modern-day grouping of 24 logical trunks onto one physical trunk.

Avoiding Glare

Similarly to the local loop, trunks require supervisory signaling. Although loop-start signaling, which is primarily used on local loops, can be used on trunks, its use on certain types of trunks can result in several problems. First, when loop-start signaling is used, only the originating instrument can release the connection. A second problem associated with the use of loop-start signaling is the fact that a trunk could be simultaneously seized from both sides, a condition referred to as *glare*.

Although glare can be tolerated on dedicated local loops, the occurrence of this condition on trunks that users are contending for cannot be tolerated. Therefore, it was necessary to develop a two-way handshaking mechanism to coordinate access to a trunk, with one end requesting access and the remote end acknowledging the request prior to the originating end grabbing the trunk. Trunk supervisory signaling methods have been developed to alleviate the problems associated with the loop-start method when applied to trunks. Some of the more popular ones are the start-dial, the ground-start, and the E&M signaling methods. Thus, let's turn our attention to each signaling method.

Start-dial Supervision

The start-dial supervision signaling method actually refers to a series of signaling methods, including wink-start, immediate-start, and tone-start signaling. Each of these trunk-signaling methods occurs in response to a subscriber going off-hook and results in the seizure of a trunk so digits can be transmitted to a remote switch.

WINK-START SIGNALING

Wink-start represents a commonly used trunk-signaling method. Under this signaling method, the originating trunk is placed in an off-hook condition, which results in the remote switch responding by transmitting an off-hook pulse of between 140 and 290 ms in duration, after which the switch returns to an idle or on-hook state. This off-hook pulse is referred to as a *wink-back*, which when detected by the originating switch results in the switch waiting for at least 210 ms and then transmitting the address digits to the remote switch. The remote switch then returns to an off-hook condition to answer the call. Figure 5-5 illustrates the sequence of operations at the originating and receiving switch during a wink-start trunk-signaling operation.

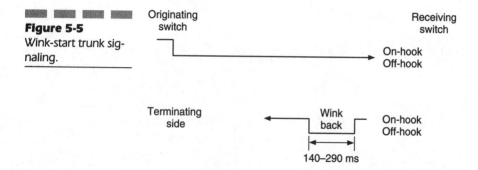

Figure 5-5
Wink-start trunk signaling.

IMMEDIATE-START SIGNALING

Immediate-start signaling represents one of the most basic trunk-signaling methods. When an immediate-start signaling method is used, the originating switch places the trunk off-hook and maintains that condition for a minimum of 150 ms, after which the switch outputs the address digits. Since there is no real handshake between switches, this type of trunk signaling is appropriate only when a dedicated logical or physical trunk is used between switches. Figure 5-6 illustrates an example of immediate-start signaling.

TONE-START SIGNALING

In tone-start signaling, the originating trunk circuit is placed in an off-hook condition. At the receiving switch, the recognition of this condition generates a dial tone. This dial tone can be used by the switch to directly output previously stored digits, or, if the switch is in a cut-through mode, the distant dial tone is passed to the user for dialing. Tone-start signaling is normally used in a private voice network formed by the interconnection of PBXs and not on the switched telephone network. Via the use of the cut-through mode, a user in New York could dial a predefined code, such as 66, and receive a dial tone from the company's PBX in Chicago, allowing the employee to dial a number as if he or she were in the Chicago office.

Ground-start Signaling

The ground-start signaling method is a modification of local loop-start signaling. It eliminates the potential for two switches to simultaneously seize both ends of a trunk. To avoid dual trunk seizure, the ground-start method provides a current-detection mechanism at both ends of the trunk, enabling each end to agree prior to the trunk being seized at one end.

To illustrate the operation of ground-start signaling, consider a PBX that needs to route a call to a telephone company switch, requiring the

Figure 5-6
Immediate-start signaling.

| Originating side | E or M | Off-hook pulse > 150 ms | Dial digits | Conversation |

| Terminating side | M or E | | Ringback | Conversation |

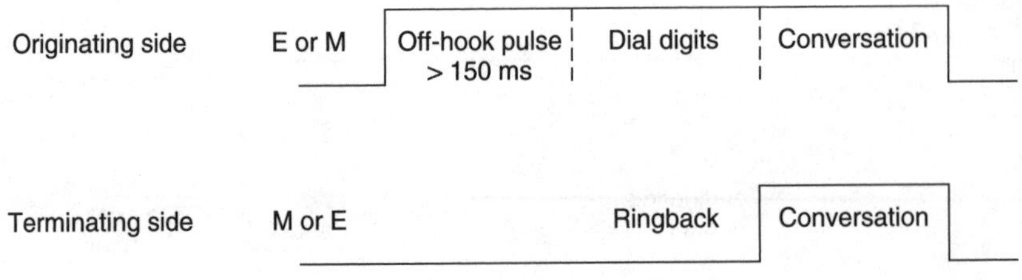

PBX to contend for a trunk. The PBX will ground the ring lead, causing current to flow from the PBX to the central office switch module across the ring circuit. At the telephone company's central office, the switch module senses the current and interprets it as a trunk-seizure request. Assuming the trunk is available, the module acknowledges the request by closing its tip switch, which in turn generates a ground on the tip lead. The flow of current across its tip lead serves as an acknowledgment to the PBX request. Then PBX will close the loop by holding a coil across the tip and ring leads and removing the ring ground. Once this is accomplished, the circuit acts like a loop-start circuit. Figure 5-7 illustrates the sequence of steps associated with ground-start signaling when a PBX initiates the seizure of a trunk. The seizure is bidirectional, allowing the central office switch to initiate the process.

When the switch initiates ground-start signaling, it requests the trunk by closing the tip switch and generating a ringing voltage over the ring lead. The PBX must recognize the incoming seizure within 100 ms to prevent glare. In response to the voltage on the ring lead, the PBX will place a holding coil across tip and ring, which completes the loop and is fol-

Figure 5-7

The steps in ground-start signaling.

PBX   Central office

A. PBX grounds ring lead, current flows on ring lead.

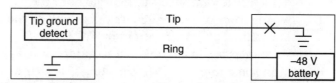

B. Central office senses ring ground from PBX and responds by grounded tip lead.

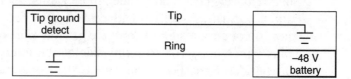

C. PBX senses tip ground, closes the two-wire loop, and removes the ring ground.

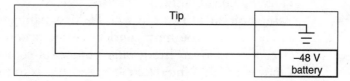

lowed by the central office switch removing the ringing voltage. Once this is accomplished, the trunk acts in a manner similar to loop-start signaling.

E&M Signaling

E&M signaling is the most commonly used method of analog trunk signaling. Under E&M signaling, separate paths are used for voice and signaling. For the voice path, the trunk can consist of either two or four wires. In comparison, for the signaling path there are five methods that can be used, referred to as Types I through V, while a sixth popular method is a British Telecom standard that, as you might expect, is popular in the United Kingdom.

Under E&M signaling, a PBX requests a trunk by raising its M lead. The distant end will honor the request by initiating the flow of the current on the E lead to the requestor. This method of signaling is used by each type of E&M signaling, with the manner in which the flow of signaling occurs used to differentiate one type of signaling from another.

TERMINOLOGY

The letters E&M are derived from the words *ear* and *mouth,* where the M lead is used to transmit signaling and the E lead is used to receive signaling information. When defining trunk signaling, it is common for vendor specification sheets to indicate both the type of trunk, based on the wiring (two- or four-wire circuit), as well as the type of E&M signaling. For example, a specification for 4W E&M TI would refer to a four-wire voice interface to a trunk that requires E&M Type I signaling.

In some respects, E&M signaling is similar to a seial port used for data transmission. That is, like serial ports, E&M signaling has a DTE/CDE type of reference. The trunking side can be viewed as being similar to the DCE and is normally associated with central office functionality. Thus, the connection of a router, FRAD, or voice gateway port commonly results in the port representing the trunking side of the interface. In comparison, the other side of the E&M interface is the signaling side. That side can be viewed as functioning similarly to a DTE. The PBX usually represents the signaling side of an E&M interface.

In addition to five types of E&M signaling, there are two types of audio interface you must consider: two-wire and four-wire. Adding a bit of confusion to an already large number of combinations is the fact that a four-wire E&M interface cable can have six to eight physical wires. This results because the difference between two-wire and four-wire circuits

TABLE 5-1

E&M Interface
Signals

Signal	Description
Ear (E)	Signal wire from trunking (CO) side to signaling (user) side.
Mouth (M)	Signal wire from signaling (user) side to trunking (CO) side.
Signal ground (SG)	Applicable to certain types of E&M signaling, provides –48 V or ground.
Signal battery (SB)	Applicable to certain types of E&M signaling, provides –48 V or ground.
Tip/ring (T/R)	Used on four-wire circuit to carry audio from signaling (user) side to the trunking (CO) side. Not used on a two-wire ciruit.
Tip-1/ring-1 (T-1/R-1)	Used on four-wire circuit to carry audio from the trunking (CO) side to the signaling (user) side. On a two-wire circuit, used to carry full-duplex audio.

depends on whether the audio path is full-duplex on one pair or two pairs of wires. Table 5-1 summarizes the possible E&M interface signals.

Now that we have some familiarity with the terminology, let's turn our attention to the types of E&M signaling.

TYPE I SIGNALING

Under E&M Type I signaling, the battery for both E and M leads is supplied by the PBX. At the PBX, an on-hook condition results in the M lead being grounded and the E lead open. In comparison, an off-hook condition results in the M lead providing the battery and the E lead being grounded. Type I signaling is the most commonly used four-wire trunk interface in North America.

Table 5-2 summarizes E&M Type I signaling. Note that if you connect a PBX directly to a voice port on a router or voice gateway, the router or gateway should normally be configured to ground its E lead to signal a trunk seizure. The PBX should apply battery to its M lead to signal a seizure.

TYPE II SIGNALING

One of the problems associated with Type I signaling is the fact that the interface can cause a high return current through the grounding system. If two PBXs were improperly grounded, this could result in current flowing down the M signaling lead, which results in a remote PBX detecting the current on the E lead. This in turn results in the occurrence of a false seizure of a trunk. To address this problem, E&M Type II signaling added

TABLE 5-2

E&M Type I
Signaling

Condition	M lead	E lead
On-hook	Ground	Open
Off-hook	Battery	Ground

two additional signaling leads: battery (SB) and signal ground (SG). Under Type II signaling, the E lead works in conjunction with the SG lead, while the M lead is strapped to the SB lead. This results in the grounding of the trunk at each end and eliminates potential grounding problems from occurring.

Table 5-3 summarizes E&M Type II signaling. Note that the connection of a voice port on a router or voice gateway is similar to the connection to E&M Type I signaling. That is, the router or voice gateway port grounds its E lead to signal a trunk seizure, while the PBX would apply battery to its M lead to signal a seizure.

TYPE III SIGNALING

Type III signaling is similar to Type I, the key difference being in the use of transmission equipment to supply the battery and ground source, which results in loop current flowing on the M lead when an off-hook condition occurs. Type III signaling was primarily used with older central office equipment and is now in very limited use because most older central office switches have been replaced.

Table 5-4 summarizes E&M Type III signaling. Note that the connection of a voice port on a router or voice gateway requires the router or voice gateway port to sense the flow of current on the M lead for an inbound seizure and ground its E lead for an outbound seizure.

TYPE IV SIGNALING

Type IV signaling is similar to Type II, but the operation of the M lead differs. In Type II signaling, the M lead states are "open" and "battery."

TABLE 5-3

E&M Type II
Signaling

Condition	M lead/SB	E lead/SG
On-hook	Open	Open
Off-hook	Battery	Ground

TABLE 5-4

E&M Type III
Signaling

Condition	M lead/SB	E lead/SG
On-hook	Ground	Open
Off-hook	Loop current	Ground

Under Type IV signaling, the states are "ground" and "open." Table 5-5 summarizes E&M Type IV signaling. Under Type IV signaling, both devices, for example a PBX and a voice port on a router or voice gateway, ground their leads to indicate a trunk seizure. The key advantage of Type IV signaling is the fact that an accidental shorting of the SB lead will not result in an excessive current flow.

TYPE V SIGNALING

Under Type V signaling, both the switch and the transmission equipment supply a battery. Here the battery for the M lead is located in the signaling equipment, while the battery for the E lead is located in the PBX.

Table 5-6 summarizes E&M Type V signaling. Under Type V signaling, the PBX side grounds its M lead to seize the trunk. In comparison, a voice port on a router, FRAD, or voice gateway supporting Type V signaling would ground its E lead to seize the trunk. Type V signaling is the ITU E&M signaling standard and represents the most common method of E&M signaling outside of North America.

INTERFACE CONSIDERATIONS

The ability to correctly connect a voice port on a router, FRAD, or voice gateway to a PBX port depends on the correct configuration of each device to be interconnected. Both the PBX and the port of the router, FRAD, or voice gateway must be configured to support the same signaling method. In addition, many products can be configured for either two- or four-wire operation and need to be compatible at both ends of the link.

TABLE 5-5

E&M Type IV
Signaling

Condition	M lead/SB	E lead/SG
On-hook	Open	Open
Off-hook	Ground	Ground

TABLE 5-6

E&M Type V
Signaling

Condition	M lead/SB	E lead/SG
On-hook	Open	Open
Off-hook	Ground	Ground

When configuring a PBX, it is important to note that many such products use dip switches rather than consoles to configure port interfaces. Even when a PBX appears to be correctly configured, it is important to check the dial plan of the PBX with the numbering plan supported by the router, FRAD, or voice gateway. For example, assume your PBX uses a four-digit-extension dial plan, while an attached voice-capable FRAD configured for four digits requires users to dial a 6 to select the FRAD trunk group. In this situation, the PBX trunk group needs to be configured for a five-digit dial plan to forward the number properly.

T1 Signaling

As previously mentioned in this chapter, T1 circuits can be viewed as representing a logical group of trunks transported on a common physical transmission facility. When used for voice transmission, the T1 circuit consists of 24 channels or time slots that repeat 8000 times per second. Each time slot represents an 8-bit encoded PCM sample. A framing bit is added to each group of 24 samples, resulting in a frame length of $24 \times 8 + 1$, or 193 bits. Since the frame repeats 8000 times per second, this results in the operating rate of the T1 line becoming 193 bits/frame $\times$ 8000 frames/second, or 1.544 Mbps.

To convey 24 analog E&M signals we would normally require 24 wire pairs. Since a T1 circuit consists of two wires in each direction, E&M signaling cannot be directly transferred over a T1 circuit. Instead, an inband signaling technique is used in which busy and idle information is periodically intermixed with digitized voice samples.

CCS

There are two methods that can be used to transmit supervisory signaling over a T1 circuit. Those methods are referred to as *common channel signaling* (CCS) and *common associated signaling* (CAS). Under the CCS method, signaling information is transmitted along the same path as the voice signal; however, it flows on a separate channel that is multi-plexed with the digitized voice signals. This type of signaling is primarily used on the 30-PCM channel circuit known as an E1 circuit line, which uses one channel for signaling and another for frame alignment, resulting in the E1 circuit having 32 channels, each operating at 64 Kbps, for a composite transmission rate of 2.048 Mbps. Although CCS signaling is primarily used with European E1 circuits, it is sometimes used on T1 circuits. When used on a T1 circuit, CCS requires one voice slot to be dedicated to transmitting signaling information.

CAS

To eliminate the necessity of using a voice slot, CAS signaling is primarily used with T1 circuits. Under CAS signaling, the seventh bit position in frames 6 and 12 in a 12-frame framing sequence are "robbed" to convey signaling information. Hence, CAS signaling is informally referred to as *bit robbing*.

Bit position 7 in frames 6 and 12 is used to convey supervisory signaling between PBXs on a private voice network between a PBX and a communications carrier's central office switch or between two switches or two PBXs. The actual pattern represented by bit 7 in frames 6 and 12 is based on the type of signaling, such as loop-start, ground-start, or E&M, and the signal being conveyed. For example, under loop-start signaling, such signaling information as loop open, loop closed, ring present, and ring removed must be conveyed. In comparison, E&M signaling only has two states: idle and busy. To differentiate between the signal bits, the seventh bit in the sixth frame is referred to as the "A" bit, while the signal bits in the twelfth frame are referred to as the "B" bits.

A second T1 framing method, called *extended superframe format* (ESF), extends the T1 frame sequence to 24 frames. Under ESF, signal bits are conveyed in frames 6, 12, 18, and 24, with the bits labeled A, B, C, and D, respectively. Due to the fact that T1 lines can be provisioned as either a 12-frame sequence known as D4 framing or a 24-frame sequence known as ESF, you must consider the compatibility between the signaling method used and the framing format when acquiring equipment to construct a voice network. In addition, when considering the transmission of voice over a data network, you must also consider the type of signaling supported by your organization's PBX and the manner in which such signaling can be conveyed over a data network, including communications equipment you may use to obtain a voice over data network transmission capability.

5-4 PBX Interface Considerations

In concluding this chapter, we will briefly discuss several items you should consider when connecting voice-compliant router, FRAD, or gateway ports to a PBX. Because most products currently on the market interface with a PBX via an analog signaling method, the key to the successful configuration of equipment is to trick the PBX into viewing the attached device as a bank of ordinary analog telephone lines. Those lines would normally be routed to a central office, and thus the PBX configuration should be set as if the PBX were connected to ordinary analog CO lines.

The connections from ports on the attached device to the PBX should behave in the same manner as analog trunk lines. That is, they should present a ringing voltage when a call is received and DTMF or pulses with appropriate make/break cycle and digits when calls arrive. In addition, when calls are forwarded through the PBX, the attached device should provide appropriate call-progress tones, such as fast busy, busy, and ringback.

As we noted earlier in this chapter, it is important to consider the dial plan used by both the PBX and the attached device. Doing so will result in the correct number of digits being passed between devices. Last but not least, it is extremely important to configure the PBX and attached ports to support the same signaling method. While these points may appear self-explanatory, they contribute to a majority of the interoperability problems that users encounter.

Voice over IP Networking

Until this chapter, we have purposely avoided any detailed discussion of a technology that for many readers is perhaps the most common method of transmitting voice over a data network: Internet telephony. The reason for this avoidance is twofold. First, Internet telephony is a term used primarily to refer to the use of software in conjunction with a sound card and microphone to provide individual PC users with the ability to initiate and receive calls over the Internet. This is a very important application and one that can be expected to continue to grow and is therefore covered in this chapter. However, it relies on the use of a separate "instrument" instead of a PC user's existing telephone, which in most organizations is connected to a PBX and provides the focal point for incoming and outgoing calls via an organization's private interconnected PBX network or the public switched telephone network (PSTN). Thus, a second reason for having avoided a detailed discussion of Internet telephony until now is that it represents more of an individual solution than an organizational solution for the transmission of voice over the Internet. However, as we will note in this chapter, there are several methods by which voice can be transported via an IP network, and for many organizations a mixture of methods may be required to satisfy both internal and external requirements, with external requirements primarily driven by potential and actual customers using the Internet to access a help desk, an order desk, or another facility operated by the organization.

In this chapter, we will first discuss the differences between Internet telephony and what this author prefers to refer to as "telephony on the Internet," by which I mean the indirect connection of standard telephones to the Internet. As we examine the basic hardware and software required to support each method of communication, including the advantages and disadvantages, we will consider the reliability issues associated with transmitting audio on the Internet and on private IP networks. From this foundation, we will review the operation and utilization of several vendor products as well as the construction of economic models to illustrate why individuals and businesses are viewing the Internet as the new audio frontier.

In concluding this chapter, we will turn our attention to a technique that can be used to obtain the reliability and predictability required to transport voice over a wide area network when you cannot obtain an IP quality of service over the WAN infrastructure. The technique we will examine involves the use of an asynchronous transfer mode (ATM) backbone network. Because many communications carriers offer ATM WAN transmission facilities, the ability to map IP datagrams into an appropriate ATM class of traffic can be used to provide the reliability and predictability required to obtain a high quality of reconstructed voice.

6-1 Internet Telephony versus Telephony over the Internet

Many years ago, the playwright Oscar Wilde, referring to the United States and the United Kingdom, noted that they were two great countries separated by a common language. If we fast-forward to our present era and discuss Internet telephony and telephony over the Internet, we could paraphrase his words as "two great techniques separated by technical incompatibilities." While the use of both techniques can be expected to significantly increase in usage, they are designed to satisfy different user and organizational requirements, and they incorporate different technologies to satisfy those requirements. To better understand the major differences between the two voice-transmission techniques, let's examine each technique in detail.

Internet Telephony

In this book, we will use the term *Internet telephony* to refer to the transmission of digitized voice conversations over the Internet by individual PC users. The technology associated with Internet telephony is primarily based on the use of sound cards installed in a PC, a microphone connected to the sound card, and appropriate software.

Overview

The basic operation of an Internet telephony system commences when a person talks into a microphone. The microphone is in turn connected to a sound card installed in the computer, which accepts an analog waveform and converts it into a digital data stream. Internet telephony software operating on the computer takes the digitized voice data stream, which normally represents a 64-Kbps PCM or a 32-Kbps ADPCM-encoded voice, and compresses the standard encoding data stream into a lower data rate based on the use of a proprietary or standardized voice-compression technique. Once this is accomplished, the software packages the digitized and compressed data stream into packets using a protocol for transmission over the Internet. Most Internet telephony products were originally developed primarily to support modem connections; however, modern products also support LAN-based operations when the LAN is connected to the Internet.

There are two primary transport protocols used for an Internet telephony session. TCP is used to transport addressing or directory information, while UDP is used for the actual transfer of voice-digitized packets. Although the actual ability to digitize voice entered through a microphone is a relatively simple process, differences in the manner in which connections are established over the Internet, voice-digitization methods, and the framing of digitized voice samples results in a high degree of incompatibility between vendor products. Before turning our attention to the operation of specific products, let's digress a bit and discuss the economic issues associated with Internet telephony and its basic operation.

Economic Issues

Any discussion of economic issues associated with Internet access must consider the method of access used. Thus, prior to discussing the economic issues associated with Internet access, let's examine the two basic methods used to obtain such access.

BASIC ACCESS METHODS

There are two basic methods associated with Internet access: dial-up and direct connection. Dial-up access is based on transmission using the Serial Line Interface Protocol (SLIP) or the Point-to-Point Protocol (PPP) to an Internet service provider's (ISP's) network access device. The ISP's network access device physically consists of a series of rack-mounted modems connected to a communications server. The server represents one of several devices connected to a local area network, with a router connected to the LAN, while the router's serial port is used to provide a high-speed communications connection from the ISP to an Internet network service provider (NSP). The NSP typically operates a high-speed backbone connection that provides interconnectivity between ISPs.

Dedicated access is normally associated with the connection of a group of subscribers located within a building or university campus. Under this access method, subscribers are connected to a corporate LAN, and the local area network is in turn connected via the use of a router and leased line to an ISP. Instead of the line terminating at an ISP's communications server, the leased line terminates at a multiport router connected to a LAN. Each subscriber PC commonly operates a browser on top of a TCP/IP protocol stack, either purchased from a third-party provider or obtained from operating systems that include built-in stacks, such as Windows 95, Windows 98, or Windows NT/Windows 2000. Figure 6-1 illustrates the two primary methods used for accessing the Internet. Now we will turn our attention to the pricing structure of each method.

Figure 6-1
Internet access
methods.

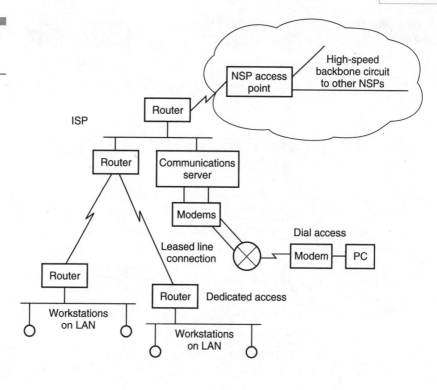

Legend: ISP = Internet service provider
NSP = Network service provider
⊗ = Switched telephone network

PRICING STRUCTURE

On an individual dial-up connection, many ISPs offer a flat-fee pricing structure, typically $19.95 per month for unlimited use. When this type of pricing structure is used, there is essentially no additional cost associated with transmitting voice over the Internet, other than the one-time cost for hardware and software and fees charged by certain vendors that now offer a voice gateway service. The voice gateway service enables calls routed via the Internet to be dialed to their ultimate destination via the public switched telephone network, as illustrated in Figure 6-2. In examining Figure 6-2, it should be noted that the voice gateway is programmed to accept calls from predefined accounts or a pay-as-you-use account based on the use of a "digital cash" or through the use of a credit or debit card. Once access is authorized, the voice gateway will out-dial the desired telephone number, billing the user for a local call and surcharge or for a long-

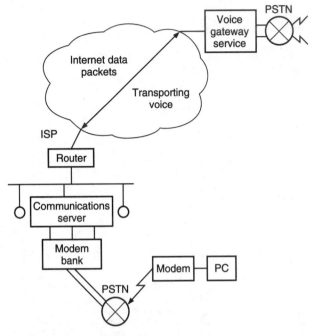

Legend: PSTN = public switched telephone network

distance call that's more economical because the gateway operator can purchase a block of minutes at a lower rate than individuals can obtain.

The use of a voice gateway is most effective for conducting international long-distance calls. For example, a voice gateway provider might bill calls received via the Internet for a gateway service in London at $.25 per minute. If you were calling via an ISP connection in New York, you could avoid a long-distance international call between New York and London that could cost between $.50 and $1.25 per minute, depending on the time of day the call is made. Thus, you might be able to save between $.25 and $1.00 per minute for this type of call.

FLAT-FEE BILLING

There are two primary methods ISPs use for billing a dedicated connection. The first is on a monthly flat-fee basis, which is based on the operating rate of the line connection. As you might expect, a 256-Kbps fractional T1 (FT1) line connection costs more than a 56-Kbps line connection, while a T1 line connection operating at 1.544 Mbps costs more than a 256-Kbps FT1 line connection. When based on the line operating rate, the cost associated with transmitting voice over the Internet depends on the capacity and cost of the current line connection. If there is sufficient capacity on the current line connection for the transmission of voice, then the cost of voice transmission is limited to the one-time expense associated with required hardware and software. If sufficient capacity is not available on the current line connection, then the cost associated with voice transmission requires you to determine the additional costs of replacing the existing connection with a higher-speed connection.

LINE-UTILIZATION BILLING

The second popular billing method used by ISPs is based on line utilization. Some ISPs will install a T1 connection that is billed at a monthly base cost for the line plus a utilization charge, with the latter based on either the average percentage, a fixed percentage, or a similar metric computed over a 24-hour period. This type of billing is more difficult to use for estimating the cost of transmitting voice, as you now have to determine the potential effect of transmitting and receiving digitized voice on the utilization level of your organization's Internet connections.

For example, if you obtain equipment that results in the digitization of speech at an 8-Kbps data rate, then every minute of speech activity results in the additional transfer of 8 Kbps × 60 seconds/8 bits/byte, or 60 Kbytes per minute. On an hourly basis, this results in the additional transfer of 3.6 Mbytes of data, without considering the effect of the overhead of frames used to transport digitized speech or the potential effect of silence suppression. The former results in additional data transfer, while the use of silence suppression results only in periods of speech actually being conveyed and reduces the amount of data transfer. Since many Internet telephony applications lack the sophistication necessary to suppress periods of silence, each hour of voice transmitted will probably result in approximately 4 Mbytes of additional activity over an Internet connection if you include frame overhead. Whether or not this level of additional activity adversely affects your organization's existing Internet connection will depend on the current operating rate of your organization's Internet connection, its current level of utilization, and the anticipated level of digitized voice expected to be transported over the connection.

UPGRADE CONSIDERATIONS

When a dedicated connection to the Internet is used, the economics associated with transmitting voice over this IP network make its use harder to justify when a line upgrade is required. This is because a line upgrade might easily increase your organization's monthly Internet usage charge by $250 to $500 per month or more. This means that when calls are national, your cost avoidance might be limited to between $.10 and $.15 per minute. Thus, if your organization's monthly Internet access billing increases by $250 per month, you would have to transmit 2500 minutes of voice per month at $.10 per minute for PSTN usage simply to break even—without even considering the one-time cost of equipment. This means you must carefully estimate your anticipated volume of voice transmission to determine if using the Internet to transmit voice via certain types of dedicated connections is economically sound. Fortunately, corporate PBX reports and communications carrier bills represent two viable sources for obtaining the information required to make a sound economic decision. Now that we have an appreciation for the general economic issues associated with the transmission of voice on the Internet, let's turn our attention to the operation of Internet telephony, including several performance issues you might wish to consider.

Internet Telephony Operations

The actual PC configuration required for Internet telephony operations depends on the software program you are using. The software program operates under a specific operating system (such as a version of Microsoft Windows or the Apple Computer Macintosh System 7.X), interfaces with a sound card to compress voice input entered through a microphone connected to the card, and coordinates a TCP/IP SLIP or PPP communications connection via the use of a modem. Originally, most sound cards were half-duplex, but recently manufactured sound cards can operate in a full mode. Thus, to obtain a full-duplex telephone connection requires the use of a full-duplex sound card as well as software that supports full-duplex operations.

Hardware and Software Requirements

Table 6-1 lists the general categories of hardware and software required for Internet telephony.

PROCESSOR AND RAM
Concerning specific hardware, at a minimum, most programs require a high-performance 486 processor or equivalent since the use of the processor to perform voice compression is processor-intensive. The actual process

TABLE 6-1

General Categories of Hardware and Software Required for Internet Telephony

Software
  Telephony program
  Operating system
  TCP/IP stack

Hardware
  Sound card (half- or full-duplex)
  Microphone
  Speaker
  Computer platform
    Microprocessor
    RAM

and RAM memory required is commonly noted in the program specification sheet for a product.

MODEM

Since the transmission of digitized voice involves some overhead resulting from the framing of voice packets, including header and trailer fields, most Internet telephony programs require the use of a modem that operates at a minimum data transfer rate of 14.4 Kbps. To put this operating rate in perspective, it is equivalent to 1800 bytes per second, while voice encoded using PCM requires 8000 bytes per second of bandwidth, which is reduced to 4000 bytes per second of bandwidth when ADPCM coding is used. Clearly, then, Internet telephony depends on the use of a vocoding or hybrid coding technique to enable 14.4-Kbps modems to support a digitized voice transmission capability. In fact, the method of voice digitization can differ between vendor products, and this is one of several issues that currently result in a high degree of noninteroperability between different vendor products.

SOUND CARD

Through the use of a full-duplex sound card and software support, you can enable both parties to talk at the same time. In actuality a full-duplex communications capability is slightly better than a half-duplex communications capability because we are able to gracefully back out of a conversation instead of having to awkwardly wait to ascertain if a person is done speaking as in half-duplex communications. Some programs enable the use of two sound cards, one for playback and one for recording the conversation. If you have an extra sound card and your program supports the use of two cards, you can avoid the purchase of a full-duplex card.

Although you might be tempted to avoid the use of a full-duplex sound card because of possible bandwidth problems, you should note that the actual bandwidth required may increase by only a few percent over the use of a half-duplex sound card. This is because many Internet telephony programs that support full-duplex operations also use silence suppression, transmitting data only when a person actually speaks.

Directory Services

Today, many Internet telephony software products are based on the use of a "directory service" server. To initiate a call, you use the program operating on your computer to access the software vendor's directory and double-click on an entry. The other party must be logged on to an Internet service provider and running the same software on his or her computer for the call to be received. Other Internet telephony software products provide a directory with a list of on-line users and chat rooms as a mechanism to allow users to meet new friends around the globe. Other programs either include a direct access capability or allow direct access after you access their central server. If you know the IP address of a user you want to call directly, you can simply enter his or her IP address and click on a call button on the program interface to initiate a call. If the called party is logged on to the Internet and running the same software program, the call will be received. Now that we have an appreciation for the basic components required to implement Internet telephony, let's look at some of the constraints and compatibility issues associated with this relatively new technology.

Constraints and Compatibility Issues

There are a number of constraints associated with the use of Internet telephony, and they are solved in a variety of ways by different vendors. Unfortunately the lack of a uniform approach to solving these constraints results in a number of compatibility issues that makes interoperability between different vendor products difficult, if not impossible. Table 6-2 lists five key areas of constraints. We will examine each of these groups in this section.

BANDWIDTH CONSERVATION METHOD

The ability to reproduce a natural-sounding conversation requires a trade-off between the speech-coding scheme and processing power of the PC. In general, the ability to highly compress speech while enabling the repro-

TABLE 6-2

Internet Telephony
Constraints

Bandwidth conservation method
  G.729
  G.728
  G.723.1

Packet delay and loss handling
  Repair lost packets with silence
  Repair lost packets with synthetic speech

LAN connectivity operation
  Requires modification to firewall and router access lists
  Products use different ports

Connection method
  Directory or IP address based
  Gateway-based

Protocols used

duction of it to produce natural-sounding conversation requires more processing power than encoding schemes that reproduce either synthetic sound or produce digitized speech at a higher data rate.

Currently Low Delay Code Excited Linear Prediction (LD-CELP), which was standardized by the ITU as the G.728 Recommendation and which results in a 16-Kbps data stream, represents one popular encoding method. Two additional voice-coding techniques used in different popular Internet telephony applications are (1) Conjugate-Structure Algebraic Excited Linear Prediction (CS-ACELP), standardized by the ITU as Recommendation G.729, which results in an 8-Kbps data stream, and (2) the dual-rate 6.3/5.3-Kbps voice-coding method recently standardized by the ITU as Recommendation G.723.1.

Until recently the G.729 coding method was very popular. However, the standardization of the G.723.1 dual-speed coding method is gaining in popularity and is also recommended as the low-bit-rate speech coder for the ITU H.323 standard for video and voice communications over packet-based networks. At one time, it was expected that most Internet telephony products would adopt the G.723.1 Recommendation. However, from a real-world operational pespective, the delay or latency associated with the G.723.1 dual-speed coding method is approximately 30 ms, which is 12 times the delay associated with the use of the LD-CELP coding method. In many situations, the additional delay is of sufficient duration to cause reconstructed voice to sound awkward. Thus, the trade-off between bandwidth and delay can represent a key item you may wish to consider when configuring an Internet telephony product that supports multiple voice coding methods. Many times, a voice coding method that results in awkward-sounding reconstructed voice at one operating rate may provide a higher quality of reconstructed voice when you select a higher operating rate.

APPLICATION NOTE   Consider varying the use of different audio codecs as a mechanism to determine if a more suitable codec is available for use.

WINDOWS CODEC SUPPORT

Although several Windows-compliant products use proprietary codecs, other products permit you to select a codec from those supported directly by Windows or by adding a codec. By using the Control Panel, you can both determine the audio codecs supported by the version of Windows used on your computer as well as observe and obtain the ability to alter the manner by which a codec is selected for many applications.

To check the codecs supported on your computer, go to Start > Control Panel and double-click on the icon labeled Multimedia Properties. Next, select the tab labeled Advanced, choose the Audio Compression codecs entry, and click on the plus mark (+) to its left. This action will result in the display of the audio compression codecs supported on your computer. Figure 6-3 illustrates the display of the Multimedia Properties Advanced tab on this author's computer after the previously described sequence of operations was performed.

You can display information about a codec by clicking on a codec to display a dialog box with a tab labeled General. An example of the dialog box displayed as a result of selecting the Microsoft CCITT G.711 A-Law and u-Law CODEC is shown in left portion of Figure 6-4. If you click on the button labeled About, a description of the codec will be displayed. The right portion of Figure 6-4 illustrates the display of information about the Microsoft G.711 codec. In examining the left portion of Figure 6-4, note the box with the down-facing arrow that has a current priority value of 2. This value is used by Windows as a criteria for using a particular audio codec. When two or more audio codecs are equally capable of compression, Windows will use them in the order of the priority assigned to them.

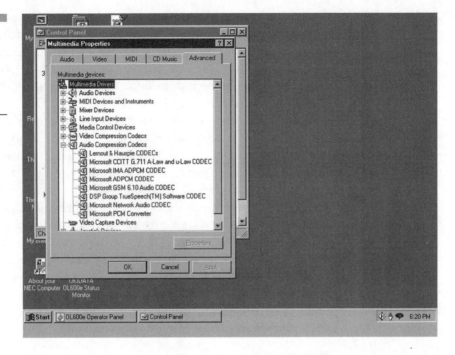

Figure 6-3
Viewing currently installed audio codecs on a Windows-based computer.

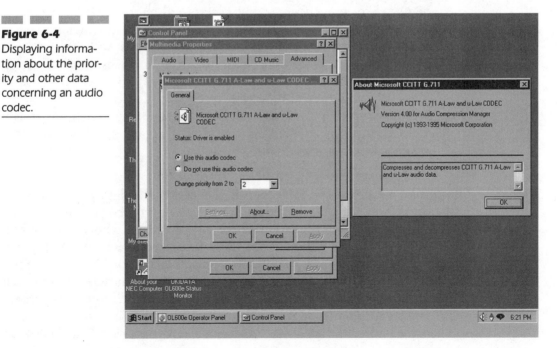

Figure 6-4
Displaying information about the priority and other data concerning an audio codec.

PACKET DELAY AND LOSS HANDLING

Two key considerations associated with the use of packet networks affect voice transmission: packet delay and packet loss. The congestion of routers and gateways—resulting from either processing packets or the inability to transfer packets onto communications facilities due to heavy line utilization—causes delay or loss of packets.

When data is being transferred, a slight delay in the arrival of one or more packets is usually not noticeable. At worst, it might result in a person waiting an extended period of time for a file transfer to complete, but the content of the transferred file would not be affected. Similarly, the loss of packets as they flow through an IP network resulting from congestion and routers, workstations, or gateway discarding packets is compensated for by the retransmission of discarded packets. However, when packets transport digitized voice, normal data transmission methods cannot be used. This is because the loss or delay of packets results in the disruption of speech intelligibility.

There are two methods that can be used to compensate for the loss or delay of packets. Those methods involve repairing lost or delayed packets with periods of silence or with synthetic speech.

Silence Generation

Currently, most Internet telephony applications simply generate periods of silence to compensate for lost packets and reproduce delayed packets. This results in the clipping of speech and a loss of its intelligibility when packets are lost in the network, and a distortion of speech when delayed packets are used to reproduce speech. At the time this book was being prepared, several Internet telephony vendors were considering the possibility of using previously received packets as a mechanism to generate synthetic speech to fill in periods of silence. In doing so, there are several methods that can be used for voice reconstruction, based on where the reconstruction process occurs.

Voice Reconstruction

Voice reconstruction can occur by the receiver attempting to reconstruct the missing segments of speech from correctly received packets preceding the packet or from packets that are lost or delayed. This can be accomplished by the repetition of a portion of the last correctly received speech waveform or via the interpolation process. When a combined transmitter and receiver method is used, extra information is included within each transmitted packet to facilitate the reconstruction and interpolation process at the receiver. Another combined transmitter and receiver technique involves the adjustment of packet sizes dynamically, based on packet delay and packet loss metrics. Making packets smaller enhances their ability to flow through a packet network, since many routers and gateways use queues that favor small-size packets. Currently, no standards exist concerning the handling of lost or delayed packets, and it may be several years until an approach is standardized. This means that the selection of a product that provides this capability should have an option to turn off lost and delayed packet handling if it is to interoperate with other products that do not offer this feature or that implement it in a different manner.

LAN Connectivity Operation

Although most Internet telephony products were originally developed to use SLIP and PPP dial connections to ISPs, many products now support the use of LAN connections, enabling the product to recognize gateway and Domain Name Server (DNS) addresses configured with the TCP/IP protocol stack operating on a computer. Since Internet telephony products can use both TCP and UDP ports for establishing connections to a directory server or directly to a distant party, the use of those ports may cause conflicts with existing firewalls or router access lists designed to provide a level of security to organizational computational equipment located behind those devices.

APPLICATION NOTE   Coordinate the use of Internet telephony products on a LAN with your organization's firewall and router administrators. Many times, Internet telephony products will fail to operate due to the ports they use being blocked by a router access list and/or a firewall.

SECURITY CONSIDERATIONS

To illustrate the effect of security implemented in the form of access lists on voice traffic, consider Figure 6-5, which shows the use of a firewall to protect a corporate LAN. DMZ is an acronym for *demilitarized,* and a DMZ LAN represents a local area network that has no workstations connected to the network. This means that inbound packets from the Internet must first flow onto the DMZ LAN, from which they are received on one port of the firewall for processing prior to being placed onto the corporate LAN. By using a DMZ LAN, the firewall is able to process every inbound packet prior to the packet being able to be received by another corporate network device.

Both routers and firewalls process packets based on access lists as well as other metrics; however, the access list can be considered the initial qual-

Figure 6-5

Using a firewall to protect a corporate LAN.

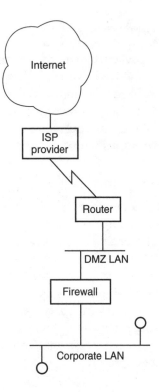

ifier, determining whether the packet reaches the next processing step or is discarded. Thus, it is extremely important for router and firewall access lists to be configured to enable the use of an Internet telephony product. For example, the Vocal Tec Internet Phone product uses two channels. It uses TCP port 6670 to connect to the vendor's Internet Phone Server's directory service, while audio is passed through UDP port 22555 on both local and remote computers. Internet Phone also uses TCP port 25793 to connect to the Vocal Tec addressing server and TCP port 1490 for whiteboard, chat, and file transfer when its conferencing option is used. This means that organizational firewalls and routers must be configured to enable data transfer on those ports if the Vocal Tec Internet Phone is used. Unfortunately, there is no standard port assignment, and not only do certain products differ in their use of TCP and UDP ports between vendor products, but there are also differences between versions of certain vendor products with respect to the use of TCP and UDP ports.

As mentioned in our discussion of TCP/IP earlier in this book, the placement of statements in an access list will affect the delay associated with allowed packets flowing through a router. In general, the router or firewall administrator should place voice-related access control list statements as high as possible in the list, usually directly after antispoofing statements.

CONNECTION METHOD

As mentioned earlier in this section, some Internet telephony products are directory based, requiring a user to first access a directory prior to establishing a call. Other products permit users to enter an IP address to establish a call. For both methods, the destination or called party must be on-line and operating the same software program.

One version of a directory service that is receiving a considerable degree of interest is the Lightweight Directory Access Protocol (LDAP), which allows a collection of directories, such as e-mail, voice mail, security, and even a PBX function, to function as a single integrated directory service.

Figure 6-6 illustrates an example of the use of an LDAP directory service. In this example, information about employees (including their e-mail address, single logon system password, telephone number, and any other directory-related information) is placed on a centralized LDAP directory. When a new employee is added to a LAN, employee information is furnished only to the LDAP directory. The LDAP protocol then disseminates appropriate information to each communications system operated by the organization that supports the LDAP. In the example shown in Figure 6-6, one entry to the LDAP directory results in the automatic update of five directories, including an Internet telephony directory.

Gateway Service

A third connection method enhances the use of the Internet, as it provides a gateway service that converts an Internet call to the PSTN. One popular example of a gateway service product is the IDT Corporation's Net2Phone program. Net2Phone functions similarly to other Internet

Figure 6-6
Using the Lightweight Directory Access Protocol (LDAP) for consolidating directory services on an organizational basis.

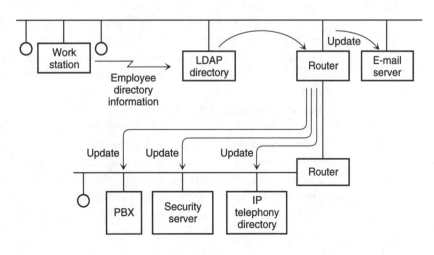

telephone products in that it operates in conjunction with a sound card, microphone, and speakers to initiate and receive calls via the Internet. Where Net2Phone differs is in its use of a central telephone switch, which functions as a gateway for out-dialing via the PSTN. This use of a centralized switch located in the United States results in all gateway calls originating in the United States. In addition, through the use of a gateway, users of Net2Phone are not limited to calling a party who is on-line and using a multimedia-equipped PC. Instead, users can call any person who has a standard telephone and the outbound call will ring the distant phone.

The current voice-digitization method used by Net2Phone requires a voice bandwidth of approximately 13 Kbps, which, with protocol overhead, results in a minimum operating rate of 14.4 Kbps. Net2Phone operates under Windows 95, Windows 98, and Windows NT version 4.0. Although you can place calls via Net2Phone, you cannot use it for faxes or even for incoming calls.

Net2Phone's key economic value is for communications between foreign locations. In the past, a number of callback companies took advantage of the high tariffs associated with the cost of calling between different non-U.S. locations by enabling users to first dial the United States. After receiving the caller ID number, but prior to answering the call, the callback service would disconnect the incoming call and dial the distant party. The distant party would enter an access code for billing purposes and receive a dial tone that allowed them to initiate a call from the United States to the distant party. Typically, the cost of the two U.S.-originated calls, one to the calling party via a callback and one to the called party, was half the cost of directly calling from one country to another. In fact, you can judge the popularity of international callback by reading a copy of the *International Herald Tribune*. In each issue you'll find a large number of advertisements for callback services.

In addition to providing a callback service for non-U.S. destinations, callback services also support calling throughout the United States. This enables users in foreign countries to call a person or business in the United States, with the cost based on prices for the callback and the long-distance call in the United States. In addition, through the use of Net2Phone, it becomes possible for U.S. businesses with 800, 888, and 887 numbers to expand on a global basis. With Net2Phone, most toll-free 800, 888, and 887 numbers become global toll-free numbers.

By applying the callback principle to Internet-originated calls, Net2Phone subscribers can use their PCs to call any city in the United States from anywhere in the world for as little as $.10 per minute. Significant savings can also be obtained when calling persons in other countries, because

IDT purchases blocks of communications capacity at wholesale prices and resells it at significant discounts. For example, Net2Phone users could dial Australia for $.10 per minute, Austria for $.15 per minute, Finland for $.17 per minute, Germany for $.10 per minute, Israel for $.17 per minute and Tel Aviv for $.10 per minute, and the United Kingdom for $.10 per minute. However, for certain countries listed in the Net2Phone rate chart, it could be more economical to use an international calling plan offered by one of the major communications carriers or the facilities of a "1010" bypass carrier. Concerning the latter, since 1995 a number of small communications resellers have been established that purchase long-distance transmission in bulk and resell international calls at rates significantly below the rates of the major communications carriers. Each of these services are accessed by dialing 1010 followed by a three-digit suffix. Since the 1010 bypasses the normally selected long-distance communications carrier, the term "1010" is commonly referred to as a *bypass carrier*. Until 1998, the digit pair 10 was used to bypass the subscriber's default long-distance carrier. However, because the number of carriers offering bypass has expanded considerably, the prefix was changed to 1010. This allows other prefixes, such as 1010, to be used once all 999 bypass carriers are assigned to the 1010 prefix. In late 1999, this author could dial Argentina and Egypt using a bypass carrier for $.35 and $.50 per minute, respectively. In comparison, Net2Phone's cost was $.42 per minute for calling Argentina and $.60 per minute for calling Egypt. Thus, for some persons, it may pay to comparison shop, especially if you anticipate frequent calling to a particular country.

FEATURES

Several common features recently added to Internet telephony products include call-progress displays and an Internet call-waiting feature. Although Internet call waiting can be implemented as a directory service by an Internet telephony company, the feature would then be limited to informing you that another caller was attempting to call you using the same directory service. Because most homes that have Internet subscribers are limited to one telephone line, the previous method of call waiting does not provide the ability to service conventional PSTN-based calls. Although many persons subscribe to call waiting, you usually turn off the service to avoid disconnecting an existing Internet connection. Recognizing this problem, Nortel Networks introduced an Internet call-waiting service that enables persons on an existing Internet connection to receive a pop-up window on their computer that alerts them to the incoming call. The user can then accept the call, forward or redirect the call, or play an outgoing message. If the subscriber decides to take the incoming call, software on the PC will accept the call via a voice over IP connection while allowing the subscriber to maintian his or her Internet connection.

Deployment of Nortel Networks' ICW is based on installing a call-waiting server in a central office and configuring the central office switch to forward calls to the server when the subscriber line is busy. The server will then communicate with the subscriber through the central office via a TCP/IP connection that pops up the previously mentioned window on the subscriber's PC. As of mid-1999, ICW service was deployed in approximately 16 cities in North America.

PROTOCOLS USED

As mentioned earlier in this section, most Internet telephony applications use TCP for addressing information and UDP for the actual transmission of packets containing digitized and compressed voice. UDP is a best-effort connectionless protocol that does not include a negotiated flow control capability. This creates two related problems. First, there is no guarantee that a packet sent will reach its destination or will reach it in a timely manner. This is because a packet can be dropped at any point in the network due to error or network congestion. Second, there is no way to control the flow of information when you are using UDP. This lack of flow control could cause UDP packets carrying Internet telephony to flood the Internet—to the detriment of other Internet applications. Based on the preceding, a mechanism is required that would reserve bandwidth from source to destination through the Internet. If this could be accomplished, voice-encoded packets could flow in an orderly manner from end to end, eliminating the possibility of packets being dropped due to network congestion or a non-steady-state arrival, with the accompanying variances in time between packets that cause distortion to reconstructed voice.

The mechanism required to accomplish this is the ReSerVation Protocol (RSVP), recently proposed as an Internet standard and discussed in Chapter 2. Unfortunately, the actual full-scale implementation of RSVP is probably many years distant, as two key issues remain to be resolved. First, RSVP requires the upgrade of all gateways and routers between source and destination. This means that one Internet user calling another may have the connection routed between one or more NSPs and two ISPs, all of which would have to have equipment upgraded to support RSVP. This upgrade could conceivably require a decade, because many routers and gateways are not upgradable and would require replacement. Second, bandwidth is not free. This means ISPs and NSPs can be expected to bill for the use of reserved bandwidth. How this will occur, how multiple providers along a reserved path will coordinate billing, and the ultimate manner of billing to ISP subscribers remains to be determined.

While RSVP may be many years away from implementation, another protocol provides the capability to support multimedia call control to include telephony services. While this new protocol is well suited for implementation by Internet telephony gateways that better represent a telephony over the Internet business solution, the protocol is also suitable for incorporation into individual protocol stacks. Thus, let's discuss it in concluding this section. The protocol we will discuss is the Session Initiation Protocol (SIP).

Session Initiation Protocol

The Session Initiation Protocol (SIP) represents an Internet Engineering Task Force (IETF) proposed standard for the control of multimedia call sessions. RFC 2543, which contains the proposed SIP standard, was published on March 17, 1999. SIP represents a lightweight transport-layer independent protocol. It is lightweight because it has six transmission method types, while its transport-layer independence results from the fact that it can be used with any datagram or stream protocol, such as TCP, UDP, or even ATM.

SIP represents a text-based client/server protocol. A SIP transmission method is formed via a textual header followed by fields that contain call properties. SIP clients, which are referred to as *user agents* (UAs), communicate with SIP servers; however, a UA also acts as a server when a SIP request reaches its final destination.

SERVER OPERATING MODES

A SIP server can operate as either a proxy server or a redirector. When acting as a proxy server, the server forwards requests to the next hop, to a SIP server, or to a user-agent within an IP network. When functioning as a redirector server, the SIP server informs its clients of the address of the requested server, which enables the client to directly contact the server.

The number of hops that can be traversed until the final destination is reached is not limited. In addition, SIP servers can be configured to contact an external location server to acquire routing information. Note that a caller does not directly interact with the location server. Instead, a redirect or proxy server queries the location server, which represents a logical abstraction to indicate where the SIP server obtains its information. The location server can be an LDAP or X.500 server, a Whois server, a shared file system or even a structured query language (SQL) database. The caller locates the proxy server by proceeding directly to a callee's domain. For example, when calling gil@fedsorus.gov, an INVITE request would be transmitted to a SIP server for the domain fedsorus.gov, with the IP address obtained via the use of DNS.

SIP TRANSMISSION METHODS

As previously mentioned, SIP supports six transmission methods. Those methods, including a brief description of each, are listed in Table 6-3.

The INVITE transmission method represents the basic mechanism used to establish a new connection and "invite" a new user to a point-to-point or conference call. Within a SIP, INVITE is text that includes three addresses: the host address where the request originated, the logical source of the request, and session description that contains one or more addresses where the caller expects audio or video to be sent. For some services, the session description address may not be the same as the logical request source address.

OPERATION

SIP provides the protocol mechanism that enables end systems and proxy servers to provide such services as call forwarding, callee and calling number delivery, terminal-type negotiation (which gives a caller options for reaching the callee, including Internet telephone and mobile phone), terminal-capability negotiation, call transfer, and invitation to multicast conferences. To illustrate how SIP operates, Figure 6-7 illustrates an example of both proxy mode and redirect mode operations.

The top portion of Figure 6-7 illustrates an example of a SIP operation in proxy mode, while the lower portion of Figure 6-7 illustrates a SIP operation in a redirect mode. For both examples in Figure 6-7 the following eight activities occur:

TABLE 6-3

SIP Protocol Transmission Methods

SIP Method	Description
INVITE	Used to invite a user to a call as well as to establish a new connection.
ACK	Used to acknowledge an INVITE.
BYE	Used to terminate an existing connection between two users or to decline an invitation.
CANCEL	Used to terminate a request or the search for a user.
REGISTER	Used for conveying information about a user's location to a SIP server.
OPTIONS	Used for soliciting information about the capabilities of a SIP server.

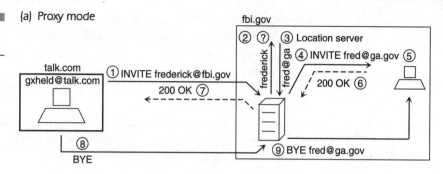

Figure 6-7
SIP operations.

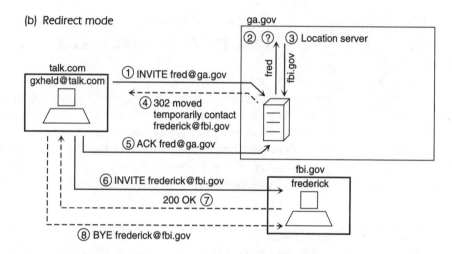

1. The caller uses a directory service, such as LDAP, to map a name to a user domain. This is accomplished through the use of an INVITE transmission method.

2. Using the caller domain, a SIP server is located via a DNS lookup.

3. The called server maps the name to the form user@host.

4. The user@host name is used to issue an INVITE to the callee. The callee can accept, reject, or forward the INVITE to a new address.

5. If the call is forwarded, the result is a return to step 2.

6. If the callee accepts the call, a confirmation is sent. Note that SIP codes are structured in increments of 100, starting at 100, with 1XX used for information purposes, 2XX for confirmations, and a 4XX range to indicate a request failure.

7. The conversation occurs.

8. The caller or callee terminates the session via a BYE.

In examining the proxy mode use of SIP in Figure 6-7a, note that the caller gxheld@talk.com issues an INVITE to frederick@fbi.com. Because the domain is known, the location server can be located via a DNS lookup, which returns the name in the form of host@domain. This enables the proxy SIP server to issue an INVITE to the proxy address associated with frederick@fbi.com, which in this example is fred@ga.gov. In the redirect mode, an INVITE to frederick@ga.gov results in a response that indicates the callee moved and the new address is frederick@fbi.gov. This results in an INVITE directly to frederick@fbi.gov.

6-2   Telephony over the Internet

Telephony over the Internet is a voice over data network transmission technique that allows a person's existing business telephone system to be used for calling persons via the Internet. The most common method used to initiate telephony over the Internet system is to connect PBXs at each corporate location to equipment that behaves in a manner similar to an analog trunk. That is, equipment presents a ring voltage when a call is received, responds to DTMF and/or rotary dialing, and passes caller ID data from an incoming call. In addition, the equipment presents each PBX with call-progress tones such as ringback and busy when outbound calls are made.

Figure 6-8 illustrates the proverbial black-box approach to telephony on the Internet, in which equipment required to perform signaling, voice digitization and compression, and packeting is labeled as a black box. Access to the black box from the local PBX is accomplished by an employee dialing a predefined prefix such as 7 followed by the extension of the called party. The analog call is routed to the black box, where it is digitized and compressed. In addition, the black box provides appropriate addressing for each packet so that the packets are routed to a similar black box at the called location. At that location, voice-digitized packets are converted back into their original analog form for routing via the destination PBX to the called party.

Although there is no technical reason to preclude the delivery of digitized voice directly to a PC equipped with a sound card and appropriate software, it is far easier to ensure compatibility between calling and called parties by routing digitized voice between pairs of black boxes manufactured by the same vendor than it is to deal with the multiple conversion operations that might be required to provide compatibility among differ-

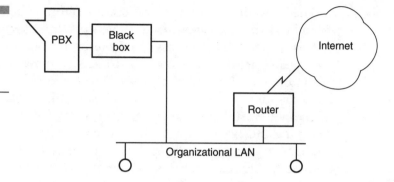

Figure 6-8
The black-box
approach to
telephony on the
Internet.

ent vendors' products, which use different packet-formation and voice-compression techniques.

In Figure 6-8, the black box represents a conversion device that interfaces with the organizational PBX, converting either analog or standard PCM-encoded digital output into a compressed digital data stream that is encapsulated in IP packets addressed to a distant black box. In doing so, the black box acts as a communications server and becomes a participant on the organizational LAN. Thus, voice-encoded packets will flow over the LAN to access the router, which simply views those packets as an additional series of packets requiring routing onto the Internet or a private IP network. This means that prior to using this approach for telephony on the Internet, you should ascertain the utilization level of your organization's LAN.

LAN Traffic Constraints

In an Ethernet environment, a utilization level above 50 percent would indicate that voice-encoded packets will more than likely flow to the router for transmission on the Internet with unpredictable delays between packets. This is because of the access protocol associated with Ethernet LANs, in which a random exponential backoff algorithm is used after a collision is detected. This means collisions that occur more frequently as utilization levels increase result in a higher probability of voice packets being delayed from their required time sequence. This in turn can be expected to result in the occurrence of distortion at the destination, when voice-encoded packets arrive with delays that preclude their reconstruction into natural-sounding speech.

The unpredictable transfer of packets transporting digitized speech from local area networks into an IP network, including processing delays at nodes, causes the transmission of a uniform data stream with supposedly predefined intervals between packets to arrive at their destination with random delays between packets. These random delays result in awkward-sounding reconstructed voice. To avoid this problem, manufacturers of the proverbial black box incorporate a *jitter buffer* into their products. The jitter buffer can be viewed as a temporary holding area, enabling packets carrying digitized speech that arrives at the destination with random delays between packets to be removed from the buffer at a uniform rate. This produces a more natural sound for the reconstructed speech.

APPLICATION NOTE Many gateways and other Internet telephony products include a selectable jitter buffer, with users able to set a delay from 0 (disabled) to 255 ms or more. When setting a selectable jitter buffer, it is important to remember that while an increase in the jitter buffer setting can improve the clarity of small blocks of reconstructed speech, the increase adds to the overall one-way delay. If there is too much delay, a person on one side of the conversation may believe the other party has stopped speaking and so may begin to talk, thus creating a "voice clash" and a requirement for both parties to listen.

Equipment Examination

Now that we have an appreciation for the black-box approach to telephony over the Internet, let's turn to the operation of equipment that provides this capability. In doing so, we will examine four specific vendor products: the Internet PhoneJACK from Quicknet Technologies, the Voice over IP (V/IP) series of products from Micom Communications Corporation, the Vocal Tech telephony gateway, and the MultiVOIP voice over IP gateway from MultiTech Systems.

Internet PhoneJACK

The Internet PhoneJACK was developed by Quicknet Technologies, Inc., of San Francisco, California, as a mechanism to allow a standard telephone to be used for making and receiving Internet telephone calls. In doing so, this product provides compatibility with a number of Internet telephony applications, including IDT's Net2Phone, Microsoft's Net Meeting and Vocal Tec's Internet Phone. Thus, the Internet PhoneJACK is considered a hybrid mechanism, as it allows a standard telephone to be used with Internet telephony applications.

VOICE SUPPORT

The Internet PhoneJACK is a sophisticated conversion device that uses a digital signal processor to perform voice compression and decompression in hardware. A user can select the voice-compression method to obtain compatibility with one of several Internet telephony applications programs. Currently the Internet PhoneJACK supports PCM A- and μ-law encoding as well as ITU G.711 and G.723.1 speech-encoding methods.

FABRICATION

From a physical perspective, the PhoneJACK is fabricated on a half-size Industry Standard Architecture (ISA) adapter card, which is inserted into a system expansion slot in the system unit of an IBM PC or compatible computer. The card contains three physical connectors for the connection of a conventional telephone. The second connector is an RJ-12, which accepts a handset or headset. The third connector is actually a pair of 3.5-mm stereo jacks, which provide support for the use of a microphone and speaker.

Through the use of the PhoneJACK, you can keep your Internet telephony calls private. Incoming calls can be answered via your telephone instead of by talking into a microphone and hearing the other party on speakers. However, the Internet PhoneJACK also supports the use of speakers and a microphone for those who prefer hands-free communications.

OS SUPPORT

Currently, the Internet PhoneJACK operates only under Windows 95. However, Quicknet Technologies plans to broaden support to include Windows 3.1 and Windows NT, which could result in the ability of its product to work with PCs using those operating systems by the time you read this book.

Micom V/IP

In 1996, Micom Communications Corporation of Simi Valley, California, introduced its V/IP (Voice over IP) telephone and fax IP gateway product, which provides the potential to integrate voice over an IP network on an enterprisewide basis. In actuality, Micom's V/IP represents a family of analog and digital voice interface cards that enable digital and analog

PBXs to be connected to the card. Each card, which services a number of voice inputs, is inserted into an IBM PC or compatible computer, which functions as a voice gateway. The gateway, which is connected to a LAN, compresses each voice conversation into an 8-Kbps data stream, packetizes the data stream, and uses a local database to map the destination office telephone number to a remote V/IP gateway's IP address.

BASIC CONFIGURATION

Figure 6-9 illustrates the basic configuration of a V/IP phone/fax gateway, based on the assumption that the organization using the gateway operates on an Ethernet LAN. In examining the use of the Micom V/IP gateway shown in Figure 6-9, several items require a bit of elaboration. First, since each V/IP card contains onboard processors that perform required compression and signaling operations, the platform for the gateway requires a minimal amount of processing power. This means you can use an Intel 486 or any type of Pentium processor—based computer as the platform for the gateway. Second, the onboard digital signal processors used on each V/IP card compress and convert both voice and fax signals into IP packets. This enables a PBX to be programmed so that both voice and fax calls can contend for the same V/IP connection between the PBX and the V/IP gateway. To better understand the capability of the V/IP gateway, let's turn to an example and discuss its operation.

OPERATION

When configuring a V/IP gateway, each gateway in a network would be connected to a LAN, resulting in an IP address being assigned to each

Figure 6-9
Using a Micom V/IP gateway.

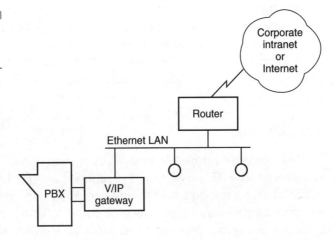

gateway. Since calls received from a directly connected PBX require routing to a different V/IP gateway, you must associate destination office numbers with the IP address of different V/IP gateways that serve different organizational locations. Thus, you would configure each gateway with a list of intracompany destination office numbers and the IP address of each.

Once the V/IP configuration process is completed and your organization's PBX is connected to one or more V/IP cards, you will also have to configure your PBX to recognize the V/IP card or cards and route calls to ports on those cards. In configuring your PBX, you would set the signaling method so that both the PBX and V/IP card ports are compatible. For example, setting both to a specific type of E&M signaling would ensure signaling compatibility. Then you would program the PBX to recognize a prefix code, such as the dialing digit 5 or 7, as a signal to route outbound calls through the PBX to the V/IP gateway. Let's assume an employee wants to dial the telephone number 555-1234 in the Chicago branch office where another V/IP gateway is installed and connected to the PBX in that office. By dialing 5-555-1234 or 7-555-1234, the call is first routed to the local V/IP gateway. That gateway looks up the destination telephone number 555-1234 in the phone directory database and extracts the IP address of the V/IP gateway in Chicago. The local V/IP gateway uses that IP address as the destination address for forming packets consisting of voice-compressed data, using a combination of the ITU's G.729 voice-compression standard with silence suppression to reduce the data stream associated with a voice conversation to approximately 4 Kbps. Due to the overhead associated with packet headers, the actual bandwidth required for a voice conversation commonly averages 6 Kbps, which is still a significant improvement over PCM's 64-Kbps operating rate.

OVERCOMING PREDICTABILITY PROBLEMS

Both the Internet and private IP networks are essentially unpredictable with respect to bandwidth allocation. This problem results from the fact that IP networks were developed primarily to interconnect local area networks, and both inter- and intra-LAN communications are random and bursty in nature. Without a priority mechanism, it becomes possible for packets transporting voice to be delayed behind long packets transporting data, resulting in a degree of distortion to reconstructed voice. Therefore, a mechanism to provide a degree of packet-arrival predictability is required to ensure reconstructed voice is not adversely distorted because of delays in the routing of packets through an IP network.

The Micom V/IP gateway attacks the predictability problem in two ways. First, it supports existing router-priority protocols based on the use of router queues that enable relatively short packets transporting voice to obtain priority over longer packets transporting data. Although this support enables voice-encoded packets to be prioritized for routing onto a wide area network transmission facility, it does not guarantee that the priority will be maintained on public networks such as the Internet, where intermediate routers may not support a specific router vendor's priority mechanism. Thus, Micom added support for the ReSerVation Protocol (RSVP) that can guarantee end-to-end bandwidth if all routers between source and destination support RSVP.

Although the support of RSVP provides an excellent mechanism to overcome the predictability problem associated with the transmission of voice on IP networks, it is currently better suited for private rather than public network use. This is because an organization can control the upgrade of its networking equipment to support RSVP. In comparison, the ability to establish an RSVP connection through the Internet depends on the support of the protocol by all equipment between source and destination. This means that anyone linked through an ISP or NSP that does not support RSVP renders the ability to reserve bandwidth inoperative. In addition, since there is no free lunch, we can expect ISPs and NSPs to bill for the use of guaranteed bandwidth. Thus, we will more than likely have to wait for those service providers to upgrade their networking equipment to support RSVP and to agree on an interservice provider revenue-sharing mechanism so users can be billed for reserved bandwidth that flows between two or more ISPs or NSPs. This means it may be at least several years and possibly well into the next millennium until the upgrade of networking equipment and the resolution of billing issues enables calls to be made over the Internet with guaranteed-reliable reconstruction of digitized voice. Thus, at the present time, the Micom V/IP gateway is a product more suitable for use over private IP networks.

ECONOMICS

To illustrate the economics associated with the use of Micom's V/IP product, we will first consider expenses associated with constructing a small V/IP gateway at two corporate locations, assuming an IP network already exists and sufficient bandwidth is available to support several compressed voice calls without requiring an upgrade to existing transmission facilities.

Gateway Cost

When this book was written, the cost of a V/IP card was approximately $770 per voice/fax channel. Since the establishment of a V/IP gateway requires the installation of one or more V/IP cards in a PC, we must also consider the cost of the personal computer. That computer, as previously mentioned in this chapter, does not require the latest in processing technology since each V/IP card contains its own digital signal processors. Thus, a minimal Pentium processor—based PC or even an older 486-based PC would be sufficient. If we assume we have to purchase a Pentium-based PC, we can do so for $1500 and obtain a sufficient platform for building a V/IP gateway. If we add $100 for an appropriate network card and $1540 for a two-port V/IP card, the total cost for a two-port voice over IP gateway becomes $3140, or $6280 for two identical V/IP gateway locations.

Computing Return on Investment

To determine the possible return on the investment required to support two V/IP gateways requires an additional set of assumptions. First, let's assume that at each corporate location employees work an average of 22 days per month. Next, let's assume that calls originating at each location destined to the other location average 30 minutes per day, which is probably not unreasonable over an 8-hour business day. Since calls are bidirectional, with an assumed 30 minutes per direction, this results in the V/IP gateways eliminating a total of 60 minutes of public switched telephone network activity per day. If we assume calls are between two offices located in the United States, our organization might be billed $.15 per minute for calls made between 8:00 a.m. and 5:00 p.m. Thus, on a daily basis our cost avoidance would be 60 minutes × $.15 per minute, or $9.00 per day. Using 22 working days per month, your monthly PSTN cost avoidance would be $9.00/day × 22 days/month, or $198.00. Thus, on an annual basis, the one-time expenditure of $6280 would result in savings of $198/month × 12 months, or $2376. This is a 37.8 percent return on your investment in voice over IP equipment, assuming a minimal amount of communications is routed via your organization's internal IP network instead of over the PSTN.

Examining Increased Usage

To illustrate how potential savings can substantially increase as usage of the V/IP cards increases, let's compute the economic savings associated with different usage scenarios. Table 6-4 lists the potential monthly and annual savings associated with eliminating between 60 and 480 call minutes per day between the two locations. In examining Table 6-4, the column labeled "Dual-port business day V/IP occupancy" indicates the percentage of usage of a dual-port V/IP gateway during an 8-hour business day. Note that 60 calling minutes per day represents only 6.25 percent of the capacity of the dual-port V/IP gateway, yet it results in an annual cost savings of $2376. Also note that an increase in usage of the V/IP gateways between the two locations to 120 minutes per day results in an annual cost avoidance of $4752, or approximately a 75 percent (4752/6280) return on the one-time expenditure required to implement this small two-site V/IP network.

If calling increases to 180 minutes per day, which represents only 18.75 percent occupancy or utilization of the V/IP gateway, the annual savings associated with the use of the dual-port V/IP gateway system increases to $7128. This level of savings pays for the equipment in less than 11 months! As you can see from Table 6-4, as usage in terms of calling minutes per day increases, the annual cost avoidance increases, resulting in a greater return on investment and a quicker payback period. Since the typical corporate return on investment of 15 to 20 percent is considered quite good, the potential return on investment from the use of Micom's V/IP gateways can be expected to warm the heart of the organization's chief financial officer. Although the preceding economic analysis was based on a cost avoidance of $.15 per minute, which may be high for large organizations with contracts for bulk-rate usage of a communications carrier's transmission facilities, such organizations may be able to use a V/IP gateway at a significantly higher level of utilization. The end result would still be an excellent return on investment. For example, assume your organization pays only $.05 per minute for calls within the United States. If your organization could use the V/IP gateway configuration for 480 call-

TABLE 6-4 Potential PSTN Cost Avoidance Based on a $.15 per minute Calling Rate	**Calling minutes/day**	**Dual-port Business Day V/IP occupancy (%)**	**Monthly cost avoidance**	**Annual cost avoidance**
	60	6.25	198.00	2,376.00
	120	12.50	396.00	4,752.00
	180	18.75	594.00	7,128.00
	240	25.00	792.00	9,540.00
	300	31.25	990.00	11,880.00
	360	37.50	1188.00	14,256.00
	420	43.75	1386.00	16,632.00
	480	50.00	1584.00	19,008.00

ing minutes per day, it would save $24 per day, or $528 for a 22-working-day month. On an annual basis, this would result in a cost avoidance of $6336, which, while substantially less than the $19,008 amount listed in Table 6-4 (based on a calling rate of $.15 per minute), still provides for the full payback of the organization's investment in less than one year.

INTERNATIONAL CALLING

When used for the routing of international calls, the higher tariffs associated with those calls can provide a substantial rate of return, even when usage between locations fills only a small fraction of the capacity of a V/IP gateway during normal business hours. For example, assume a bank installs V/IP gateways in branches located in Chicago and London. A discount PSTN rate for a call between the two locations of $.50 per minute would represent an attractive rate for calling between the two locations. Assuming 60 calling minutes per day between the two locations, the use of two V/IP gateways would save $660 per month, or $7920 on an annual basis. In this example, the return on investment occurs in less than one year even though the actual occupancy of the V/IP gateways is less than 6.25 percent over an 8-hour business day. Although your organization's actual return will vary based on the projected amount of calling and the cost per minute of the call, you can normally expect to obtain significant economic savings by transmitting voice on a private IP network.

Vocal Tec Internet Telephony Gateway

Vocal Tec's Internet Telephony gateway represents a logical extension of this vendor's Internet Phone product. In fact, the core software of the Internet Phone was used in its new product. Although the Internet Telephony gateway has many similarities to the previously discussed Micom V/IP gateway, the design and operation of these products have significant differences that warrant coverage of both devices in this chapter.

OVERVIEW

Vocal Tec markets its Internet Phone Telephony gateway as both an integrated hardware and software package and as an unbundled software program. The complete hardware and software package consists of a slim-line PC containing a Dialogic voice processing card for PBX and PSTN access and a LAN adapter card to enable the gateway to become a participant on a local area network connected via a router to an Internet service provider. This turnkey system with one voice port has a retail price of $3995 as this book is being written. As an alternative, you can purchase a software-only package for $1295 per simultaneous process and supply your own Win-

dows NT Pentium 133-, 166-, or 200-MHz computer. Up to two simultaneous processes can be supported on a Pentium 133-MHz computer and
up to four on a 166-MHz computer, while a 200-MHz Pentium with 48
Mbytes of memory can be used to support up to eight voice channels. For
each platform, you would also have to install a four-port Dialogic D/41ESC
voice-processing board for every two voice channels. That board has a retail
cost of $1095 as we go to press.

As with the Micom V/IP gateway, you can use the Vocal Tec Internet
Telephony gateway by connecting a PBX at each gateway location to a
voice gateway PC. By configuring a PBX code for each voice gateway, you
enable a caller to reach extensions on a remote PBX connected to a remote
Internet Telephony gateway. Unlike the Micom V/IP gateway, which relies
on a configured database of gateway IP addresses and associated telephone numbers, the Vocal Tec Internet Telephony gateway includes a
built-in interactive voice response (IVR) system. If a call is disconnected,
instead of the usual silence followed by a dial tone, the IVR system tells
the call originator the reason for the disconnection or inability to establish a call. For example, the IVR system might tell you the called number
was busy, the local or remote telephone gateway was busy, or you entered
an invalid telephone number.

CALLING SUPPORT
The Vocal Tec Internet Telephony gateway supports four types of calls:
telephone to telephone, computer to telephone, telephone to computer,
and World Wide Web page plug-in to telephone.

Telephone-to-telephone Calling
Telephone-to-telephone call support enables dialing from behind a PBX or
via regular telephone lines on a Touch-Tone phone. This makes it possible,
for example, for an employee working at home to dial the PBX and enter
an access code and destination telephone number to have a call routed over
the Internet without having to be in the office. Concerning access, the
Internet Telephony gateway offers several levels of caller authentication
that can be set separately for each line connected to the gateway. A *full
access control setting* requires callers to enter a password regardless of the
calling destination. A *limited access control setting* results in callers being
prompted for a password when the destination number is an outside call
on a gateway while passing calls to PBX extensions.

A third access control method is to use the PBX for access control.
Known as *PBX access control*, this setting allows an administrator to configure the PBX to restrict access to an extension number assigned to each

gateway in a network or to specific extensions reached through different gateways. The fourth access control method involves *no access control.* When this setting is used, all calls are immediately passed through the gateway.

Internet Phone-to-telephone Calling

Since Vocal Tec developed both the Internet Phone and Internet Telephony gateway, they are compatible, just as you might expect. This compatibility enables any person connected to the Internet to use Internet Phone software on his or her computer to reach a person whose telephone is connected to an Internet Telephony gateway via a PBX. When the call is received at the gateway it can be routed directly to an extension off the PBX or, if authorized, out-dialed from the PBX. The latter feature enables the Internet Telephony gateway to provide low-cost, international, long-distance service. In fact, several communications carriers—including Taiwan Telecommunications Network Services Co., Telecom New Zealand, and Telecom Finland either offer or have announced plans to offer Internet telephony services based on the use of the Vocal Tec Internet Telephony gateway product line.

Telephone-to-Internet Phone Calling

Reversing the previous call direction, the Internet Telephony gateway enables regular telephone users to communicate with persons using Vocal Tec's Internet Phone software. When dialing to the Internet, the gateway will prompt the call originator to enter the destination IP address, using the pound (#) button to delimit the IP address number. The telephone-to-Internet call-routing capability of the gateway could be useful for catalog sales, help desks, order desks, and similar organizations that would like to respond directly to a customer query received via e-mail from a Web browser. This capability can be taken to the extreme by noting a person browsing an organization's Web page and allowing an operation to initiate a conversation with a friendly "Can I help you?" query.

Browser-to-telephone Calling

Since most order departments and help desks use conventional telephones, any mechanism that permits Web browser—initiated calls to be routed to existing telephones will increase the productivity of personnel and enable a common set of telephones to be used for answering Internet and switched network—originated telephone calls. This method of gateway usage probably will increase as Internet commerce increases, since it allows potential customers to obtain real-time answers to their questions as they view products on a Web page.

OTHER FEATURES

In addition to supporting four gateway calling methods and four methods of access control, the Vocal Tec Internet Telephony gateway incorporates a number of features that make it suitable for internal corporate use on a private IP-based network, for use by organizations connected to the Internet, or as a mechanism for an organization to become a communications carrier. For use on private IP networks or via the Internet, the Vocal Tec Internet Telephony gateway's network monitor feature provides an alternate routing capability. That is, each gateway in a network will periodically poll the other gateways to ascertain the availability of those gateways. If an originating gateway cannot access the distant gateway or if it notes an unacceptable delay that degrades the reconstruction of voice, it can initiate alternate routing. Then, in a worst-case scenario, calls would be routed over the switched telephone network.

Through the use of a monitoring toolkit, organizations can obtain a "mini" call control center capability. In addition to providing a graphical representation of the call status for each line connected to the gateway, you can use the toolkit to establish different types of accounts, restricting different types of subscribers to different types of dialing. Through the gateway's billing management option, you can log incoming and outgoing calls, time-stamp each call, and record the caller's IP address. This provides the foundation for reselling Internet telephony services or for developing a charge-back mechanism that can be used to allocate the cost associated with communicating over an IP network to the departments in an organization that are using this facility.

MultiTech MultiVOIP

In concluding this section, we will turn our attention to the MultiTech MultiVOIP voice IP gateway. This relatively recent product, initially marketed in early 1999, has a suggested retail price of $1749, which represents an extremely low cost for a gateway. The MultiVOIP gateway, illustrated in Fig. 6-10, is manufactured as a stand-alone device. Each gateway has five connectors, including an RJ-45 Ethernet port, an Ethernet-to-serial port connection to connect a controlling PC, an AC power connector, and two ports for connecting analog devices. The two analog connection ports support two- or four-wire Types I, II, IV, and V E&M signaling as well as foreign exchange (FX) and loop-start 2-wire connections.

There are a large number of voice over IP network options to consider; however, it is important to first determine how your organization plans to use this capability. This information will enable you to select a solution commensurate with satisfying those requirements.

Figure 6-10
The MultiTech Multi-VOIP voice over IP gateway. (Photograph courtesy of MultiTech Systems.)

FEATURES

Although the MultiTech MultiVOIP voice over IP gateway weighs only 2 lbs and is housed in a relatively small $6 \times 1.6 \times 9$ inch package, it supports a full range of vocoders. Vocoder families supported include ITU G.711, G.723, G.726, and G.727. In addition, the MultiVOIP gateway also supports a series of proprietary NetCoder voice-compression methods that results in users having 22 vocoders from which to select.

In addition to a wide choice of vocoders, the MultiVOIP gateway is scheduled to add a gatekeeper/billing service option in a pending update. Although this can be used for charge-back purposes, you should note that while the current product is ideal for small-office utilization, its lack of scalability makes it difficult for large-scale implementations, as doing so would require the setup and management of one gateway for every two analog ports.

UTILIZATION ECONOMICS

Figure 6-11 illustrates the use of a pair of MultiVOIP gateways to support the transport of voice over the Internet or a corporate intranet. Because of the relatively low cost of a MultiVOIP gateway, for an approximate one-time cost of $3500 you can obtain the ability to continuously transmit two voice calls. If your organization can configure PBXs to first attempt to use the two ports and keep them busy 8 hours per day, 22 days per month, you would obtain:

$$8 \text{ hours/day} \times 22 \text{ days/mo} \times 60 \text{ min/hr}$$

$$\times 2 \text{ ports} = 21{,}120 \text{ call minutes/month}$$

At a cost avoidance of just 10 cents per minute, a pair of MultiVOIP gateways would pay for themselves in under two months. Even at half occupancy during the business day, the payback period is approximately three

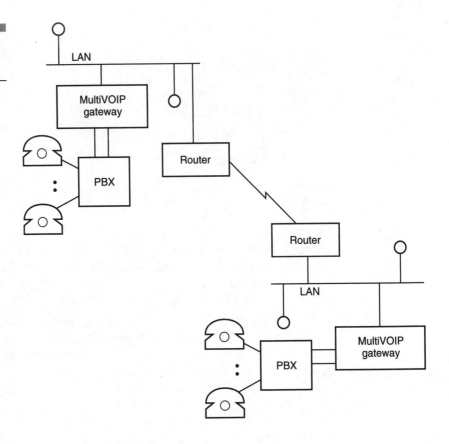

Figure 6-11
Using the MultiTech
MultiVOIP gateway.

months, while two hours of voice activity per port per day results in a still very attractive payback period of six months.

6-3 IP over ATM

In concluding this chapter, we will turn our attention to a transmission technique that for many organizations can make both Internet telephony and telephony over the Internet a practical reality. That transmission technique involves taking advantage of the use of ATM in a wide area infrastructure. Because ATM supports multiple service types with varying levels of service guarantees, it becomes possible with the appropriate hardware and software to take advantage of appropriate ATM classes of service to obtain the predictability and reliability required to transport voice end-to-end and obtain a high quality of reconstructed voice at the destination.

Overview

The key to routing IP over ATM to support the reliable and predictable transport of digitized voice is threefold. First, a mechanism is required to map IP datagrams into an appropriate ATM class of service. Second, an appropriate ATM class of service must be used. Third, equipment must be used that supports the flow of IP traffic, and its conversion into ATM cells, provides priority queuing for the conversion, and at the egress from the ATM network performs an appropriate reverse translation from ATM cells into IP datagrams. Because Cisco Systems provides equipment that can be used to obtain this capability, our examination of several aspects of IP over ATM will include a discussion of the features accompanying certain products manufactured by that vendor.

IP Datagram Considerations

Because either digitized voice or data can be transported within an IP datagram, it is important to differentiate between the two. In addition, because your organization may wish to prioritize the flow of certain types of data, such as encapsulated SNA over e-mail, it becomes important to divide traffic types and users into classes and treat each class differently during peak traffic periods.

When traffic flows on an intranet, it is possible to provide a quality of service (QoS) by implementing RSVP or by adding bandwidth. However, when data flows over a wide area network operated by one of more third-party communications carriers, it may be difficult or impossible to control QoS via IP. Fortunately, ATM has a built-in class-of-service capability. However, as illustrated in Figure 6-12, a mechanism is required to map IP datagrams into an appropriate ATM class of service at the ingress and from ATM cells to IP datagrams at the egress from the ATM network.

Figure 6-12
Using ATM to interconnect IP networks.

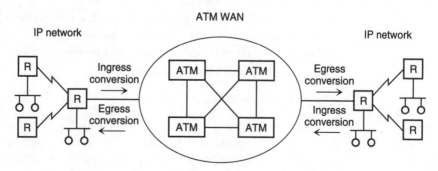

One method that can be used to differentiate IP datagrams is by setting appropriate bits in the Service Type byte, which is also referred to as the Type of Service (ToS) byte. RFC 791 defines eight levels of precedence that can be assigned to the Precedence field in the ToS byte. Those settings were previously discussed in Chapter 3. Thus, setting the Precedence field in the ToS byte represents a method to classify traffic. Because the resulting series of datagrams from different locations transporting different applications can be differentiated from one another, Cisco Systems refers to the newly classified traffic as *differentiated service classes.*

ATM Classes of Service

Under ATM, multiple traffic classes that are commonly referred to as *service types* are supported. Each traffic class or service type has a predefined characteristic as well as a level of service guarantee. Each traffic class definition is based on the use of three attributes: the timing relationship between the source and destination, the variability of the bit rate, and its connection mode.

Timing Relationship

The timing relationship between the source and destination defines the ability of the receiver to receive the original data stream at the same rate at which it was originated. For example, a voice conversation digitized at 64 Kbps via PCM must be "read" by the receiver at that data rate to be correctly interpreted. In comparison, a file transfer occurring via a T1 line into the Internet at a data rate of 1.544 Mbps could be correctly received via an egress access line operating at 56 Kbps. Although the reception of the file requires additional time, different transmission and reception rates do not inhibit the actual data transfer.

Bit Rate Variability

The second attribute governing the class of traffic is the bit rate. Some applications, such as digitized real-time voice, require a constant bit rate. Other applications, such as a file transfer, can occur successfully with either a constant or a variable bit rate.

Connection Mode

A third attribute governing the class of traffic is its connection mode. The connection mode can be either connection-oriented or connectionless. *Connection-oriented* means a connection must be established prior to actual data transfer occurring, while *connectionless* references transmission occurring on a best-effort basis, with an acknowledgment flowing back only after transmission was initiated. Examples of connection-oriented applications include voice calls and IBM SNA data sessions. Examples of connectionless applications include Ethernet transmission and applications that use UDP. Table 6-5 indicates the relationship between key ATM classes of service and their three key attributes.

ATM's Class A is also commonly referred to as a Constant Bit Rate (CBR) class of service. CBR is well suited for transporting digitized voice and in fact was designed primarily for supporting voice communications. CBR allows the amount of bandwidth, end-to-end delay, and the delay variation to be specified during call setup. Class B traffic is commonly referred to as Variable Bit Rate Real Time (VBR-rt) as it requires a timing relationship. In comparison, because Class C traffic does not require a timing relationship, it is commonly referred to as Variable Bit Rate Non-Real Time (VBR-nrt). Finally, Class D traffic is commonly referred to as Unspecified Bit Rate (UBR).

As IP datagrams are processed by an internal IP network, the setting of the appropriate ToS bits occurs. Prioritized datagrams that transport digitized voice should be mapped into ATM CBR cells. In doing so, ATM traffic shaping on a CBR ATM permanent virtual circuit (PVC) must occur to provide a constant intercell gap, which is the characteristic of ATM CBR shaping.

In a Cisco Systems router environment, certain vendor router ATM interfaces provide an ATM traffic-shaping capability. In doing so, Cisco equipment supports the configuration of parameters that define the average sustainable cell rate (SCR), peak cell rate (PCR, and maximum burst size (MBS). By configuring the average cell rate and the peak cell rate to the same bandwidth through the use of a Cisco routers atm pvc command, you will shape the resulting ATM cell flow with a constant intercell gap. This in turn results in a CBR data flow, because a constant intercell gap represents the characteristic of CBR shaping.

TABLE 6-5

ATM Classes of Service

Class	Timing	Bit	Connection
A	Required	Constant	Connection-oriented
B	Required	Variable	Connection-oriented
C	Not required	Variable	Connection-oriented
D	Not required	Variable	Connectionless

Ingress Considerations

In addition to prioritizing IP datagrams and converting traffic to an appropriate ATM class of service, it is important to ensure that ingress traffic is prioritized. This is because the router connected to the ATM backbone must place traffic into different virtual circuit queues as well as extract data from those queues based on precedence. To accomplish this, certain Cisco routers support a prioritization technique referred to as Weighted Random Early Detection (WRED).

WRED provides a mechanism to obtain service differentiation across different ATM classes of service based on the setting of the ToS byte in an IP datagram. Under WRED, an exponential weight factor can be assigned for a WRED parameter group.

The parameters are used in an equation to define the probability of a packet being dropped. That probability depends on a mapping from the IP precedence value to a WRED parameters value as indicated in Table 6-6.

The following equation defines the WRED average value, with n ranging between 1 and 16.

$$\text{Average} = (\text{old average} \times 1\tfrac{1}{2}\,\char`\^ n) + \text{current queue size} \times \tfrac{1}{2}\,\char`\^ n)$$

Note that the higher the value of n, the more dependent the average is on the previous average. Thus, a large value of n serves to smooth out the peaks and valleys in queue length. Cisco routing packets are marked with a precedence of 6, resulting in a selective discard with a very low loss prob-

	IP precedence	WRED minimum threshold values
TABLE 6-6	0	8
Default WRED Minimum Threshold Values Based on IP Precedence	1	9
	2	10
	3	11
	4	12
	5	13
	6	14
	7	15

ability. Thus, you should configure a Cisco router to use precedence 6 and 7 for digitized voice traffic, while data traffic should use precedences 0 to 5.

As a practical matter, the average queue size is unlikely to change very quickly and avoids drastic swings in queue length. However, Cisco recommends that users start operation or testing with the default value of n, which is 9, because the fine-tuning of WRED to achieve a specific IP service differentiation is a "delicate exercise."

Economics

Although each communications carrier can be expected to price the use of ATM differently, we will conclude this section with an example of the cost associated with the use of an ATM backbone network. In 1999, Quest billed ATM CBR service at \$.02 per Mbyte of traffic. If we are not greedy, and we assume a voice-digitization rate of 8 Kbps, then a one-minute conversation results in the transmission of 8 Kbps × 60 seconds/minute × 8 bits/byte, or 60 Kbytes/minute. On an hourly basis this results in 60 Kbytes/minute × 60 minutes/hour, or 3.6 Mbytes/hour. Thus, at a cost of \$.02/Mbyte of traffic, a one-hour voice call would cost \$.072. While you must still consider the cost of voice over IP equipment, the ability to use an ATM backbone for under 8 cents per hour to obtain quality of service represents an ideal mechanism to lower the cost of voice.

Voice over Frame Relay

In previous chapters in this book, we examined the operation of frame relay and the effect of using different methods on the bandwidth required to digitize voice. In this chapter, we will put that knowledge to use as we investigate the transmission of voice over frame relay networks. First, we will examine some key technical issues associated with the transmission of voice over a frame relay network. Then we'll turn our attention to the operation and utilization of several types of vendor equipment developed to provide users with the capability to transmit voice over their frame relay network connections. As we cover the operation and utilization of vendor equipment, we will also look at the development of economic models you can use to estimate the cost of adding a voice transmission capability to your organization's public or private frame relay network. Finally, because the Frame Relay Forum is so important, we will conclude this chapter with a discussion of the FRF.11 Implementation Agreement (IA), which sets the standard for the transmission of voice over frame relay.

Although just about all equipment vendors were offering proprietary solutions for transmitting voice over frame relay as this book was written, the reason for the proprietary nature of products was the lack of standards in this area. Now that the Voice over Frame Relay Implementation Agreement is a fact, we can expect that vendors will announce compliant products in the near future, assuming that they have not done so by the time this book is published. In fact, based on telephone conversations with several vendor representatives while preparing this book, this author found a willingness of vendor personnel in both engineering and product marketing divisions at several firms to predict that they would eventually modify their existing products to become fully compliant with the FRF.11 Implementation Agreement.

7.1 Technological Issues

Frame relay was developed as a fast packet switching technology designed to eliminate the delays associated with the use of an X.25 packet network. In doing so, frame relay became a suitable transport for interactive query-response applications in which a client was located on one network and the server was located on a geographically separated network, with both networks linked together through the use of a frame relay network. The fact that CRC checking was employed only at switches to determine whether or not to drop a frame (instead of using full error detection and correction by retransmission) enabled data to flow end to end with minimal delay. This capability was extremely important to support query-response applications in which client-station users would enter a variety of short queries that would otherwise be significantly delayed through a conventional packet switching network and would degrade the ability of the user to type in a normal manner, adversely affecting productivity.

Although the use of a frame relay network enables access to SNA mainframes as well as LAN-to-LAN connectivity that otherwise might be awkward when using an X.25 network, frame relay uses a variable-length information field. Thus, from a technical perspective, the variable frame length can adversely affect the arrival and interpretation of the digitized-voice frame when its contents are examined and used to reconstruct voice. In addition to the variable-length frame presenting problems with respect to the transportation of digitized voice, a variety of other technical issues face equipment developers. Table 7-1 lists ten of the key issues faced by equipment developers and voice over frame relay implementers. In the remainder of this section, we will examine each issue. Not only will this give you an appreciation for the obstacles equipment developers and implementers had to overcome, it will also help to clarify the technological features so you can compare equipment manufactured by different vendors.

Frame Length Handling

As noted earlier in this chapter and in Chapter 3, the information field in the frame relay frame is variable in length. To illustrate the problem this

TABLE 7-1

Voice over Frame
Relay Technical
Issues

Frame length handling
Frame prioritization
Frame loss handling
Echo cancellation
Frame delay handling
Silence suppression
Voice-compression method
Telephony signaling
Multiplexing technique
Using frame relay over ATM

Figure 7-1

A lengthy frame transporting data that is serviced between frames transporting digitized voice can adversely delay the reconstruction of speech at its destination, making it sound awkward.

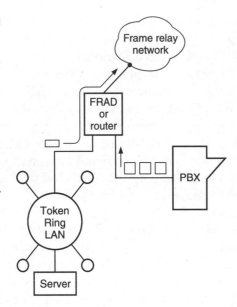

can cause, consider the FRAD or router in Figure 7-1, which provides a connection to a frame relay network for a transmission to and from a LAN and a PBX. In this example, there is one serial port connection used to link the FRAD or router, which services the LAN and the PBX, to the frame relay network. This means that the transfer of a file, a long response from the server to a client query from another location connected to the LAN shown in Figure 7-1 via the frame relay network, or another lengthy data transfer will tend to fill the information field in the frame relay frame.

Effect of Variable-length Frames

Although an Ethernet LAN limits the information field length to 1500 bytes, a Token Ring LAN operating at 16 Mbps can have an information field that can be up to approximately 18 Kbytes in length. If a LAN station obtains access to the serial interface of the router or FRAD between frames transporting digitized speech, the delay will depend on the operating rate of the serial connection to the network and the length of the frame. Concerning the former, there are significant delay differences between accessing a frame relay network at 56/64 Kbps and a T1 operating rate of 1.544 Mbps. For example, at 64 Kbps, one 8-bit byte carried in the information field of a frame relay frame requires 125×10^{-6} seconds (8/64,000) for transmission. Thus, a 1500-byte information field in a frame relay frame that results from the transportation of data in the maximum-length Ethernet information field to the FRAD or router would require 0.1875 seconds $(125 \times 10^{-6} \times 1500)$ to be transmitted to the network, without considering the overhead associated with control fields. This means that, excluding frame overhead and processing time associated with the FRAD or router forming a frame for placement onto the access line connected to the frame relay network, a lengthy Ethernet LAN packet could delay a frame transporting voice by almost 0.2 second.

APPLICATION NOTE FRADs or frame relay—compliant routers must be configured to place a limit on the length of frames transporting data to minimize their effect on frames transporting digitized voice.

Considering End-to-end Delay

It should be noted that the previously described delay represents only the delay associated with accessing the frame relay network. The actual end-to-end delay can be significantly higher, since slight delays are introduced at each node in the frame relay network, and additional delay may result if a frame transporting data arrives at a network node prior to a frame transporting digitized voice. The latter situation can easily occur if your organization uses a frame relay network to interconnect a number of LANs, with PVCs set up to provide an any-LAN-to-any-LAN communications capability. In this situation, there is a higher probability that a frame transporting data will arrive between a sequence of frames transporting digitized speech at a network node for delivery to a FRAD or router via an access line from the network to a subscriber's location. In fact, a station on a LAN at the originating site could be transmitting to a different destination than the destination of the frame carrying digitized voice, while a station on a LAN at a third location could be transmitting a sequence of frames carrying data to the destination location of the digitized-voice frame. If any frame carrying data arrives before the frame carrying digitized voice, then the delay in effect doubles. Thus, the use of 64-Kbps access lines could result in an end-to-end delay of 0.3750 seconds, a gap sufficient in duration to result in the distortion of reconstructed speech.

Worst-case Delay

Although a delay of 0.375 seconds is significant, that delay assumes a worst-case situation when frames transporting digitized speech are delayed by frames transporting data in an information field 1500 bytes in length.

Now let's assume that the LAN used is a Token Ring network operating at 16 Mbps. As previously discussed, this network can transport frames with an information field of up to 18,000 bytes in length. Since the maximum length of the information field of a frame relay frame is 8192 characters, this means that the FRAD or router would fragment the contents of a lengthy Token Ring information field that exceeds 8192 bytes into two or more frame relay frames, with the first frame always having a maximum-length information field of 8192 bytes. Again, returning to an access line operating rate of 64 Kbps, this means that the worst-case delay resulting from a frame transporting data will be 125×10^{-6} seconds/byte $\times$ 8192 bytes, or 1.024 seconds, clearly a most unsuitable situation. Once again, it becomes possible for a long frame transporting data from a different location to arrive at the destination FRAD slightly ahead of the frame transporting digitized voice. This action doubles the 1.024-second delay between frames transporting voice to 2.048 seconds, making a bad situation intolerable.

Varying the Access Line Operating Rate

Now let's assume our organization installs a T1 circuit as the local access line to a frame relay network operator. Although this transmission facility operates at 1.544 Mbps, the operating rate includes an 8-Kbps sequence of framing bits that cannot be used for the transmission of the contents of frame relay frames. This means that the data transmission capacity of the access line will be 1.536 Mbps, or 24 times the capacity of a 64-Kbps circuit. This also means that the latency or delay resulting from a frame transporting data being processed by a router or FRAD just prior to a frame transporting digitized voice will adversely affect the digitized voice frame by 1/24th the time indicated by our prior computations for the same situation, resulting from the use of a 64-Kbps access line. Table 7-2 summarizes the one-way delays resulting from 1500- and 8192-byte frames carrying data being processed by a FRAD or router prior to a frame transporting digitized voice via 64-Kbps and 1.544-Mbps access lines.

In examining the entries in Table 7-2, your first instinct to solve the delay problem caused by a variable-length information field may be to sig-

TABLE 7-2

Data Frame Delay Times (in seconds)

Frame Length	Access Line Operating Rate	
	64 Kbps	1.544 Mbps
1500 bytes	1.875	0.0078
8192 bytes	1.024	0.0427

nificantly increase the operating rate of the access line to the frame relay network. Although this would undoubtably reduce the delay time caused by frames that transport data arriving at a FRAD or router prior to frames that transport digitized voice, it is also important to note that very rarely does a frame transporting data arrive at a FRAD or router as a single entity. That is, if a workstation initiates a file transfer, there is a high probability that a flow or sequence of LAN frames will arrive at the FRAD or router, and in fact may fill its buffer memory unless there is a mechanism that subdivides buffer memory into independent queues and uses a priority mechanism to service data placed in each queue. Even then, separate queues and a priority scheme may not be sufficient, because at certain access line operating rates, a lengthy frame transporting data can adversely delay a frame transporting digitized voice. Thus, a better solution to this problem is both fragmentation and prioritization of data.

Fragmentation

Fragmentation provides a mechanism to subdivide relatively long frames into a series of shorter, less-delay-creating frames. Through a fragmentation process, an even flow of minimized-length frames will be created, such that frames transporting digitized voice do not have to wait too long behind frames transporting data. This concept is illustrated in Figure 7-2, which shows how a long data frame is subdivided into a sequence of shorter-length frames by a FRAD or router. In this example, it was assumed that the FRAD or router was programmed to interleave frames transporting voice and data. However, in many operational situations, fragmentation by itself or with simple interleaving is not sufficient. What is then needed is a frame-prioritization scheme that works in conjunction with frame fragmentation.

Figure 7-2

Through the fragmentation of lengthy frames into short blocks of data, the delay resulting from a frame transporting data on a frame transporting digitized voice is minimized.

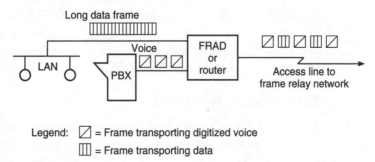

One important factor you must recognize is the effect of fragmentation. Although the fragmentation of packets transporting voice is a necessity to minimize delays to packets transporting digitized voice, the fragmentation process increases network overhead. Simply put, prior to implementing a voice over frame relay application it is extremely important to determine the potential effect of fragmentation on your data transportation.

APPLICATION NOTE Although frame fragmentation is vital for the success of mixed voice and data applications flowing over a common serial port, the fragmentation process introduces additional overhead that adversely affects the transfer of data.

Frame Prioritization

Prioritization is a technique in which frames are processed based on predefined criteria. When a FRAD or router is servicing both data and digitized voice, it logically makes sense to prioritize delay-sensitive traffic, such as digitized voice, ahead of non-delay-sensitive traffic or less-delay-sensitive traffic.

Memory Partitioning and Priority Queues

Prioritization must be used with fragmentation to be effective. Many equipment vendors will partition the memory of their FRAD or router into priority queues. Frames containing data that exceed a predefined length are first fragmented. Then, all frames transporting data, including fragmented and nonfragmented frames, are placed into a low-priority queue. Similarly, frames transporting digitized speech that exceed a predefined length are also fragmented. However, unlike frames transporting data, frames carrying digitized voice are placed into a high-priority queue. The primary reason frames transporting digitized voice are fragmented is that the sampling source produces a lengthy frame, and fragmentation will produce a more regular flow of voice information. It also reduces the potential that the loss or delay of a packet as it flows through the network will adversely affect the reconstruction of the voice signal at its destination.

Prioritization Techniques

The method used to prioritize traffic will obviously provide a preference to voice. However, depending on the type of data presented to the FRAD or router, there may be certain types of frames transporting different types of data that also require prioritization. For example, the transmission of SNA traffic can result in session timeouts if frames carrying such data are adversely delayed. Thus, prioritization techniques must consider the type of data being transmitted as well as the fact that frames transporting digitized speech should receive a higher priority than most frames transporting data.

APPLICATION NOTE It is important to examine the manner by which queue servicing occurs and whether such servicing is adjustable.

Frame Loss Handling

When data are transmitted over a frame relay network, the loss of a frame due to congestion or error results in higher layers at the endpoints performing a retransmission of the lost frame. Although the retransmission process is commonly used to correct a previously lost frame, it introduces a delay that is not suitable for handling digitized speech. That is, if a frame transporting digitized speech is for some reason dropped by the network, the retransmission of the frame results in an arrival delay that distorts the reconstruction of the digitized voice signal. Recognizing this fact, equipment vendors handle frame loss with respect to the transportation of digitized speech in one of two ways. Some vendors simply generate a period of silence, while other vendors use the contents of a sequence of previously arrived frames to generate speech for the missing interval. This is accomplished by means of an interpolation technique based on the contents of the last or a few previously arrived frames. For both techniques, vendor equipment will not retransmit lost frames, as their arrival at the destination would result in a sufficient degree of delay that would render their use impractical.

It is important to note that the second technique actually represents a combination of techniques. A short period of time can transpire prior to a frame either being marked as missing or delayed and an interpolation of the prior frame being used. That period or gap is commonly compensated for by the generation of noise; however, because the gap is a very short period of time that is commonly unnoticeable to the human ear, some vendors may elect to use a period of silence. Thus, interpolation may be combined either with noise or silence.

Echo Cancellation

Echo is a phenomenon resulting from the connection of two-wire subscriber access lines to the four-wire infrastructure used to form the long-distance trunks that interconnect telephone company central offices to one another. The actual connection of two-wire to four-wire circuits is performed by a device referred to as a *hybrid*. When energy is transmitted across the hybrid, a portion is reflected back, and this reflection is called an *echo*. The echo can be an annoyance to the speaker, especially when the reflection of his or her voice is delayed sufficiently to become highly noticeable.

There are actually two types of echoes in voice conversations: near-end and far-end. The *near-end echo* results from the reflection of energy at the hybrid in the caller's central serving office. The *far-end echo* is caused by the hybrid located in the central office serving the called party. From the perspective of degree of disturbance, the far-end echo travels a much longer distance and would therefore usually arrive at the talker's location well after he or she spoke, causing an echo similar to what you might encounter in a canyon. To suppress the effect of echoes, communications carriers use *echo suppressors*. An echo suppressor is an electronic device inserted into a four-wire circuit to function as a blocking mechanism with respect to reflected energy.

Frame relay networks do not use echo-suppression equipment in their networks. This is because those networks were constructed to support the transfer of digital data. However, since the annoyance factor of an echo is a function of its delay, the transmission of digitized speech over a frame relay network can result in disturbing echoes when two sites separated by a sufficient distance are interconnected via a frame relay network. Since the network operator does not use echo-suppression equipment, this becomes the responsibility of equipment vendors.

Although most equipment vendors who market products for the voice over frame relay market include an echo-suppression or echo-cancellation capability, not all do. However, prior to using this feature as an evaluation discriminator, it is important to note that only when the average round-trip propagation time exceeds 25 to 50 ms is the use of echo suppression recommended. Otherwise, the use of a frame relay network to connect a few locations in close proximity to one another may not be necessary.

Frame Delay Handling

As frames are routed through a network, they will encounter a variety of nonuniform processing delays. These delays, which depend on such factors as the activity level of a switch, the length of a frame processed ahead of another frame, and the processing power of the switch, result in a uniform data stream by the time it is transmitted into a frame relay network being received at its destination with random delays between frames. This is illustrated in Figure 7.3, which shows how precise time intervals between a sequence of frames presented to a frame relay network could be altered during their flow through the network, resulting in random delays between received frames.

Jitter and Jitter Compensation

The delay between received frames is commonly referred to as *jitter* and can result in awkward-sounding regenerated speech. Recognizing this problem, many voice over frame relay equipment vendors incorporate a buffer area in their products. Buffering the frames that transport digitized speech removes the variable delays, in effect facilitating the process by which voice is reconstructed to prevent annoying periods of random delays.

APPLICATION NOTE Many equipment vendors have selectable-delay jitter buffers, typically supporting 0 to 255 ms of delay. Although a longer delay facilitates the reconstruction of voice, it also adds to the overall latency. Too high a setting can force users into a CB mode of having to say "over" to alert the other party to proceed.

Figure 7-3
Delays associated with switch processing capability and the traffic load presented to each switch result in frames presented to a network at a constant rate being received from the network with random delays between each frame.

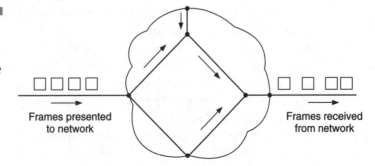

Frames presented to network

Frames received from network

Silence Suppression

Although many frame relay network providers do not bill for the number of bytes transmitted, from a practical standpoint it makes no sense to transmit digitized voice samples that contain only a period of silence. Frames containing a period of silence add to network traffic and can adversely affect the transmission and delivery of other frames carrying digitized voice samples from the same or different callers. Recognizing this problem, some equipment vendors include a silence-suppression capability in their equipment.

The effective implementation of silence suppression requires the use of a time tag for each frame transporting a digitized speech sample. This time tag enables the receiver to reconstruct a person's voice, including gaps and pauses between words and sentences, which results in the ability to maintain the natural quality of a person's speech. Unfortunately, the method used to suppress periods of silence currently varies between vendor products. However, the adoption of the Frame Relay Forum Voice over Frame Relay Implementation Agreement (FRF.11 IA) facilitates the interoperability between vendor equipment.

Voice-Compression Method

Although many technical issues can affect the quality of reconstructed voice, the most important long-term factor is the method of voice compression used. As previously discussed in Chapter 4, voice-compression methods can be generally grouped into three distinct categories: waveform coding, vocoding, and hybrid coding, with the latter representing a combination of the first two categories. Although such waveform-encoding methods as PCM and ADPCM result in very high quality reconstructed speech, they also require a large amount of bandwidth to transmit a digitized conversation, with PCM consuming 64 Kbps and ADPCM requiring 32 Kbps to provide a toll-quality conversation. Waveform coding provides such a high level of reconstructed voice that it serves as a benchmark for users to compare the quality of other compression methods, but it does not maximize the utilization of bandwidth. In fact, on certain access lines, such as a 64-Kbps connection to a frame relay network, the use of PCM or ADPCM would either preclude the use of the connection for data or consume all or half of the bandwidth of the access line—neither of which is a pleasant situation. Thus, a more practical employment of voice on a frame relay network requires the use of low-bit-rate compression algorithms, either resulting from vocoding or hybrid coding techniques.

Low-Bit-Rate Coding

Currently, equipment vendors offer products that support a variety of voice-compression algorithms, with many vendors using algorithms in the Code Excited Linear Prediction (CELP) family, whose employment can result in voice digitization rates from a high of approximately 16 Kbps down to 2.4 Kbps. Table 7-3 lists three examples of low-bit-rate standardized voice-compression algorithms commonly supported by frame relay equipment vendors.

In examining the low-bit-rate voice-compression methods listed in Table 7-3, you should consider the ability of equipment to support multiple methods. Doing so provides you with the ability to select an alternative if for some reason the primary method results in reconstructed voice that is not to your liking.

Telephony Signaling

The effective transmission of voice over a frame relay network requires the ability to alert the destination to an incoming call and to inform the originator of the progress of the call. Such activities are associated with telephony signaling, and a FRAD or voice-compliant router must be able to transfer appropriate telephony signaling. In doing so, it is important to note that the meaning of a telephone signal can be represented by a transition as well as by time between pulses and the sequence of pulses. This makes the appropriate coding and transfer of telephony signaling much more challenging than the simple passage of data signals that are represented by a transition from a high to low pulse or a low to high pulse.

TABLE 7-3	ITU Standard	Compression Method	
Low-Bit-Rate Standards-Based Voice-Compression Methods	G.723.1	ACELP	5.3/6.3 Kbps
	G.728	LD-CELP	16 Kbps
	G.729	CS-ACELP	8 Kbps

Since PBXs may use different signaling methods, it is important to ensure compatibility between the signaling method supported by the FRAD or router and the signaling method used by the PBX.

Multiplexing Technique Used

In their quest to enhance the performance of voice over frame relay and to develop a mechanism that can differentiate their products from those of others, vendors offering voice-capable FRADs have incorporated different bandwidth-optimization methods into their products. Two such techniques that are incompatible with one another are *logical link multiplexing* and *subchannel multiplexing.*

Logical Link Multiplexing

Logical link multiplexing (LLM) enables frames transporting voice and data to share the same PVC. This technique is suitable for the situation in which your organization uses a voice server on a LAN to digitize voice. It requires both digitized voice-encoded frames as well as frames transporting LAN data to be carried via a common frame relay connection to the LAN. By using logical link multiplexing, you can more than likely reduce your organization's cost to use a frame relay network, since most network operators include a cost component based on the number of PVCs used.

Subchannel Multiplexing

A second multiplexing technique used by some FRAD manufacturers is subchannel multiplexing (SM). Under subchannel multiplexing, portions of multiple voice conversations are combined within one frame. By transmitting samples of several voice conversations within one frame, the overhead of the frame in comparison to its payload is reduced. This can be an especially important consideration when transmitting multiple digitized voice conversations over a low-speed frame relay access circuit, such as a 56- or 64-Kbps access line. Now that we have a general appreciation of the major technologically related issues concerning the transmission of voice over a frame relay network, let's turn our attention to the operation and utilization of vendor equipment developed to provide this capability. We will also discuss the general cost of acquiring certain types of equipment, and we'll combine that with the cost of using a frame relay network to develop economic models for voice over frame relay transmission under several networking scenarios.

Frame Relay over ATM

Similar to our discussion of transporting IP over an ATM network in Chapter Six, you can also consider transporting frame relay over an ATM network. In fact, there are two standardized methods for doing so. One method is referred to as Data Exchange Interface (DXI), while the second method is referred to as Frame-based User-to-Network Interface (FUNI). Both methods represent access protocols standardized by the ATM Forum.

Overview

Both the DXI and FUNI access protocols enable frame relay transmission to be carried over an ATM network. Although both access protocols have a high degree of commonality, there are certain key differences between the two. The primary difference is the use of different hardware and the location of the hardware that provides a frame-to-cell and cell-to-frame translation. Other differences between the two reside in the efficiency and the internetworking capability of each method.

Both DXI and FUNI access protocols require appropriate software operating on a router to generate FUNI or DXI frames. When FUNI is used, FUNI frames flow directly to a serial port, as illustrated in Figure 7-4a. The ATM switch then performs the segmentation and reassembly (SAR) process, converting frames to cells and vice versa. When a DXI access protocol is used for the connection, an ATM CSU/DSU performs the frame-to-cell and cell-to-frame conversion process. This is illustrated in Figure 7.4b.

In examining Figure 7.4, note that the use of the DXI access protocol results in variable-length frames being segmented into ATM fixed-length cells at the subscriber's premises. Because each ATM 53-byte cell includes 5 bytes of overhead, in almost all transmissions the use of the FUNI access protocol will be a more efficient transport mechanism into an ATM network. For example, a 75-byte frame would fill the 48-byte payload of one cell and result in the use of a second cell with only 27 bytes in its 48-byte payload being filled. Because ingress and egress lines into and out of the ATM network normally operate at a much lower rate than the backbone of the ATM network, the inefficiency of the DXI access protocol may not be suitable for some latency-critical applications, including voice over frame relay.

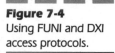

Figure 7-4
Using FUNI and DXI
access protocols.

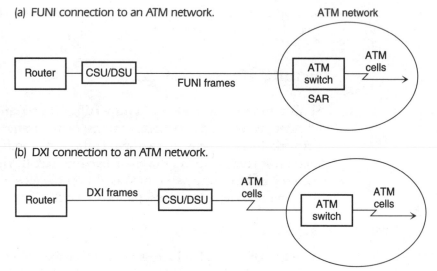

(a) FUNI connection to an ATM network.

(b) DXI connection to an ATM network.

Legend: SAR = segmentation and reassembly.

APPLICATION NOTE When considering frame relay versus ATM, the use of the FUNI access protocol should be considered over the use of the DXI access protocol when ingress and egress occur at relatively slow data rates. This is because the FUNI access protocol transmits more-bandwidth-efficient frames to the ATM switch, while the DXI access protocol uses less-bandwidth-efficient fixed 53-byte cells.

Frame Structure

The basic structure of the DXI, FUNI, and frame relay frames is the same. It differs only in the composition of the frame relay header field. The top portion of Figure 7-5 illustrates the structure of the basic frame that is common to all three access protocols. The lower portion of Figure 7-5 illustrates the associated header changes for each access protocol.

When FUNI and DXI frames are segmented into cells, their frame addresses are mapped into ATM VPI/VCI (virtual path identifier/virtual connection identifier) using similar procedures. Those mapping procedures result in certain values in the FUNI and DXI frame fields being placed in appropriate fields withing the ATM cell header. For example, the Congestion Notification (CN) bit is mapped to the CN bit position in the ATM cell header. The CN bit performs the same function as the frame relay FECN bit, being set by the network during periods of congestion. However, nei-

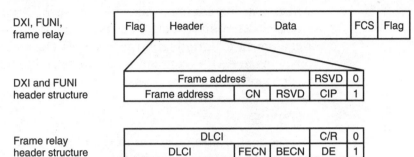

Figure 7-5

Comparing DXI, FUNI, and frame relay frame structures.

Basic frame structure

Legend:
BECN = Backward-explicit congestion notification
CLP = Cell-loss priority
CN   = Congestion notification
C/R = Command/response
DE   = Discard eligibility
DLCI = Data link connection identifier
FCS = Frame check sequence
FECN = Forward-explicit congestion notification
RSVD = Reserved

ther FUNI nor DXI provides for a BECN bit setting. This is because there is no function similar to BECN in ATM. The DXI and FUNI access protocols use the cell-loss priority (CLP) bit to perform the same function as the frame relay discard-eligible (DE) bit. Last but not least, the frame relay C/R does not have a corresponding bit in either the FUNI or SXI header.

Mapping Issues

FUNI mandates the support of ATM Adapter Layer 5 (AAL 5) in the ATM switch that supports the connection; however, AAL 3/4 is optional. It is important to note that although neither AAL 3/4 nor AAL 5 supports the constant bit rate (CBR) required for voice circuit emulation, the ATM network operator can specify cell loss and latency for either adaption layer that provides a guaranteed level of deliver. Thus, depending on the latency and loss guarantees specified for mapping frames into variable-bit-rate cells, the use of ATM in this manner may be suitable for connecting frame relay devices or networks transporting voice. Similarly, DXI frames are segmented into AAL 5 cells.

One problem that results from the use of AAL 5 is the fact that it performs error detection and correction, which adversely affects the transmission of real-time voice. Thus, another consideration prior to using ATM to transport frame relay, which in turn is transporting digitized voice, is to determine the error rate of the ATM backbone and the ability of equipment to discard retransmitted cells. Obviously, if you can obtain a mapping to AAL 1's constant bit rate designed to transport voice, all of the previously mentioned problems are eliminated.

Economics

One the the possible questions in the mind of many readers is the economic trade-offs associated with the use of pure frame relay versus frame relay over ATM. For many economic comparisons, you must examine the cost components of each service. However, this can be a bit difficult with certain comparisons because most frame relay operations do not include a cost component based on the quantity of data transmitted, which most ATM operators do. Another problem associated with comparing the use of the two technologies involves comparing frames and cells when changes are based on the quantity of data transmitted. To provide you with an indication of how you can compare apples and oranges by costing frame relay and ATM service usage, this author will use prices that Quest publicized in early 1999 for frame relay non-discard-eligible, ATM variable-bit-rate, real-time, and ATM available-bit-rate services. Those prices per Mbyte of traffic transmitted were 4 cents, 3 cents, 1.2 cents, and .55 cents, respectively.

FRAME RELAY COST

An 8-Kbps voice-digitization rate, we noted earlier in this book, is equivalent to 3.6 Mbytes/hour. If we assume voice is packetized in 70-byte segments, the 3.6 Mbytes equates to 51,429 frames (3.6 Mbytes/70 bytes per frame). Because each frame has 6 bytes of overhead, total overhead becomes 51,429 frames × 6 bytes/frame, or 308,574 bytes. Thus, an hour of 8Kbps digitized voice results in 3.6 Mbytes plus 308 Kbytes of overhead, for a total of 3.9 Mbytes. Based on Quest's rate of 4 cents and 3 cents per Mbyte for non-discard-eligible and discard-eligible transmission, the cost of an hour of digitized voice is either 15.6 cents or 11.7 cents!

ATM COST

Prior to computing the cost of ATM, we need to determine the number of cells and cell overhead. Because we assumed voice was digitized into 70-byte frames, each frame must be converted into two 53-byte cells. Thus, the 51,429 frames becomes 102,858 cells. Since each cell is 53 bytes, the total amount of data, including cell overhead, payload, and cell pads, becomes 102,858 cells × 53 bytes/cell, or 5.45 Mbytes. Because we assumed the per-Mbyte cost of ATM to be 1.2 cents for VBR-rt and .55 cents for ABR, the cost per hour for each type of ATM class of traffic becomes 5.45 Mbytes × 1.2 cents/Mbyte, or 6.54 cents, and 5.45 Mbytes × 0.55 cents/Mbyte, or 3.0 cents. Thus, in this example, if we do not consider the cost of equipment and focus our attention on transport charges, the use of an ATM backbone can result in significant savings.

7-2 Equipment Operation and Utilization

Since 1995, a number of vendors have introduced equipment that supports the transmission of voice over a frame relay network. These vendors include ACT Networks, Fast Comm Communications Corporation, Memotec Corporation, Motorola Corporation, Nuera Communications, and Castleton Network Systems Corporation. In addition, due to the potential economic savings associated with the use of this technology, additional vendors were introducing new products as this book was written. Thus, a viable market of voice over frame relay equipment providers is being established that will competitively offer equipment to satisfy organizational networking requirements. In addition, the Frame Relay Forum's Voice over Frame Relay Implementation Agreement provides the foundation for interoperability between different vendor products. Thus, an expanding and eventually interoperable series of products should be available for consideration by the time you read this book.

In this section, we will examine the operation and utilization of several commercially available products. We'll learn how they facilitate the transmission of voice over a frame relay network, and we'll weigh the economics associated with using certain types of vendor products. This indepth economic analysis will include both the cost of hardware and the cost of frame relay network services.

ACT Networks

ACT Networks is one of several vendors of communications products with a relatively long history in the development of frame relay products. In fact, ACT was the first company to commercially market frame relay access devices (FRADs) that could be used to transmit voice, fax, and data over public and private frame relay networks. In addition to manufacturing customer-provided equipment (CPE) for frame relay operations, ACT also manufactures a carrier class central office voice FRAD for use by communications carriers or for use on the backbone used to form high-speed internal networks. In this section, we will examine the operation and utilization of two ACT Networks products—its Integrated FRAD and a specific model of its IFRAD called the SN-8800 IFRAD. We will also examine the economics associated with using the SN-8800 to transmit voice over a frame relay network.

The Integrated FRAD

As previously noted in this chapter, there are a large number of technical issues associated with obtaining the ability to effectively and efficiently transport digitized voice over a frame relay network. Recognizing those technical issues, ACT Networks developed a family of FRADs designed from the ground up as a mechanism to transmit voice, data, and fax via public or private frame relay networks. Since these FRADs provide an integrated transmission capability, ACT Networks refers to them as Integrated Frame Relay Access Devices, or IFRADs. Such IFRADs are designed to do the following: fragment data frames to alleviate the potential adverse effect of those frames on frames transporting digitized speech; use buffers to minimize the effect of jitter for frames transporting speech; employ a priority scheme to prioritize voice and fax over data; and use a combination of silence detection and digital speech interpolation to take advantage of the half-duplex nature of voice communications.

OPERATIONAL FEATURES

The best way to obtain an appreciation of the capability and functionality of ACT Networks' IFRADs is to examine their operating features. We'll discuss seven features that enable Integrated FRADs to transport voice, data, and fax over a frame relay network in an effective and efficient manner, resulting in the reconstruction of speech almost identical to its original quality. These features are as follows:

1. Signal prioritization

2. Frame fragmentation

3. Predictive congestion management

4. The use of jitter buffers to alleviate signal sampling delays

5. The implementation of silence detection and the application of Digital Speech Interpolation to take advantage of the half-duplex nature of human conversations

6. The support of four speech compression methods

7. Signaling and telephone operational support features necessary to convey telephone calls across a frame relay network

Signal Prioritization

An ACT IFRAD supports the use of three priority queues. By assigning delay-sensitive traffic to high-priority queues and delay-insensitive traffic to lower-priority queues, you can facilitate the transfer of delay-sensitive information through the IFRAD. In doing so, ACT Networks recommends assigning faxes to the highest-priority queue, as such signals are more sensitive to delay than is voice when transmitted on a real-time basis. It is important to note that if you are using a store-and-forward fax system through a frame relay network, fax files would be handled in a manner similar to conventional data files. That is, you would assign the transfer of data files, including those containing digitized fax, to a low-priority queue.

In addition to providing a signal-prioritizing method via the assignment of different categories of information to different queues, the IFRAD supports the selling of the discard eligibility (DE) bit on selected channels. This additional feature enables users to specify to the network which data sources the network can selectively drop during periods of congestion.

Although queuing is an important mechanism for servicing high-priority traffic over delay-insensitive traffic, by itself it only ensures that information in high-priority queues is serviced before information in lower-priority queues. This means that a relatively long frame transporting data that arrives at an IFRAD slightly before a frame containing digitized speech will be serviced first, which can adversely affect the arrival of digitized speech at its destination. This in turn could result in an awkward portion of reconstructed voice. To prevent this situation from occurring, ACT Networks' IFRADs include a frame fragmentation feature.

Frame Fragmentation

ACT's IFRADs attack the previously mentioned problem through the use of a frame fragmentation process. An ACT Networks' IFRAD limits the length of frames based upon the type of information they transport. Frames transporting voice are limited to a maximum of 83 bytes. Frames transporting data are limited to a maximum length of 71 bytes for asynchronous data and 72 bytes for synchronous data. In comparison, frames transporting fax are limited to a maximum length of 58 bytes.

By limiting the length of packets the ACT Networks' IFRAD fragmentation process ensures that those frames transporting voice and fax are not significantly delayed by the prior servicing of data packets. Thus, prioritization and fragmentation go hand in hand to facilitate the transfer of frames carrying time-sensitive information through an IFRAD while minimizing the potential delay effect when a packet transporting data is serviced by the device.

Predictive Congestion Management

The use of FECN and BECN bits by a frame relay network for congestion control can be viewed as a reactive, after-the-fact method of congestion control. This is because network congestion has already occurred when the network sets those bits. Recognizing this problem and its potential effect on frames transporting time-sensitive information, ACT Networks included a feature called predictive congestion management in its IFRADs. Under predictive congestion management, an IFRAD responds to variances in traffic loading by varying the length of queues before congestion occurs. This enables frames transporting time-insensitive data to be further delayed, reducing the load on the network and in effect reducing the probability of congestion adversely affecting frames presented to the network. Predictive congestion management supplements the network's use of FECN and BECN bits but does not replace it. This means that an IFRAD on receiving frames with those bits set by a network switch, will reduce traffic to the network on the data link control identifier(s) associated with the set bit or bits.

Jitter Buffers

Instead of accepting received packets and immediately delivering them to their destination, an IFRAD employs a jitter buffer to remove random time delays between frames transporting digitized voice. Those time delays result from different processing requirements occurring at each switch as frames flow through a network. Thus, although a sequence of frames transporting digitized speech may be presented at a uniform rate to a frame relay network, it will more than likely be received from the network with variable delays between frames. Since variable delays would result in awkward-sounding reconstructed speech, ACT Networks' IFRADs incorporate a configuration jitter buffer. This buffer can be set to hold a maximum of 255 msec of speech and serves as a mechanism to remove the variable time gaps between frames received from the network. That is, after frames are temporarily stored in the IFRAD's jitter buffer, they are dumped from the buffer at a constant rate.

Silence Detection

Most human conversations are fairly civil. When we speak, there are gaps between words, pauses between sentences, and slight delays as we form responses mentally prior to vocalizing them. Thus, human conversations are inherently half-duplex in nature and contain frequent short pauses between sentences, and even between words in a sentence. To take advantage of these characteristics of human speech, the ACT Networks' IFRAD uses the gaps in speech from one ongoing conversation in another conversation. This technique is more formally referred to as Digital Speech Interpolation. When conversations are truly half-duplex, this technique can result in the ability to improve bandwidth utilization by up to 50 percent.

Voice-compression Support

IFRADs are modular in design, obtaining support for voice and fax via the installation of a voice/fax card. Each voice channel on the vendor's voice/fax card supports four voice compression methods, ranging in bandwidth from PCM's 64-Kbps operating rate to Algebraic Code Excited Linear Prediction's (ACELP's) 4.8-Kbps operating rate. This extended voice-compression support enables users to select an appropriate voice-compression algorithm based on a particular application and the level of background noise (or lack thereof). For example, if a connection to a voice/fax card occurs from a telephone in an industrial area, background noise commonly has a significant effect on vocoding-based voice-compression techniques. In comparison, the low background noise associated with a normal office environment would have a negligible effect.

Telephone Signaling Support

As we discussed in Chapter 5, there are several methods by which telephone signaling can be conveyed across a network. ACT Networks' IFRADs support four types of signaling, and they perform adaptive echo cancellation to ensure delays in the reflection of speech energy do not adversely affect a voice conversation.

The SN-8800 NetPerformer

In concluding our examination of ACT Networks' IFRADs, we will turn our attention to the use of this vendor's SN-8800 NetPerformer, which represents a small branch office IFRAD. We will use this IFRAD for our economic analysis because of its proven suitability for connecting small branch offices and its relatively limited expansion capability. Unlike other IFRADs that have the ability to be expanded in a manner that provides an almost unlimited number of networking configurations, the SN-8800 contains only two expansion slots and supports only three types of cards that can be used in those slots. This makes the use of the SN-8800 relatively straightforward and easy to price. In addition, the SN-8800 comes equipped with two built-in voice channels in its base unit, which facilitates its use for voice over frame relay in small branch offices that might have a limited voice-transmission requirement to other branch offices or to headquarters.

The SN-8800 base unit consists of four serial data ports and two voice channels. Two expansion slots are available on the base unit for the installation of Ethernet or Token Ring LAN adapters or a T1/E1 CSU1/DSU. At the time this book was written, the retail price of the SN-8800 was $3995, with an Ethernet LAN card priced at $395, a Token Ring LAN card priced at $895, and a T1/E1 CSU/DSU card priced at $795.

Figure 7-6 illustrates the use of an ACT Networks' SN-8800 IFRAD to support the communications requirements of a typical branch office into a frame relay network. In this example, the SN-8800 is used to support the connection of an IBM 3174 control unit that supports an SNA connection for a group of legacy SNA terminals accessing a mainframe, as well as for LAN-to-LAN connectivity via the use of an Ethernet adapter that connects the IFRAD to an Ethernet network. Since the SN-8800 has two built-in voice channels, we will assume that we connected two ports on a PBX at the branch office to the SN-8800 and programmed the PBX to route calls to the IFRAD when employees dial a 6 prefix.

The actual cost of an ACT Networks SN-8800 based on its list price would be $5185 per IFRAD to support two channels of voice along with the transmission of Ethernet and SNA traffic via a common frame relay network access line. Since the voice ports are built into the SN-8800, we cannot directly break out the cost associated with transporting voice. However, from a network perspective, the addition of voice would require the addition of only two PVCs, each at a very low CIR. Assuming the cost of a PVC at a 16-Kbps CIR is $10 per month, which represents an average of several frame relay network provider billings obtained during 1999, then the cost for adding four PVCs to enable communications between two branch offices would be $40 per

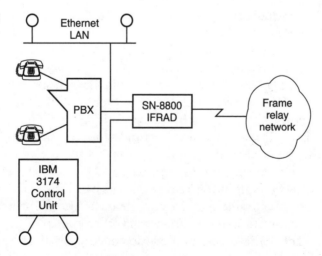

Figure 7-6
Using the ACT Networks SN-8800 to support the transmission of voice and data over a frame relay network.

month. Assuming you were calling only at night (which is unreasonable for a business), and you obtained the Sprint "dime lady" rate of $.10 per minute, you would need to use the two voice channels a total of only 400 minutes per month, or approximately 18 minutes per day (based upon 22 working days per month), to recover the added cost of the PVCs. Thus, the use of the SN-8800 IFRAD provides a very economical method for adding a voice communications transmission capability to a branch office to bypass the PSTN. If the branch office is located overseas, where the per-minute cost of using the PSTN might be $.30 to $.50 per minute or higher, you would need to use the voice transmission provided by the SN-8800 IFRAD only a few minutes per day to recover the cost of the PVCs. In other words, if it takes only one short call per day to break even, subsequent calls may provide significant savings that can make the person who acquired the SN-8800 the economic champion of the organization.

Now that we have an appreciation for the general features of one vendor's voice over frame relay products, let's look at a few other products and the economics associated with using a pair of FRADs to transport voice over a frame relay network.

Memotec

Memotec Corporation, which is headquartered in Montreal, Canada, is a well-known manufacturer of communications products, including a series of FRADs developed to provide support for the transmission of voice, data, and legacy communications protocols over a frame relay network. In April 1996, Memotec announced its CX900 "flex-FRAD," which provides a modular solution for users needing to support a variety of traffic over a frame relay network. The vendor's CX900 flex-FRAD was followed by the introduction of its CX900e frame relay access switch, which is based on a chassis design that permits the addition of various types of modules so that you can custom-tailor a configuration to satisfy your requirements. The best way to understand the versatility of a FRAD is to study its features. In doing so, we will focus our attention on the CX900e, a recent addition to the Memotec product line.

CX900e FRAD

As previously discussed, the CX900e is a modular FRAD that is fabricated as a chassis into which different modules are installed so that device functionality can be customized to a specific set of user requirements. The CX900e supports six types of modules, including LAN, Voice, Serial Port, ISDN, DSU/CSU, and V.34 Dial Modem modules. The ISDN Modules can be used as a primary method for network access or as backup to the frame relay network, while the V.34 Dial Modem module is used only for dial backup in the event of a primary-link failure.

Currently, Memotec markets both Ethernet and Token Ring LAN modules, enabling the FRAD to function as a LAN bridge/router supporting either type of LAN network over a frame relay network. The serial port module provides device connectivity to a wide area network via V.24, V.35, or X.21 interfaces, while the DSU/CSU module represents an integrated DSU/CSU required for transmission onto a digital access line. The ability to integrate support for voice and fax via the Memotec FRAD is accomplished through the use of one or more voice modules. Each voice module supports one voice/fax connection, and a CX900e can support up to four voice modules. The voice/fax capability of the CX900e is based on the functionality of the vendor's voice modules, so let's turn our attention to the characteristics of the voice modules supported by the FRAD.

VOICE MODULE SUPPORT

Voice/fax support is accomplished through the installation of one or more voice I/O cards into the FRAD chassis, with a maximum of four I/O cards supported per FRAD. Each voice I/O card contains an analog voice/fax port that is controlled by a specific type of line interface driver. Memotec offers foreign exchange drivers as well as a two-wire and four-wire E&M driver support for each voice card.

OPERATION

The Memotec CX900e is similar to the ACT Networks' IFRAD with respect to the manner in which it supports the transmission of time-sensitive information and its removal of random spacing between received frames carrying digitized speech. That is, the CX900e prioritizes frames, using fragmentation to facilitate the transfer of frames carrying voice and fax, while employing an elastic buffer to alleviate the effect of jitter caused by the flow of frames through the network. Concerning fragmentation, although the Memotec FRAD uses default parameters to define the maximum-length default of frames transporting voice, fax, and asynchronous and synchronous data, a network manager or administrator can change those values. Similar to the IFRAD, the CX900e permits a user to set the discard eligibility (DE) bit for individual channels. Also similar to the

ACT Networks' IFRAD, the Memotec CX900e supports the use of Digital Speech Interpolation to take advantage of the half-duplex nature of human conversation and the pauses that occur during speech. One area of significant differences between ACT and Memotec products is in their support of different voice-digitization methods. Unlike the ACT Networks' IFRAD, which supports the use of four distinct methods of voice compression, including toll-quality PCM, Memotec's voice-digitization support is limited to 8- and 5.8-Kbps versions of the ITU G.729 Algebraic Code Excited Linear Prediction (ACELP), with the method used software selectable. The actual voice-digitization method supported by Memotec is referred to as ACELP II, which is considered to represent a superset of the ITU G.729 standard.

Nuera Communications

One of the more interesting vendor products located by this author during the preparation of this book was the Access Plus F200ip from Nuera Communications of San Diego, California. Unlike previously mentioned products that support either voice over frame relay or voice over IP, the F200ip supports both. Thus, it provides a degree of flexibility beyond that obtainable with other products. Since this chapter is focused on voice over frame relay, we will limit our coverage of the Nuera Communications F200ip to its frame relay capability, which is essentially equivalent to the vendor's F100 FRAD, whose operation was rated number one in quality for voice over frame relay by listeners during a test performed by *Data Communications Magazine*. Thus, in this section we will review the functional capability of the Nuera Communications F100 FRAD and then examine the economics associated with its use.

The F100 FRAD

The Nuera Communications F100 FRAD is based on an eight-slot chassis. The chassis accepts the installation of one port analog or four port digital/fax cards, with each card containing its own digital signal processor to perform all required voice-coding operations. Included in the chassis is a dedicated frame relay serial port and three data ports for connecting the FRAD to routers and other network devices. This means that you can easily use the F100 to compress 24 voice channels from a PBX T1 connection or up to 30 from an E1 connection to a PBX, which exceeds the capacity of competitors' products. The use of built-in dedicated serial ports frees the chassis for a full installation of eight voice I/O cards. Users need not worry about the support of a wide area connection degrading from the functional capacity of the FRAD to support certain voice communications requirements.

Within the F100 chassis is a network processor that performs such functions as echo cancellation and frame prioritization. A separate packet processor is employed to perform call-processing functions, including the ability to switch each call independently of the others. This enables the connection of a T1 or E1 line from a PBX to have up to 24 or 30 calls routed to appropriate digital/fax cards, unlike some other FRAD designs that require a sequence of individual PBX connections from a PBX to individual ports on voice/fax cards installed in a FRAD. Thus, the design of the F100, which is illustrated in Figure 7-7, facilitates cabling between a PBX and the FRAD. However, unlike some other FRADs that support the installation of LAN adapter cards to enable the FRAD to become a direct participant on a local area network, the F100 connects to a LAN via a serial interface to a router. Although this requires the use of a router instead of a network adapter card, it frees slots in the chassis for use by other types of cards.

Figure 7-7
The Nuera F100 FRAD includes built-in serial ports, which frees the chassis for supporting up to eight four-port digital cards.

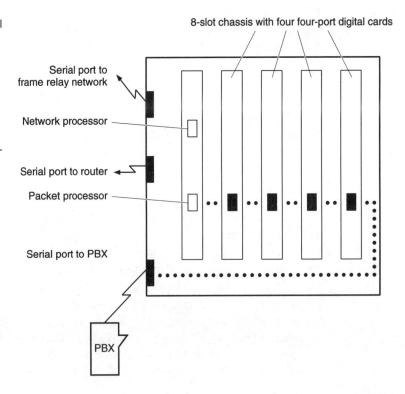

The Nuera Communications F100 FRAD includes features such as silence suppression, frame fragmentation, prioritization, and the use of a jitter buffer that functions in a manner similar to voice-capable FRADs manufactured by other vendors. However, the F100 also includes several unique features that provide an additional margin of performance to facilitate the transmission of voice over a frame relay network. Those features include the use of asymmetric fax channels, adaptable echo cancellation, the use of digital voice/fax cards that support five types of voice compression, and the capability to support the use of eight four-port voice cards. These features can be an important consideration when evaluating equipment, so let's briefly discuss them.

ASYMMETRIC FAX CHANNELS

Fax transmission results in the majority of data flowing in one direction, while a limited amount of control information flows in the reverse direction. This transmission characteristic enables the use of asymmetric fax channels to considerably reduce the use of bandwidth, which can then be used by other traffic.

ADAPTABLE ECHO CANCELLATION

The F100 includes an adaptable echo canceler. This canceler measures reflected energy and adapts from 0 to 49 msec to provide a consistent voice quality for all calls serviced by the FRAD.

DIGITAL VOICE/FAX CARD SUPPORT

The F100 uses digital voice/fax cards that support up to four voice channels per card and up to 30 channels per system, providing one of the highest voice support of products currently marketed for transmitting voice over a frame relay network. Each voice/fax card supports five methods of voice compression: (1) ATC, from 7.4 to 32 Kbps; (2) G.729 CS-ACELP at 8 Kbps; (3) G.728 LD-CELP at 16 Kbps; (4) G.726 ADPCM at 32 Kbps; and (5) E-CELP at 4.8, 7.47, and 9.6 Kbps. Between the voice-call capacity and the ability to select from five voice-compression methods, the F100 gives users a significant capability to "test the concept" and, once the concept proves justifiable, to significantly expand the capacity of the FRAD.

ECONOMICS OF USE

To obtain an appreciation for the economics associated with the use of the Nuera Communications F100 FRAD, let's examine the use of a pair of FRADs, each containing four voice ports and several low-speed ports to enable you to route SNA and perhaps both asynchronous and synchronous data traffic through a common frame relay access line. Although the cost of each F100 obviously varies by configuration, the basic price of the FRAD just mentioned will be between $6000 and $7000 per unit. Let us further assume the use of a T1 access line results in an average cost of $625 per month to obtain a fractional T1 (FT1) access to a frame relay network at a data rate of 128 Kbps. The monthly cost of a 128-Kbps network port will be assumed to be $415, while PVCs with a 16-Kbps CIR will be assumed to cost $10 per month. Based on the use of four PVCs to support voice and data, we can now compute the cost of adding voice to an SNA or a mixture of formerly data-only applications, including both hardware and network operation cost. However, prior to doing so, it is important to note that the one-time cost associated with the purchase of communications equipment should be amortized over its lifetime to determine the monthly cost. This can be added to the monthly fee of the communications carrier to obtain the total monthly cost for both equipment and the use of a transmission facility. Once this is determined, it becomes relatively easy to estimate the cost per minute for the transmission of voice over a frame relay network for different potential levels of voice traffic.

Amortizing One-time Equipment Cost

Assume the cost of F100s is $7000 each, or $14,000 for a pair that will be used to enable two branch offices to exchange both data and voice over common access lines routed to a frame relay network. If we assume the equipment has a four-year (48-month) life, then the cost per month becomes $14,000/48, or $292 per month.

Adding the Network Cost

Assuming that the monthly cost of the frame relay service is $1080 per site, which includes the access line, port cost, and individual PVCs, the monthly network cost for two sites becomes $2160. Thus, the total monthly cost of equipment plus a frame relay network provider is $2160 plus $292, or $2452.

Computing the Cost Per Minute

Since the cost per minute depends on the volume of voice traffic carried by FRADs between network endpoint locations, we will first make some assumptions concerning the potential use of the four voice ports per FRAD and then use those assumptions as a basis to project additional usage of the FRADs to transport varying amounts of voice traffic via a frame relay network. First, let's assume there are 22 working days per month during which the voice capability of the FRADs will be used. Second, assume we will use the port on each voice card 12.5 percent of the business day, or one hour during an eight-hour business day (probably a very low level of utilization for an organization considering the use of voice over frame relay). Based on the preceding assumptions, we anticipate four hours of voice communications per day, occurring collectively on all four voice ports, or 88 hours on a monthly basis. This means that on a per-minute basis, we will begin our economic analysis by assuming the pair of FRADs are used to provide 88 hours × 60 minutes/hour, or a total of 5280 call minutes of voice transmission per month. Based on the previously computed monthly cost of equipment and frame relay service of $2452, this results in a per-minute cost of $2452 divided by 5280 call minutes, or $.464 per minute. At this rate, it would appear that transmitting voice over frame relay would pay off only for expensive international calls. While this may be true for a low volume of call minutes, consider the possibility of adding voice-transmission capacity to an existing FRAD or of increasing the volume of usage. For our example, let's do both, starting with the latter by examining the effect of increased call volume on the cost per minute.

Examining the Effect of Increased Call Volume

Table 7-4 summarizes the cost per minute based on varying the occupancy rates of the four voice ports. Note that you have to keep the ports on the voice/fax card fairly well occupied to obtain a reasonable per-

TABLE 7-4

Economics of Increased Call Volume

Full Cost of Equipment and Network Considered			
Hours/day	Percent port occupancy	Monthly call hours*	Cost/min
1	12.5	88	46.4
2	25.0	176	23.2
3	37.5	264	15.5
4	50.0	352	11.6
5	62.5	440	9.3
6	75.0	528	7.7
7	87.5	616	6.6
8	100.0	704	5.8

*Four ports, 22 business days per month.

minute cost that is less expensive than normal commercial service via the PSTN. However, Table 7-4 is based on the full purchase cost of a pair of FRADs for voice transmission via frame relay. If we already have an existing pair of FRADs we wish to upgrade to support voice over frame relay, or if we originally intended to acquire a pair of FRADs to support data transmission and added voice and fax transmission capability, we should consider only the cost of a pair of voice/fax cards and the PVC cost for voice. This is because we would still have to purchase the chassis and pay a monthly fee for the access line and network port. Thus, let's again revise our computations.

Examining the Incremental Cost of Voice

We can examine the economics associated with transmitting voice over frame relay by assuming that the basic expense of obtaining a pair of FRADs, a pair of access lines, and a pair of network ports would be incurred even if we were simply transmitting data over the network. Thus, the cost of transmitting voice involves the *incremental* cost associated with adding this transmission capability. To determine the incremental cost associated with transmitting voice, let's assume that each four-port card can be purchased for $1500, resulting in the equipment expense being reduced to $3,000, or $62.50 per month when amortized over a 48-month period. Instead of considering monthly access line charges and the monthly cost of two network ports, let's assume we simply add a PVC for each PBX-to-PBX transmission, which adds $20 per month to our frame relay network carrier bill. Thus, our total monthly cost now becomes $82.50.

If we use the same network usage assumptions as before, then a 12.5 percent occupancy rate generates 5280 call minutes of voice transmission per month. This results in a per-minute cost of $82.50/5280, or approximately $.016 per minute, which is supercompetitive. Table 7-5 indicates the economics associated with an increased call volume for the situation where we amortize only the additional cost associated with adding a voice and fax transmission capability to FRADs that we would have had to purchase anyway to satisfy a data transmission requirement. As indicated in Table 7-5, the cost per minute can get so low that you may consider becoming a communications carrier in competition with the big firms!

General Observations

In comparing the costs listed in Tables 7-4 and 7-5 for increased call volumes, we can make some general observations. First, unless you anticipate

TABLE 7-5

Economics
of Increased Call
Volume

	Only Incremental Cost of Voice Capability Considered		
Hours/day	Percent Port Occupancy	Monthly Call Hours*	Cost/min
1	12.5	88	1.56
2	25.0	176	0.78
3	37.5	264	0.52
4	50.0	352	0.39
5	62.5	440	0.31
6	75.0	528	0.26
7	87.5	616	0.02
8	100.0	704	0.19

*Four ports, 22 business days per month.

an extremely high level of voice communications, the transmission of voice over a frame relay network may be hard to justify from an economic perspective. Second, if you have an existing frame relay connection using FRADs that can be upgraded to support voice, or if you need to acquire hardware and establish a connection to a frame relay network to support data transmission, then the incremental cost associated with adding a voice transmission capability will normally result in a very low level of call volume being sufficient to justify the additional cost of supporting voice. Now that we have an appreciation for the economics associated with transporting voice over a frame relay network, let's conclude this section with a feature checklist to facilitate our potential equipment-acquisition process.

Feature Checklist

In concluding this section, Table 7-6 provides you with a comprehensive checklist of voice/fax-related features to consider when evaluating different vendor products. It includes a column for listing your requirements with respect to a particular voice FRAD feature as well as two columns labeled "Vendor A" and "Vendor B." Use these to compare products from two vendors against your specific requirements. You can add more vendors if you wish.

TABLE 7-6

FRAD Voice-Related Features to Consider

Feature	Requirement	Vendor A	Vendor B
DE bit setting	_____	_____	_____
Echo cancellation adjustability	_____	_____	_____
Fax support			
V.21 300 bps	_____	_____	_____
V.27ter 2.4/4.8 Kbps	_____	_____	_____
V.29 9.6 Kbps	_____	_____	_____
V.17 14.4 Kbps	_____	_____	_____
Fragmentation			
Fixed	_____	_____	_____
Adjustable	_____	_____	_____
Logical link multiplexing	_____	_____	_____
Jitter buffer			
Adjustable	_____	_____	_____
Prioritization			
Fixed queues	_____	_____	_____
Selectable	_____	_____	_____
Subchannel multiplexing	_____	_____	_____
Voice/fax card			
Type			
Analog	_____	_____	_____
Digital	_____	_____	_____
Ports/card			
Number	_____	_____	_____
Maximum supported on FRAD	_____	_____	_____
Compression method(s)	_____	_____	_____
Voice signaling support			
Foreign exchange office (FSO)	_____	_____	_____
Foreign exchange station (FXS)	_____	_____	_____
Off-hook	_____	_____	_____
Ear and mouth (E&M type)	_____	_____	_____

7-3 The Frame Relay Forum VoFR IA

In concluding this chapter, we will focus our attention on the recently announced Frame Relay Forum Voice over Frame Relay (VoFR) Implementation Agreement (IA). Frame Relay IAs are based on relevant ANSI,

ITU, or other standards and highlight areas where the agreements differ from existing standards. Thus, IAs are developed to provide unambiguous agreements between switch equipment vendors and network operators on how options within a standard may be implemented to facilitate true worldwide multivendor interoperability. Thus, IAs are meant to be read along with relevant standards.

Overview

The Frame Relay Forum FRF.11 IA consists of four sections and eight annexes. The first section is introductory in nature and covers the purpose of the IA, includes an overview of its contents, and provides a list of abbreviations used in the document and the relevant standards. The second section, titled "Reference Model and Service Description," illustrates how a Voice Frame Relay Access Device (VFRAD) would exchange voice and signaling information with another VFRAD via the use of a network reference model. In doing so, this section refers to the use of different voice compression schemes that are contained in Annex A of the IA and the packaging of data frames according to rules specified in Annex C of the IA. Other portions of Section 2 discuss the use of encoded fax, how periods of silence can be encoded, the use of signaling bits, and similar information, with detailed information provided by references to appropriate annexes in the IA.

With the exception of some of the annexes, Section 3, "Frame Formats," is probably the most important section with respect to interoperability between vendor equipment. It provides a detailed description of how voice and data payloads are multiplexed within a frame. This section uses the term *subframe* to refer to a payload package that is placed in a frame's information field.

The fourth and final section in the document, entitled "Minimum Requirements for Conformance," defines the support vendors must provide to ensure that their products can interoperate with other vendor products that support the VoFR IA.

We will now turn our attention to the formation of subframes and the basic compliance requirements a FRAD must support to conform to the VoFR IA.

Subframes

The use of subframes is optional; however, they serve as a mechanism to enable more efficient processing and transmission of frames containing

Figure 7-8
The use of subframes
reduces overhead
and enables voice-
encoded frames to be
transported across a
frame relay network
more efficiently.

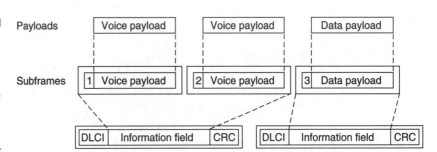

digitized speech. Each subframe contains its own header and payload, with the header identifying the voice/data subchannel that originated the payload and, optionally, the type of payload and its length.

Figure 7-8 illustrates the relationship between frames and subframes. In this example, a single DLCI is used to support two voice channels and one data channel. This is accomplished by two voice payloads being packaged in the first frame, while a data payload is shown being placed into the second frame.

In examining Figure 7-8, it is important to note that payloads can transport voice, fax, data, or signaling information. To provide a mechanism for interoperability, the format of the subframe is defined in the IA. Figure 7-9 illustrates its format.

Figure 7-9
The subframe format.

Bit position	8	7	6	5	4	3	2	1
Octet 1	EI	LI	Subchannel identifier (CID)					
Octet 1a	CID		Spare	Spare	Payload type			
Octet 1b	Payload length							
Octet n	Payload							

Notes:

1. When the EI bit = 1, the structure of octet 1a's payload type field applies as follows:

Bits	4	3	2	1	
	0	0	0	0	Primary payload transfer
	0	0	0	1	Dialed digit transfer
	0	0	1	0	Signaling bit transfer
	0	0	1	1	Fax relay transfer
	0	1	0	0	Silence information description

2. When the LI bit = 1, the structure of octet 1b applies.

The Subframe Format

In examining Figure 7-9, note that 6 bits in the first byte and 2 bits in the second byte can be used to define the subchannel identification, providing the ability to multiplex up to 256 channels within a common DLCI. The actual structure of the first two octets and the inclusion of octets 1a and 1b depend on the settings of the extension indication (EI) and length indication (LI) bits in the subframe. Those settings are indicated in the lower portion of Figure 7-9. For example, when the EI bit is set to a value of binary 1, it serves as a flag to indicate the presence of octet 1a. This extends the subchannel identification to 8 bits. Otherwise, when the EI bit is set to a value of 0, the CID uses 6 bits, and the maximum value of the subchannel identification is limited to 63. Returning to the setting of the EI bit to 1, as indicated in Figure 7-9, this setting in conjunction with the payload type field values defines how the entries in the Payload Type field are interpreted. Note that although 4 bits are used to define the payload type, only 5 out of 16 possible values are presently defined.

Through the use of the setting of the EI and LI bits and the values assigned to the payload type field, there are a number of possible combinations of subframes as well as variances in the information transported in those frames. Figure 7-10 illustrates two examples of the formation and composition of subframes. In Figure 7-10a, setting the EI and LI bits to 0 results in the elimination of the need to include octets 1a and 1b in Figure 7-9. Thus, the payload directly follows the CID.

In the example illustrated in Figure 7-10b, both the E1 and LI bits are set to values of binary 1. The setting of the EI bit to a value of 1 means that octet 1a will be included in the header. That byte includes a payload

Figure 7-10
The composition of
subframes within a
frame depends on
the setting of the EI
and LI bits.

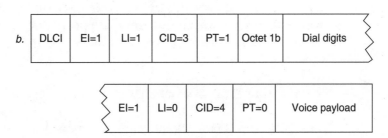

a. | DLCI | EI=0 | LI=0 | CID=3 | Voice payload |

b. | DLCI | EI=1 | LI=1 | CID=3 | PT=1 | Octet 1b | Dial digits |

| EI=1 | LI=0 | CID=4 | PT=0 | Voice payload |

type (PT) field whose value is shown set to 1. As indicated in Figure 7-9, this signifies that dialed digits are being transferred in the payload. The setting of the LI bit informs the receiver that octet 1b, which defines the payload length, follows, and it is simply labeled "octet 1b" in Figure 7-10. Once the payload in the form of dial digits is used to complete the subframe, a second subframe is included in the frame. The following subframe is transmitted on a different CID and has its LI bit set to 0, which indicates that no payload-length octet follows. Instead, the use of a payload type field value of 0 indicates to the receiver that the information directly following the payload type field represents the primary payload transfer in a standard voice payload field.

Conformance Issues

The key to equipment interoperability is the ability of different vendor products to support a minimum number of common functions. Under the VoFR IA, there are two classes of compliance requirements. Vendor products must satisfy one or the other or both to provide interoperability with other vendor products. Class 1 compliance is for products that support high-bit-rate voice digitization at 32, 24, or 16 Kbps, while Class 2 compliance is for products that support low-bit-rate voice-digitization methods. Thus, a vendor product can be Class 1 compliant, Class 2 compliant, or both Class 1 and Class 2 compliant.

For both Class 1 and Class 2 compliance, equipment must support the frame structure defined in the IA, including the subframe format. For Class 1 compliance, equipment at a minimum must support the ITU G.727 ADPCM voice-compression method for transmission at 32 Kbps and for the receiver at 32, 24, and 16 Kbps. The support of all other payload transfer methods, including fax, is optional; however, the IA conformance section defines the support for signaling bits that enables voice calling information to be passed between vendor products. Class 2 compliance is similar to Class 1, with the key difference being that CS-ACELP voice digitization is mandatory in place of G.727 voice digitization. Under Class 2 compliance, a vendor product must support either the ITU G.729 or the G.729 Annex A method of voice encoding.

For Further Reference

The Voice over Frame Relay Implementation Agreement uses a series of annexes to the 16-page four-section document to specify the exact details necessary for vendors to develop products that can interoperate with one another. Annex A covers the syntax of dialed digit transfers, which provide a uniform method for transmitting and interpreting both dialed digits and the power level of frequencies used for DTMF signaling. Annex B specifies the structure and procedure for the transfer of signaling bits across a frame relay network. In Annex C, the structure of the subframe payload is defined, while Annex D provides detailed information concerning the transport of fax data. Annexes E through I focus on the coding of voice digitized by different encoding methods. Thus, the annexes provide detailed information necessary for vendors to design and manufacture VoFR-compliant products. A complete copy of the Voice over Frame Relay Implementation Agreement is included in the appendix of this book courtesy of the Frame Relay Forum. Readers should also access the Frame Relay Forum's World Wide Web site at http://www.frforum.com. This site provides a wealth of material, from frame relay background to technical information to copies of various Implementation Agreements. Visit this Web site to explore additional aspects of frame relay, such as data compression, that are beyond the scope of this book.

CHAPTER

Management Issues

In this concluding chapter we will turn our attention to several management issues related to the ability of an organization to transport voice over IP or voice over frame relay. Instead of focusing attention on traditional management issues, such as charge-back, equipment selection, and acquisition, we will turn our attention to a key area you need to explore prior to considering implementation of a voice over data network—knowledge about its practicality. In other words, will it work?

Recognizing the Rosetta stone of latency introduced in Chapter 1, we can predetermine the potential of success or failure of a voice over data network if we can determine the latency or delay through a network. Once we determine the routing delay, we can use that information with ingress and egress delays and codec delays. The total delay would then be used to determine whether the end-to-end delay will be under 250 ms. If it is not, we would more than likely be wasting our time and money in attempting to implement a voice over data network facility. However, because in certain situations a lengthy routing delay may be modified to a lower value by the selection of another path or replacement of a bottleneck in the path, we also need to examine the path of the route from the ingress point to the egress point. Fortunately, the TCP/IP protocol stack contains some built-in management tools that can be used to facilitate our examination of both delay and route structure.

8-1 Using TCP/IP Applications

The TCP/IP protocol suite includes several utility application programs that provide network users with the ability to test and troubleshoot a variety of potential problems. From a voice over data network perspective, there are two key TCP/IP utility application programs you can consider using to obtain information about networking devices, network usage, and the general state of a network. Those utilities are PING and TRACEROUTE.

PING

PING represents a TCP/IP utility application program that is included in every protocol stack this author has worked with. Those protocol stacks include NetManage and FTP software TCP/IP protocol stacks developed for use with Windows 3.1 and several versions of Unix, Windows 95, Windows 98, Windows NT, and the beta version of Windows 2000.

The name PING can be traced to two separate historical developments. First, according to some persons, because PING operates by generating an Internet Control Message Protocol (ICMP) Echo Message that results in the destination address issuing an Echo Response message, it is similar to radar and shipboard sonar. That is, a ship generates a sonar signal and uses the ping response from the target to obtain a bearing and distance to the target by timing the delay between transmitting the signal and receiving its pinged reflection. That time represents the round-trip delay. Thus, dividing the time by 2 represents the time to the target. Because the velocity of propagation of a sonar wave is known, the time to the target multiplied by the velocity of propagation equals the distance to the target. According to legend, the Echo Response generated by an Echo Request was viewed similarly to sonar pinging, thus resulting in the term PING being used for this TCP/IP application.

A second commonly told tale concerning the name of the PING application program maintains that the name resulted as an acronym for Packet Internetwork Groper. In this tale, the Echo Request message generated by the client is used to elicit, or "grope," a response from the destination. Because the application was designed to cross network boundaries, it supported internetworking. Thus the name PING was used as an acronym for Packet Internetwork Groper.

Regardless of how the name PING evolved, this application utility program typically represents the first tool commonly used to test and troubleshoot network devices. For example, you can use PING to determine whether a workstation, server, or another TCP/IP network device recently connected to a network is correctly cabled to the network and whether the protocol stack is operational and correctly configured. That is, after a device is connected to a network and its TCP/IP protocol stack is configured, you can test the cabling to the network and the operational state of the protocol stack by PINGing the device from another station on the network or from one located on a different network. If the PING elicits a response, the response informs you that the device is correctly cabled to the network and that the TCP/IP protocol stack is operational. Based on the fact that PING will also return the round-trip delay between source and destination, this application can also provide you with indirect information about network activity. That is, if round-trip delay time is relatively long in comparison to previously obtained round-trip delay times, the cause would normally be attributable to network congestion.

For planning a voice over data network implementation, the round-trip delay caused by the use of PING provides the information necessary to determine the delay from a workstation doing the PINGing to the destination by dividing the delay by 2. However, a word of caution is warranted concerning the time reported by PING. If you enter a host name instead of an IP address, the first PING will require a name to address resolution because all routing is via IP addresses. Thus, this action will add to the round-trip delay time. In addition, because the characteristics of a network dynamically change during the day, it's best to use PING periodically throughout the day to examine changes in the round-trip delay.

If you receive a timeout in response to issuing a PING that denotes the absence of an Echo Response message after a predefined period of time, you should not automatically assume the destination is not available or improperly cabled to a network. If the destination is on a different network, it's possible that one or more intermediary devices, such as a router or gateway, is not operational and the PING cannot reach its destination. As we will note later in this section, if you obtain a timeout response to the use of PING when attempting to access an address on a different network, you should turn to the use of the TRACEROUTE utility program prior to concluding that the destination is not operational. In addition, if the round-trip delay appears excessive, you can turn to TRACEROUTE to determine the route and the delays along the route. If you can identify a bottleneck, it may be possible to request your Internet service provider (ISP) to upgrade equipment or a transmission facility. If this is not possible, the ISP might be able to reroute your connection or arrange for a different peering agreement where ISP traffic flows between networks to facilitate obtaining a lower latency.

Command Format

Although most modern operating systems are based on the use of a graphic user interface (GUI), most implementations of the PING utility program require the use of a command-line interface. One common command-line interface is as follows:

```
PING [-q] [-v] [-c count] [-s size] {Host_name|IP_Address}
```

where the command-line parameters are as follows:

-q implements the quiet mode, resulting only in the display of summary lines at start-up and completion.

-v implements verbose mode, resulting in the listing of ICMP packets received in addition to each Echo Response message.

-c specifies the number of Echo Requests (count) sent prior to concluding the test.

-s specifies the number of data bytes (size) transmitted with each Echo
   Request message.

Host_name or IP_Address identifies the target to be PINGed.

   To illustrate an example of the use of the PING utility, assume you just
installed a computer with the IP address 198.78.46.8 and the host name
gil.feds.gov. To test the cabling of the computer to the network and the
operation of the protocol stack on the computer you could go to another
station on the network and enter the following command:

```
PING -c 5 gil.feds.gov
```

The preceding command line would result in the transmission of five
Echo Request messages to the host address gil.feds.gov. Let's assume the
response was five PING timeout messages, each indicating the lack of a
response from the destination host. Although you might assume that
there is a problem with the destination, it's important to note that routing is based on the use of IP addresses. Because TCP/IP-compliant devices
respond to IP addresses, it's quite possible the host is up and operational
but, for some reason, an appropriate entry was not made into the local
DNS server to enable the host name to be resolved into an appropriate IP
address. Recognizing this potential problem, you would then retry PING
using the IP address of the destination as follows:

```
PING -c 5 198.78.46.8
```

The response to the PING would appear similar to the following:

   72 bytes from 198.78.46.8 time = 12.2 ms

   72 bytes from 198.78.46.8 time = 12.2 ms

   72 bytes from 198.78.46.8 time = 12.2 ms

   72 bytes from 198.78.46.8 time = 12.2 ms

   72 bytes from 198.78.46.8 time = 12.2 ms

   If you do not specify the number of data bytes to be used in each
Echo Request, a default of 64 is used, with an 8-byte ICMP header resulting in the count of Echo Response packet size being displayed as 72 bytes.
Although the round-trip time for each Echo Request to Echo Response
message is shown as being the same at 12.2 ms, it's important to note that
this is not always true. When you use a host address instead of an IP
address, it's important to note that most times the issuance of multiple

Echo Requests will result in the first round-trip delay having a longer time value than succeeding times. As previously explained, the reason for this is the fact that the first PING is delayed by the address resolution process. During the address resolution process, the host name is converted into an IP address to enable the Echo Request to be routed toward its destination. If you are using PING to obtain a precise round-trip delay time, such as to determine if a network structure can support voice over IP, which requires a very low level of latency, it is important to recognize the potential of the first round-trip delay time to significantly exceed succeeding delay times. Thus, it's a good and recommended procedure to issue at least two separate PING commands, permitting the first one to obtain the host IP address via the Address Resolution Protocol (ARP) and place that entry in the ARP table maintained by the PINGing device. Then the second PING command to the same destination will reflect round-trip delay times that do not include the address resolution process.

In concluding our examination of the use of the PING application utility program, we will turn our attention to the format and utilization of the program supported by Microsoft Corporation in Windows 95, Windows 98, and Windows NT/2000. Figure 8-1 illustrates the command format for PING displayed in response to entering the command without any command-line parameters.

In examining the command-line entries supported by Microsoft's implementation of PING, note the -t option. The use of that option results in a continuous PINGing of the destination until the CTRL-BREAK key combination is pressed to interrupt the program.

Figure 8-1

Microsoft Windows 95/98 PING utility program command-line format.

```
Command Prompt                                                        _ □
Microsoft(R) Windows NT(TM)
(C) Copyright 1985-1996 Microsoft Corp.

C:\>PING

Usage: ping [-t] [-a] [-n count] [-l size] [-f] [-i TTL] [-v TOS]
            [-r count] [-s count] [[-j host-list] | [-k host-list]]
            [-w timeout] destination-list

Options:
    -t                 Ping the specified host until interrupted.
    -a                 Resolve addresses to hostnames.
    -n count           Number of echo requests to send.
    -l size            Send buffer size.
    -f                 Set Don't Fragment flag in packet.
    -i TTL             Time To Live.
    -v TOS             Type Of Service.
    -r count           Record route for count hops.
    -s count           Timestamp for count hops.
    -j host-list       Loose source route along host-list.
    -k host-list       Strict source route along host-list.
    -w timeout         Timeout in milliseconds to wait for each reply.

C:\>_
```

Continuous PINGing requires a continuous response from the destination. Because the destination must suspend what it is doing to respond to the PING, its ability to perform its intended function, such as a Web server responding to HTTP queries, is degraded. In effect, continuous PINGing is often considered as an unsophisticated hacker denial-of-service attack.

Another area of concern with respect to PING is that it can be used to discover network devices. That is, a sophisticated programmer can use PING within a shell program in an attempt to learn the addresses of network devices and then target those devices. To protect against the adverse effects of PING, some organizations either use a firewall or program a router's access list to prevent PINGs from reaching their network. If a router's access list is programmed, the denial of PINGs is usually expressed on a universal basis. However, it is possible for the router access list administrator to reprogram the list to enable you to issue PINGs for determining the round-trip delay to a predefined destination. Because a firewall has a more sophisticated filtering capability, many network managers and LAN administrators will configure the firewall to permit up to five PINGs per source IP address within a predefined period of time. This action permits a reasonable level of PINGing for a legitimate purpose to occur from users outside the organization's network while precluding denial-of-service attacks based on the use of PINGs. An alternate option some network managers use is to program a firewall to allow employees behind the firewall to issue outbound PINGs while barring inbound PINGs. The problem with this solution is the fact that if every organization implemented it, nobody would be able to legitimately use PING. Based on the preceding, you should consider coordinating the use of PING with your firewall or router administrator. If PING is barred, you can usually use a workstation to issue PINGs. All you need is the IP address of the workstation and about two minutes to enable a change to a firewall policy or perhaps a few minutes longer to change a router access list.

Figure 8-2 illustrates the use of PING twice to ping the server at American University. If you examine the round-trip delay times shown in Figure 8-2, you will note they vary significantly between each issue of PING that occurred only a half minute from one another. This illustrates a key problem with the use of the public Internet for voice over IP: its variable and unpredictable delay makes it currently unsuitable for many business applications.

Now that we have an appreciation for the operation and utilization of PING, let's turn our attention to the utility program that should be considered as a follow-up to its use—the TRACEROUTE program.

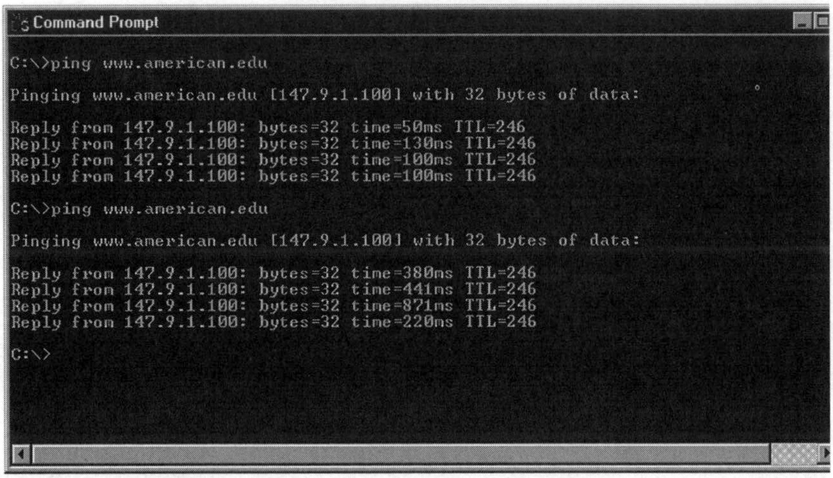

Figure 8-2
PINGing the
American University
Web server.

```
Command Prompt                                                    _ □

C:\>ping www.american.edu

Pinging www.american.edu [147.9.1.100] with 32 bytes of data:

Reply from 147.9.1.100: bytes=32 time=50ms TTL=246
Reply from 147.9.1.100: bytes=32 time=130ms TTL=246
Reply from 147.9.1.100: bytes=32 time=100ms TTL=246
Reply from 147.9.1.100: bytes=32 time=100ms TTL=246

C:\>ping www.american.edu

Pinging www.american.edu [147.9.1.100] with 32 bytes of data:

Reply from 147.9.1.100: bytes=32 time=380ms TTL=246
Reply from 147.9.1.100: bytes=32 time=441ms TTL=246
Reply from 147.9.1.100: bytes=32 time=871ms TTL=246
Reply from 147.9.1.100: bytes=32 time=220ms TTL=246

C:\>
```

TRACEROUTE

The TRACEROUTE command invokes a program by that name which
provides information about the route that packets take from source to destination. If you PING a device on a different network, the lack of a
response via a timeout condition does not necessarily mean that the destination device is not operational. Instead, it's possible that one or more
intermediary routers or gateways that provide a connection between networks are not operational. In addition, if PING shows a lengthy round-
trip delay, it does not indicate whether most or a portion of the delay
results from a single bottleneck whose removal might enable an unworkable solution to become doable. Thus, TRACEROUTE can be used to
examine the route from source to destination to determine whether a
path to the destination is available and, if so, the delays along the path.

Operation

TRACEROUTE operates by transmitting a series of User Datagram Protocol (UDP) datagrams to an invalid port address at the destination device.
First, the program transmits three datagrams in sequence, with each datagram having its IP time-to-live (TTL) field value set to unity. This action
results in each datagram timing out as soon as it is processed by the first
router in the path between the source and destination networks.

After the first router decrements the TTL field value by one and notes
its value is zero, it generates an ICMP Time Exceeded Message (TEM)

response, which indicates the datagram expired, and sends it to the great bit bucket in the sky. The TEM response enables the device issuing the TRACEROUTE to compute the round-trip delay to the router for each of the three datagrams in the sequence. Next, the issuing device sets the TTL field value to 2 and transmits another sequence of three UDP datagrams. This sequence of three datagrams flows through the first router, which decrements their TTL field values to 1. However, the next router decrements their TTL field values to zero and returns TEM responses to each datagram, enabling the round-trip delay to the second router in the path to be determined.

The previously described process continues until the datagrams either reach their destination or encounter a broken path. If the datagrams reach their destination, the use of an invalid port number in the UDP header results in the destination device generating an ICMP Destination Unreachable message in response to each of the three datagrams. This message tells the TRACEROUTE program that the destination was reached and that it should terminate its operation. In the event an open path is encountered due to a router or gateway failure, TRACEROUTE uses a timer and will terminate its operation when the timer expires. By noting that the last router that responded was not connected to the destination network, you can observe that a wide area network connection or router failure is the reason behind the inability to access a destination device.

Command Format

The following is a commonly used TRACEROUTE command-line format:

```
TRACEROUTE [-m ttl] [-q packets] {IP_Address| Host_name}
```

where

-m represents the maximum allowable time-to-live (ttl) value, which is the number of hops allowed prior to the program terminating. The typical default ttl value used by most implementations of TRACE-ROUTE is 30.

-q represents the number of UDP packets transmitted with each time-to-live setting. The common default value is 3.

Figure 8-3 illustrates the Microsoft command format for the implementation of TRACEROUTE, which is referred to as TRACERT. Note that you can use the -w option to specify a longer timeout value if the use of the utility results in timeouts. Also note that if the default maximum of

Figure 8-3
The Microsoft
TRACERT command
format.

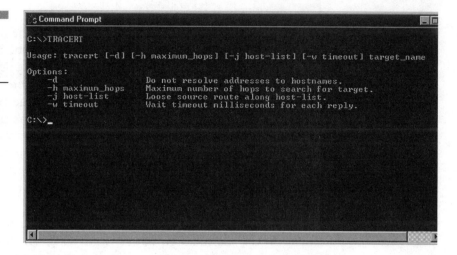

```
  Command Prompt                                                        _ □

C:\>TRACERT

Usage: tracert [-d] [-h maximum_hops] [-j host-list] [-w timeout] target_name

Options:
    -d                     Do not resolve addresses to hostnames.
    -h maximum_hops        Maximum number of hops to search for target.
    -j host-list           Loose source route along host-list.
    -w timeout             Wait timeout milliseconds for each reply.

C:\>_
```

30 hops prevents the use of the program to determine the full path, you can use the -h option to change the default to a higher value.

Figure 8-4 illustrates the use of TRACERT from a Windows NT client to determine the path to the American University Web server. It should be noted that the author used a commercial Internet service provider's network to access the Internet. From the access point, a total of 10 hops were required to reach the destination. In examining the entries in Figure 8-4, you will note that typically routers are configured to return a description in addition to the TEM message. That description typically provides an indication of the location and organization operating the router. For example, hop 4 and hop 5 represent routers operated by BBN Planet in Vienna, Virginia. Because BBN Planet was acquired over a year ago by GTE, it's also apparent that the description of the router was not updated.

Although the Microsoft implementation of TRACEROUTE, which is known as TRACERT, uses a default of three datagrams to obtain three round-trip delay times per hop, it does not average those times. Other implementations of TRACEROUTE provide a statistical summary of round-trip response time. Similarly, other implementations may have one or more optional parameters that permit you to control timeout delays. Because all versions of TRACEROUTE work in a similar manner, it is important to note that regardless of implementation, its use provides you with the ability to determine whether a path is available to the destination. In addition, it also provides you with the ability to note the delays associated with different points on the route to the destination.

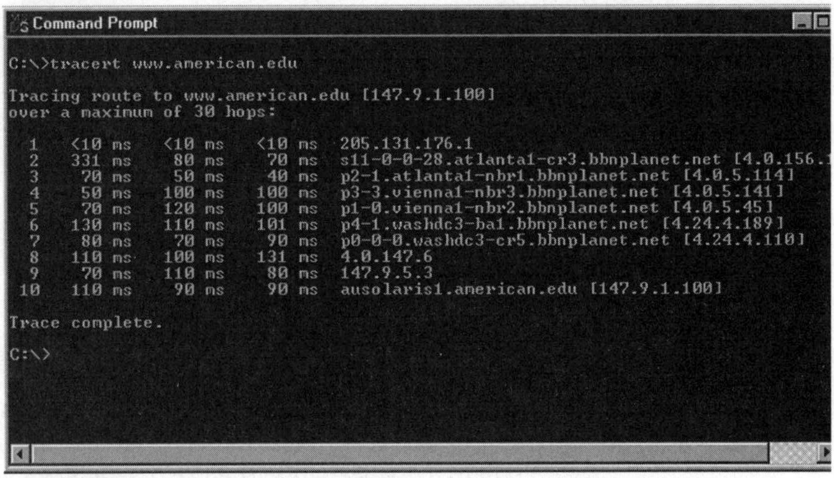

Figure 8-4
Using TRACERT to
examine the path to
the American University Web server.

```
Command Prompt                                                        _ □

C:\>tracert www.american.edu

Tracing route to www.american.edu [147.9.1.100]
over a maximum of 30 hops:

  1   <10 ms   <10 ms   <10 ms  205.131.176.1
  2   331 ms    80 ms    70 ms  s11-0-0-28.atlanta1-cr3.bbnplanet.net [4.0.156.1
  3    70 ms    50 ms    40 ms  p2-1.atlanta1-nbr1.bbnplanet.net [4.0.5.114]
  4    50 ms   100 ms   100 ms  p3-3.vienna1-nbr3.bbnplanet.net [4.0.5.141]
  5    70 ms   120 ms   100 ms  p1-0.vienna1-nbr2.bbnplanet.net [4.0.5.45]
  6   130 ms   110 ms   101 ms  p4-1.washdc3-ba1.bbnplanet.net [4.24.4.189]
  7    80 ms    70 ms    90 ms  p0-0-0.washdc3-cr5.bbnplanet.net [4.24.4.110]
  8   110 ms   100 ms   131 ms  4.0.147.6
  9    70 ms   110 ms    80 ms  147.9.5.3
 10   110 ms    90 ms    90 ms  ausolaris1.american.edu [147.9.1.100]

Trace complete.

C:\>
```

8-2 Traffic Prioritization Considerations

As mentioned several times in this book, the key to operating an effective voice over data network facility is to obtain predictability and reliability. If your organization is considering implementing voice over IP or voice over frame relay, you need to consider the equipment along the path between source and destination. In concluding this book, we will briefly discuss some additional items you may wish to investigate to ensure that your implementation is headed for success.

Shared versus Switched Operations

If organizational users that will take advantage of voice are LAN-based, you more than likely should consider the use of switches instead of a shared media environment. A shared media Ethernet represents an unpredictable technology, as its basic mode of operation is one of contention for the media. This means that unless LAN utilization is very low, the ability of digitized voice packets to reach a router can be expected to have a considerable variance in delays. If your organization has or can obtain a switch-based infrastructure that supports IEEE 802.1p, you obtain the ability to make packets transporting voice a higher priority than packets transporting data, thus obtaining predictability at the edge of the network.

Ingress Operations

There are three functions necessary to enable packets transporting digitized voice to correctly flow into a packet network. First, due to the effect of long packets upon packets transporting voice, the size or length of all packets must be adjusted. This adjustment is necessary to ensure that when a long packet is processed, its time onto the network does not adversely affect to a significant degree the latency of the packet behind it transporting digitized voice. Second, the ingress device must prioritize packets transporting voice over those carrying data. This will also minimize delays. Last but not least, the line access rate that provides egress to the network must be carefully examined. As we noted earlier in this book, a T1 line results in an insignificant delay for transporting a packet carrying digitized voice, while the use of a 56-Kbps access line results in a significant degree of latency.

Egress Operations

Although it may appear that because data flows into the destination network as a serial bit stream, equipment at the egress location does not require the functionality of ingress equipment. This is not true. Remember that voice conversations are bidirectional. Thus, the three key functions mentioned earlier in this section for ingress equipment are also necessary for egress equipment.

Summary

By carefully examining the features and operational characteristics of potential equipment in conjunction with the use of utility programs, you can obtain a reasonable expectation of the potential success or failure of a voice over data application implementation. Although the techniques mentioned in this chapter require a bit of time (no pun intended), it may result in valuable information that sheds light on the potential success or failure of a voice over data network application. The best advice this author can provide is that you should use the information in this book to be prepared.

APPENDIX A

APPENDIX A

VOICE OVER FRAME RELAY
IMPLEMENTATION AGREEMENT

FRF.11

Frame Relay Forum Technical Committee

Note: The user's attention is called to the possibility that implementation of the frame relay implementation agreement contained herein may require the use of inventions covered by patent rights held by third parties. By publication of this frame relay implementation agreement the Frame Relay Forum makes no representation that the implementation of the specification will not infringe on any third party rights. The Frame Relay Forum take no position with respect to any claim that has been or may be asserted by any third party, the validity of any patent rights related to any such claims, or the extent to which a license to use any such rights may not be available.

Editors:

Ted Hatala

Ross Kocen

Kenneth Rehbehn

For more information contact:

The Frame Relay Forum

Suite 307

39355 California Street

Fremont, CA 94538 USA

Phone: +1 (510) 608-5920

FAX: +1 (510) 608-5917

E-Mail: frf@frforum.com

CONTENTS

1. Introduction

1.1 Purpose

Frame relay is now a major component of many network designs. The protocol provides a minimal set of switching functions to forward variable sized data payloads through a network. The basic frame relay protocol, described in the Frame Relay Forum User to Network (UNI) and Network to Network (NNI) Implementation Agreements, has been augmented by additional agreements which detail techniques for structuring application data over the basic frame relay information field. These techniques enabled successful support for data applications such as LAN bridging, IP routing, and SNA.

This specification extends frame relay application support to include the transport of digital voice payloads. Frame formats and procedures required for voice transport are described in this Implementation Agreement. This specification addresses the following requirements:

- Transport of compressed voice within the payload of a frame relay frame

- Support a diverse set of voice compression algorithms

- Effective utilization of low-bit rate frame relay connections

- Multiplexing of up to 255 sub-channels on a single frame relay DLCI

- Support of multiple voice payloads on the same or different sub-channel within a single frame

- Support of data sub-channels on a multiplexed frame relay DLCI

Transport of compressed voice is provided with a generalized frame format that supports multiplexing of sub-channels on a single frame relay DLCI. Support for the unique needs of the different voice compression algorithms is accommodated with algorithm-specific "transfer syntax" definitions. These definitions establish algorithm specific frame formats and procedures. Annexes describing different transfer syntax definitions are found at the end of this document.

Transport of supporting information for voice communication, such as signalling indications (e.g., ABCD bits), dialed digits, and facsimile data, is also provided through the use of transfer syntax definitions specific to the information being sent.

1.2 Overview of Agreement

A description of the reference model and service description for the voice over frame relay (VoFR) service is provided in Section 2, along with the concept of a Voice Frame Relay Access Device (VFRAD).

Specification of the frame formats and procedures is provided in Section 3.

Transfer syntax definitions for individual voice compression algorithms as well as generic supporting information (e.g., dialed digits) are provided in Annex sections at the conclusion of the document. Figure 1-1 illustrates some of the transfer syntax definitions used for Voice Over Frame Relay.

1.3 Voice Frame Relay Access Device (VFRAD)

A voice over frame relay access device supports voice services. A VFRAD may be positioned between a PBX or key set and the frame relay network. Alternatively, the VFRAD may be integrated into an end-system that directly supports telephony applications and frame relay. The VFRAD multiplexes voice and fax traffic along with data traffic from a variety of services/sources into a common frame relay connection.

1.4 Definitions

Must, Shall or Mandatory—the item is an absolute requirement of this implementation agreement.

Figure 1-1
Transfer syntax examples

Vocoders					Other			
G.729	G.728	G.723.1	G.726/G.727	G.711	Dialed	CAS	Data	Fax
CS-ACELP	LD CELP	MP-MLQ	ADPCM	PCM	Digits		Transfer	Relay

Should—the item is desirable.

May or Optional—the item is not compulsory, and may be followed or ignored according to the needs of the implementor.

1.5 Acronyms

ADPCM	Adaptive Differential Pulse Code Modulation
AIS	Alarm Indication Signal
B_c	Committed Burst
B_e	Excess Burst
BECN	Backward Explicit Congestion Notification
BER	Bit Error Rate
CAS	Channel Associated Signalling
CS-ACELP	Conjugate Structure—Algebraic Code Excited Linear Predictive
CELP	Code Excited Linear Prediction
CID	Channel Identification
CIR	Committed Information Rate
CCS	Common Channel Signalling
DE	Discard Eligibility
DLCI	Data Link Connection Identifier
DTMF	Dual Tone Multi-Frequency
E-ADPCM	Embedded Adaptive Differential Pulse Code Modulation
FAX	Facsimile Group 3
FECN	Forward Explicit Congestion Notification
FRAD	Frame Relay Access Device
HDLC	High Level Data Link Control
IA	Implementation Agreement
I/F	Interface
IWF	Inter-working Function
LD-CELP	Low Delay—Code Excited Linear Prediction
lsb	Least Significant Bit
MP-MLQ	Multi Pulse Maximum Likelihood Quantizer
msb	Most Significant Bit

PCM   Pulse Code Modulation

PVC   Permanent Virtual Connection

SID   Silence Information Descriptor

UNI   User Network Interface

VAD   Voice Activity Detection

VFRAD   Voice Frame Relay Access Device

VoFR   Voice over Frame Relay

Vocoder   Voice coder/decoder

1.6   Relevant Standards

[1]   FRF.1.1   Frame Relay User-to-Network Implementation Agreement, January 1996

[2]   FRF.3.1   Multiprotocol Encapsulation Implementation Agreement, June 22, 1995

[3]   FRF.12   Frame Relay Fragmentation Implementation Agreement, 1997

[4]   ITU G.711   Pulse Code Modulation of Voice Frequencies, 1988

[5]   ITU G.723.1 Dual Rate Speech Coder for Multimedia Communications Transmitting at 5.3 & 6.3 kbit/s, March 1996

[6]   ITU G.726   40, 32, 24, 16 kbit/s Adaptive Differential Pulse Code Modulation (ADPCM), March 1991

[7]   ITU G.727   5-, 4-, 3- and 2 bits Sample Embedded Adaptive Differential Pulse Code Modulation, November 1994

[8]   ITU G.728   Coding of Speech at 16 kbit/s Using Low-Delay Code Excited Linear Prediction, November 1994

[9]   ITU G.729   Coding of Speech at 8 kbit/s using Conjugate Structure—Algebraic Code Excited Linear Predictive (CS-ACELP) Coding, March 1996

[10]   ITU G.764   Voice Packetization—Packetized voice protocols, December 1990

[11]   ITU T.30   Terminal Equipment and protocol for Telematic Service/Procedure for Facsimile General Switch Networks, March 1993

2. Reference Model and Service Description

2.1 Frame Relay Access

A VFRAD uses the frame relay service at the UNI as a transmission facility for voice, voice signalling, and data. The reference model for voice over frame relay is shown in Figure 2-1. Using the Voice over Frame Relay (VoFR) service, it is possible for any type of VFRAD on the left-hand side of Figure 2-1 to exchange voice and signalling with any type of VFRAD on the right-hand side of Figure 2-1.

Three types of devices are shown in Figure 2-1. The top layer shows end-system devices similar to telephones or FAX machines. The middle layer shows transparent multiplexing devices similar to channel banks. The bottom layer shows switching system devices similar to PBX's.

A VFRAD connects to a frame relay UNI via physical interfaces as defined in [1].

2.1.1 End-System Devices

The top left device in Figure 2-1 could be a PC with FAX or telephony application software using a frame relay network port for connectivity to other VFRAD devices. Such an end-system could use the VoFR protocol stack on a frame relay connection to another end-system (top right). It could also use the VoFR protocol stack on a connection to a transparent channel bank into a private network (middle right) or to a PBX (bottom right).

2.1.2 Transparent-Multiplexing Devices

The middle left device in Figure 2-1 could be a Channel Bank connected via analog trunks to an external PBX (not shown). Such a multiplexing device could use the VoFR protocol stack on a frame relay connection to an end-system (top right), another channel bank (middle right) or a PBX (bottom right).

2.1.3 Switching-System Devices

The bottom left device in Figure 2-1 could be a PBX using a frame relay network for connection to off premise extensions (end-systems) or as

Figure 2-1
Voice over Frame
Relay network
reference model

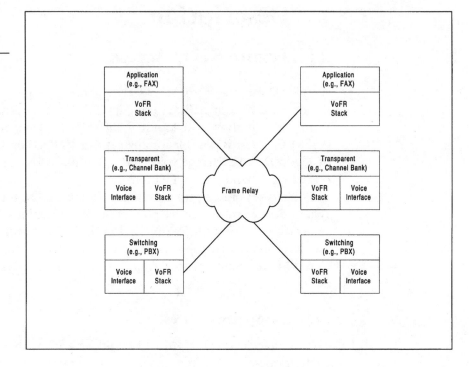

trunks to other PBX devices. Such a switching system device could use the VoFR protocol stack on a frame relay connection to an end-system (top right), a channel bank (middle right), or another PBX (bottom right).

2.2 Voice Interfaces

The requirements for implementation of voice interfaces are beyond the scope of this implementation agreement.

2.3 Voice Over Frame Relay Service Description

This implementation agreement defines formats and procedures that support a VoFR service. Elements of the VoFR service support various types of service users that may be performing any of the following voice applications:

1. Call origination and termination—for an end-system

2. Transparent interworking between individual sub-channels on a VoFR interface and sub-channels on another type of voice interface.

3. Call-by-call Switching—for a switching system to terminate an incoming call and originate a call on another voice interface.

To support the VoFR service, the underlying protocol stack must provide a full duplex transport service. The service users can use the following service elements to operate a voice connection. The service elements support the transport of two types of payloads: primary payloads and signalled payloads. Refer to Section 3.1 for a discussion of payload types.

2.3.1 Primary Payloads

2.3.1.1 ENCODED VOICE

This service element conveys voice information supplied by the service user. The voice information is packaged according to the rules specified by a voice transfer syntax. Voice transfer syntax definitions for various voice compression schemes are described in the annexes of this IA.

2.3.1.2 ENCODED FAX OR VOICE-BAND MODEM DATA

The service users can exchange digital data in a "baseband" format suitable for re-modulation into a FAX or analog modem signal. The VoFR service transports this information between the two service users.

The transmitting service user may locally detect the presence of a FAX or voice-band modem signal for the voice connection and demodulate it before sending it. The receiving service user can detect arriving packets that contain demodulated data and can reconstruct the original modulated signal instead of reconstructing a speech signal.

The encoded FAX or voice-band data payload format is within the scope of this IA. The algorithms used for demodulation and re-modulation of FAX and/or voice-band data are outside the scope of this IA.

The transfer syntax for FAX is described in Annex D.

The transfer syntax for voice band modem data is for further study.

2.3.1.3 DATA FRAMES

This service element conveys data frames supplied by the service user. The frames are packaged according to the rules specified by Annex C.

The content of the data frames is transparent to the VoFR service.

One application of the data frame service element enables transparent tunneling of common channel signalling messages between two compatible end-points (e.g., PBX interfaces). Common channel signalling message formats and procedures are beyond the scope of this agreement.

2.3.2   Signalled Payload

2.3.2.1   DIALED DIGITS
This service element transparently conveys DTMF, pulse, or other dialed digits supplied by the service user. These digits may be sent during the voice call setup or following call establishment to transfer in-band tones.

2.3.2.2   SIGNALLING BITS (CHANNEL ASSOCIATED SIGNALLING)
This service element transparently conveys signalling bits supplied by the service user. These bits may indicate seizure and release of a connection, dial pulses, ringing, or other information in accordance with the signalling system in use over the transmission facility.

2.3.2.3   FAULT INDICATION
The service users can use this service to convey an alarm indication signal.

2.3.2.4   MESSAGE-ORIENTED SIGNALLING (COMMON CHANNEL SIGNALLING)
Refer to section 2.3.1.3

2.3.2.5   ENCODED FAX
Refer to Section 2.3.1.2
Encoded FAX may be transmitted on a sub-channel that utilizes a primary payload for encoded voice. In this case, the sub-frames containing the encoded FAX must be sent as a signalled payload.

2.3.2.6   SILENCE INFORMATION DESCRIPTOR
Silence Information Descriptor (SID) sub-frames indicate the end of a talk-spurt and convey comfort noise generation parameters. These SID indications support voice activity detection (VAD) and silence suppression schemes.

When VAD is utilized, a SID sub-frame may optionally be transmitted following the last encoded voice sub-frame of a talk-spurt. Reception of a SID sub-frame after a voice sub-frame may be interpreted as an explicit indication of end of talk-spurt. In addition, SID sub-frames may be transmitted at any time during the silence interval to update comfort noise generation parameters.

The SID payload is defined for PCM and ADPCM encoding in the appropriate annexes (Annex F and Annex G). The SID payload definition for other voice encoding algorithms is for further study and can be null.

SID sub-frames should not be sent if VAD is not utilized.

2.4   VFRAD Configuration Requirements

VoFR devices compliant with this implementation agreement are not required to negotiate operational parameters. Negotiation procedures are for further study. Therefore, at the time of provisioning, the network manager must configure end-to-end configuration parameters (e.g., Vocoder.). Endpoint devices providing the VoFR service are configured with compatible sub-channel assignments, signalling, compression algorithms, and other options.

2.5   VoFR Service Block Diagram

The relationship of the Voice Over Frame Relay service, VoFR Service user and the frame relay service is shown in Figure 2-2.

2.6   Service Multiplexing

The Frame Relay UNI can support multiple PVCs, each of which can provide VoFR service. The VoFR service supports multiple voice and data channels on a single frame relay data link connection. The VoFR service delivers frames on each sub-channel in the order they were sent.

Figure 2-2
VoFR service block diagram.

Voice Over Frame Relay Implementation Agreement – FRF.11

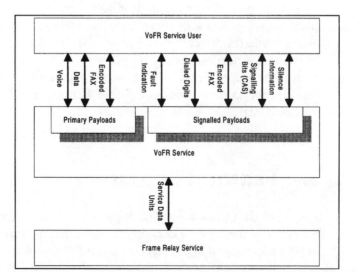

Figure 2-3
Voice over Frame
Relay multiplexing
model.

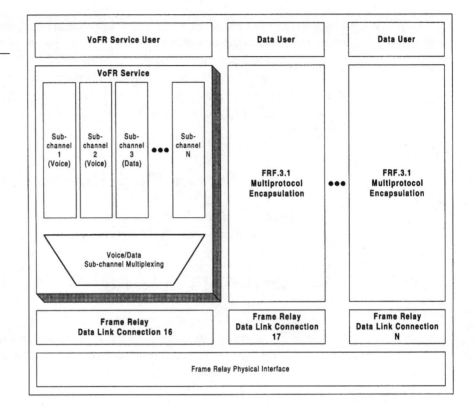

As shown in Figure 2-3 each instance of the voice/data multiplexing layer can support one or more voice connections and data protocol stacks over a single frame relay PVC. The mechanism for separation of the voice and data connections being supported over a single frame relay PVC is within the scope of this IA. The mechanisms and protocol stacks used for data connections are covered in other Frame Relay Forum IA's and relevant standards.

3. Frame Formats

Voice and data payloads are multiplexed within a voice over frame relay data link connection by encapsulation within the frame format specified in [1]. Each payload is packaged as a sub-frame within a frame's informa-

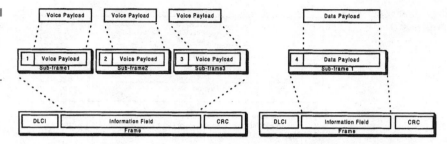

Figure 3-1
Relationship between frames and sub-frames.

tion field. Sub-frames may be combined within a single frame to increase processing and transport efficiencies. Each sub-frame contains a header and payload. The sub-frame header identifies the voice/data sub-channel and, when required, payload type and length. Refer to Figure 3-1 for an illustration of sub-frames. In this example, a single DLCI supports 3 voice channels and 1 data channel. Three voice payloads are packaged in the first frame and a data payload is contained in the second frame.

3.1   Payloads

3.1.1   Primary Payload

Each sub-channel of a VoFR connection transports a primary payload. A primary payload contains traffic that is fundamental to operation of a sub-channel. Other payloads may be sent to support the primary payload (e.g., dialed digits for a primary payload of encoded voice). These additional payload types are differentiated from the primary payload by a signalled encoding in the payload type field of the sub-frame. A payload type of all zeros always indicates the primary payload.

Three basic types of primary payloads are utilized: encoded voice payloads, encoded FAX payloads, and data payloads. Refer to the appropriate annex for a description of the transfer syntax which supports these payload types.

3.1.2   Signalled Payload

Payloads containing in-band information, which augment the primary payload flow, are indicated using payload type codings. These signalled payloads include information such as channel-associated signalling, dialed digits, in-band encoded FAX relay, and fault indications. Refer to the appropriate annex for a description of the service elements which support the signalled payloads.

Figure 3-2
Sub-frame format.

Bits								Octets
8	7	6	5	4	3	2	1	
EI	LI	Sub-channel Identification (CID) (Least significant 6 bits)						1
CID (msb)	0 Spare	0 Spare	Payload Type					1a (Note 1)
Payload Length								1b (Note 2)
Payload								p

NOTES:
1. When the EI bit is set, the structure of Octet 1a given in Table 3-1 applies.
2. When the LI bit is set, the structure of Octet 1b given in Table 3-1 applies.
3. When both the EI bit and the LI bit are set to 1 both Octet 1a and 1b are used.

3.2 Sub-frame Format

Each sub-frame consists of a variable length header and a payload. The minimal sub-frame header is a single octet containing the least significant bits of the voice/data channel identification along with extension and length indications. An extension octet containing the most significant bits of the voice/data channel identification and a payload type is present when the Extension Indication is set. A payload length octet is present when the Length Indication is set. Refer to Figure 3-2 and Table 3-1 for a description of the sub-frame structure.

TABLE 3-1

Sub-frame Format.

Voice Over Frame Relay Implementation Agreement – FRF.11

Extension indication (octet 1)

The extension indication (EI) bit is set to indicate the presence of octet 1a. This bit must be set when a sub-channel identification value is > 63 or when a payload type is indicated. Each transfer syntax has an implicit payload type of zero when the EI bit is cleared.

Length indication (octet 1)

The length indication (LI) bit is set to indicate the presence of octet 1b. The LI bit of the last sub-frame contained within a frame is always cleared and the payload length field is not present. The LI bits are set for each of the sub-frames preceding the last sub-frame.

Sub-channel identification (octets 1 and 1a)

The six least significant bits of the sub-channel identification are encoded in octet 1. The two most significant bits of the sub-channel identification are encoded in octet 1a. A zero value in the two most significant bits is implied when octet 1a is not included in the VoFR header (EI bit cleared). Sub-channel identifiers 0000 0000 through 0000 0011 are reserved in both the short and long format.

Payload type (octet 1a)

This field indicates the type of payload contained in the sub-frame.

Bits				
4	3	2	1	
0	0	0	0	Primary payload transfer syntax
0	0	0	1	Dialed digit transfer syntax (Annex A)
0	0	1	0	Signalling bit transfer syntax (Annex B)
0	0	1	1	Fax relay transfer syntax (Annex D)
0	1	0	0	Silence Information Descriptor

A zero value for the payload type is implied when octet 1a is not in included in the header (EI bit cleared).

Payload length (octet 1b)

Payload length contains the number of payload octets following the header. A payload length indicates the presence of two or more sub-frames packed in the information field of the frame.

Payload (octet p)

The payload contains octets as defined by the applicable transfer syntax assigned to the sub-channel or as indicated by the payload type octet 1a.

3.3 Sub-frame Examples

The diagrams in this section illustrate some of the possible combinations of sub-frames. Figure 3-3 shows a frame which contains a single voice payload for a low-numbered sub-channel. Octets 1a and 1b are not required. The payload, a CS-ACELP sample, starts after octet 1.

Figure 3-3
Frame containing one sub-frame.

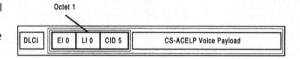

Figure 3-4 shows a frame which contains a single voice payload for a high-numbered channel (>63). Octet 1a must be included. Note that the payload type is zero, indicating the transfer syntax that has been configured for the channel. In this example, the transfer syntax is the CS-ACELP syntax.

Figure 3-4
Frame containing one subframe for a high numbered channel.

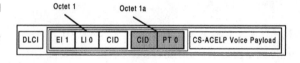

Figure 3-5 shows a frame which contains multiple sub-frames for channels 5 and 6. In this case, the payload type is non-zero and octet 1a is required to encode the payload type. The first of the two sub-frames includes octet 1b with the encoding of payload length.

Figure 3-5
Frame containing multiple sub-frames.

Figure 3-6 shows a frame which contains multiple sub-frames for channels 5 and 6. In this case, the payload type is zero and the payload length (octet 1b) appears in the first of the two sub-frames.

Figure 3-6
Frame containing multiple sub-frames.

4. Minimum Requirements for Conformance

This agreement provides support for several optional transfer syntax definitions. Interoperability between VoFR devices is possible only when both devices share support for one or more common transfer syntax definitions. VoFR devices are classified based on the support provided for the common transfer syntax definitions. Class 1 compliant devices support capabilities suitable for high bit-rate interfaces. Class 2 compliant devices support capabilities that enable optimal performance over low bit-rate frame relay interfaces. An implementation is compliant with this agreement if the requirements for at least one of the two classes are met.

4.1 Class 1 Compliance Requirements

4.1.1 Frame Formats

1. Support the frame structure described in section 3.
2. Received optional frames may be discarded.

4.1.2 Primary Payload Types

1. Support of G.727 as described in Annex F is mandatory. Support of other vocoders described in Annex F is optional.
2. A transmit rate of 32Kbps is mandatory.
3. Support for rates of 32kbps, 24kbps, 16kbps are mandatory at the receiver.
4. Support for other primary payload transfer syntax definitions (e.g., FAX) is optional.

4.1.3 Signalled Payload Types

1. Support for the dialed digit signalled payload type is optional.
2. Support for the signalling bits signalled payload type (CAS and AIS) is mandatory.
3. Support for the encoded FAX signalled payload type is optional.

4.2 Class 2 Compliance Requirements

4.2.1 Frame Formats

1. Support the frame structure described in section 3.
2. Received optional frames may be discarded.

4.2.2 Primary Payload Types

1. Support for Annex E CS-ACELP G.729 or G.729A voice transfer syntax is mandatory.
5. Support for other primary payload transfer syntax definitions (e.g., FAX) is optional.

4.2.3 Signalled Payload Types

1. Support for the dialed digit signalled payload type is mandatory.
2. Support for the signalling bits signalled payload type (CAS and AIS) is mandatory.
3. Support for the encoded FAX signalled payload type is optional.

Annex A—Dialed Digit Transfer Syntax

A.1 Reference Documents

None

A.2 Transfer Structure

The Dialed Digit Transfer Syntax is comprised of the Dialed Digit Payload Format and the Dialed Digit Transfer Procedure.

A.3 Dialed Digit Payload Format

At the originating VFRAD the detected digits are inserted into a Dialed Digit Payload by the Dialed Digit Service element. Payload carrying dig-

	Bits							
8	7	6	5	4	3	2	1	Octet
Sequence Number								P
reserved 000			Signal Level					P+1
Digit Type [0]			Edge Location [0]					P+2
reserved 000			Digit Code [0]					P+3
Digit-Type[-1]			Edge-Location[-1]					P+4
reserved 000			Digit-Code[-1]					P+5
Digit-Type[-2]			Edge-Location[-2]					P+6
reserved 000			Digit-Code[-2]					P+7

its will be identified using the VoFR sub-frame payload type field code-point for the Dialed Digit transfer syntax. The digits will automatically be associated with the corresponding voice traffic based on the Channel ID field.

Each Digit Payload contains three windows of digit transition. The first window represents the current 20 ms period [0], the second [–1] is the recent period and the third [–2] is the previous.

A.3.1   Sequence Number

The sequence field is an 8-bit number that is incremented for every fragment transmitted. The sequence field wraps from all ones to zero in the usual manner of such sequence numbers. Each increment of the sequence represents a period of 20 ms.

A.3.2   Signal Level

The power level of each frequency is between 0 to –31 in –dBm0. Power levels above zero dBm0 are coded 00000. In the event that one dialed digit payload contains a transition from one dialed digit to another dialed digit, the signal level field applies to the dialed digit in the "current" 20 ms period.

A.3.3   Digit Type

A 20 ms window is used to encode the edge when a digit is turned on and off. This is the edge time, 0 ms (00000) to 19 ms (10011), from the beginning of the current frame in ms. If there is no transmission, the edge location will be set to 0 and the Digit Type of the previous windows will be repeated.

A.3.4   Digit-Code

The following DTMF digit codes are encoded when dialed digit type = DTMF ON.

Figure A-2
Signal level.

Code	Power Level dBm0
00000	0
00001	-1
000010	-2
000011	-3
00100	-4
00101	-5
00110	-6
00111	-7
01000	-8
01001	-9
01010	-10
01011	-11
01100	-12
01101	-13
01110	-14
01111	-15
10000	-16
10001	-17
10010	-18
10011	-19
10100	-20
10101	-21
10110	-22
10111	-23
11000	-24
11001	-25
11010	-26
11011	-27
11100	-28
11101	-29
11110	-30
11111	-31

Figure A-3
Digit types.

Code	Digit Type
000	Digit Off
001	DTMF On
010-111	Reserved

Figure A-4
DTMF digit codes.

Digit Code	DTMF Digits
00000	0
00001	1
00010	2
00011	3
00100	4
00101	5
00110	6
00111	7
01000	8
01001	9
01010	*
01011	#
01100	A
01101	B
01110	C
01111	D
10000-11111	Reserved

A.4 Dialed Digit Transfer Procedures

A.4.1 Procedure for Transmission of Dialed Digit Payloads

When the transmitter detects a validated digit, or has addressing information to send it will start sending a Dialed Digit Payload every 20 ms. Since each payload covers 60ms of Digit on/off edge information, there is redundancy of the edge information. The sequence number is incremented by one in each transmitted payload.

When the digit activity is off, the transmitter should continue to send three more Dialed Digit Payloads for 60ms.

A.4.2 Procedure for Interpreting Received Dialed Digit Payloads

When the receiver gets a Dialed Digit Payload or accepts the received addressing information, it will generate digits according to the location of the on and off edges. Silence will be applied to the duration after an off edge and before an on edge. Digits will be generated after an on edge and before an off edge.

If the sequence number is one greater than the last received sequence number, the receiver appends the Current edge information to the previously received information.

If the sequence number is two greater than the last received sequence number, the receiver appends the Recent and Current edge information to the previously received information.

If the sequence number is three greater than the last received sequence number, the receiver appends the previous, recent and current edge information to the previously received information.

If the sequence number is more than three greater than the last received sequence number, the receiver appends the previous, recent and current edge information to the previously received information. It fills in the gap with the static values based on the previously received payload.

On a given sub-channel, if a voice payload is received at any time, an off edge should be appended to the previously received digits on/off edge information.

Annex B—Signalling Bit Transfer Syntax

B.1   Reference Documents

None

B.2   Transfer Structure

The Signalling Bit Transfer Syntax is comprised of payload formats and transfer procedures for alarm indications and channel associated signalling bits.

B.3   Payload Format

Payloads carrying signalling bits will be identified using the payload type field in the VoFR Header. The signalling bits will automatically be associated with the corresponding voice traffic based on the Channel ID field.

The first byte following the VoFR header contains a seven-bit sequence number with the most significant bit assigned as an Alarm Indicator Signal (AIS) bit. A value of 1 signifies an alarm condition.

The sequence number starts at 0 and increments by 1 up through 127 and rolls over back to 0.

Figure B-1

Signalling Bit Transfer Syntax payload format.

		Bits						
	8	7	6	5	4	3	2	1	Octet
	AIS		Sequence Number						P
Previous	D[t-56ms]	C[t-56ms]	B[t-56ms]	A[t-56ms]	D[t-58ms]	C[t-58ms]	B[t-58ms]	A[t-58ms]	P+1
	D[t-52ms]	C[t-52ms]	B[t-52ms]	A[t-52ms]	D[t-54ms]	C[t-54ms]	B[t-54ms]	A[t-54ms]	P+2
	D[t-48ms]	C[t-48ms]	B[t-48ms]	A[t-48ms]	D[t-50ms]	C[t-50ms]	B[t-50ms]	A[t-50ms]	P+3
	D[t-44ms]	C[t-44ms]	B[t-44ms]	A[t-44ms]	D[t-46ms]	C[t-46ms]	B[t-46ms]	A[t-46ms]	P+4
	D[t-40ms]	C[t-40ms]	B[t-40ms]	A[t-40ms]	D[t-42ms]	C[t-42ms]	B[t-42ms]	A[t-42ms]	P+5
Recent	D[t-36ms]	C[t-36ms]	B[t-36ms]	A[t-36ms]	D[t-38ms]	C[t-38ms]	B[t-38ms]	A[t-38ms]	P+6
	D[t-32ms]	C[t-32ms]	B[t-32ms]	A[t-32ms]	D[t-34ms]	C[t-34ms]	B[t-34ms]	A[t-34ms]	P+7
	D[t-28ms]	C[t-28ms]	B[t-28ms]	A[t-28ms]	D[t-30ms]	C[t-30ms]	B[t-30ms]	A[t-30ms]	P+8
	D[t-24ms]	C[t-24ms]	B[t-24ms]	A[t-24ms]	D[t-26ms]	C[t-26ms]	B[t-26ms]	A[t-26ms]	P+9
	D[t-20ms]	C[t-20ms]	B[t-20ms]	A[t-20ms]	D[t-22ms]	C[t-22ms]	B[t-22ms]	A[t-22ms]	P+10
Current	D[t-16ms]	C[t-16ms]	B[t-16ms]	A[t-16ms]	D[t-18ms]	C[t-18ms]	B[t-18ms]	A[t-18ms]	P+11
	D[t-12ms]	C[t-12ms]	B[t-12ms]	A[t-12ms]	D[t-14ms]	C[t-14ms]	B[t-14ms]	A[t-14ms]	P+12
	D[t-8ms]	C[t-8ms]	B[t-8ms]	A[t-8ms]	D[t-10ms]	C[t-10ms]	B[t-10ms]	A[t-10ms]	P+13
	D[t-4ms]	C[t-4ms]	B[t-4ms]	A[t-4ms]	D[t-6ms]	C[t-6ms]	B[t-6ms]	A[t-6ms]	P+14
	D[t]	C[t]	B[t]	A[t]	D[t-2ms]	C[t-2ms]	B[t-2ms]	A[t-2ms]	P+15

The transfer syntax for signalling bits contains 60 milliseconds worth of samples for up to four signalling bits. Each sample has a time resolution of 2.0 milliseconds. Each payload contains ten "new" samples for the current 20 millisecond time interval and a repetition of the ten samples for each of the two immediately preceding 20 millisecond time intervals.

This will result in 15 bytes of packed signalling bit values.

For sixteen state coding, all four bits are independent. For four state coding, the A and B bits are repeated in the C and D bit fields respectively. For two state coding, the A bit is repeated in the B, C, and D bit fields.

B.4   Procedures for Transmission of Payloads

While there are transitions occurring in the signalling bit values, the transmitter sends a signalling bit payload every 20 milliseconds. Since each payload covers 60 milliseconds of signal bit states, there is redundancy of signal bit information. The sequence number is incremented by one in each transmitted payload.

When the signal bit values have been static for 500 milliseconds, the transmitter switches frequency of transmission and sends a signal bit payload only once in every 5 seconds. During this time, the sequence number is not incremented.

When transitions start occurring again, the transmitter resumes incrementing the sequence numbers by one and sending payloads every 20 milliseconds.

The first such payload contains ten static previous and ten static recent values with ten new current samples. The second such payload contains ten static previous values with the ten previous values that were current in the first payload, and ten new current samples. This restarts the overlapping redundancy of information.

The transmitter may debounce the sequence of signalling bit values prior to transmission, but is not required to do so.

B.5   Procedures for Interpreting Received Payloads

When the receiver gets a signalling bit payload, it processes the bits based on the sequence number.

If the sequence number is one larger than the last received sequence number, the receiver appends the Current signal bits to the previously received values.

If the sequence number is two larger than the last received sequence number, the receiver appends the Recent and Current signal bits to the previously received values.

If the sequence number is three larger than the last received sequence number, the receiver appends the Previous, Recent, and Current signal bits to the previously received values.

If the sequence number is more than three larger than the last received sequence number, the receiver appends the Previous, Recent, and Current signal bits to the previously received values. It fills in the gap with static values based on the previously received payload.

If the sequence number is the same as the last received sequence number, the receiver takes the first value and uses it to set its current values for the signalling bits. (The signal bit values are static.)

The transmitter may or may not have debounced the signal bit values before transmission. If the receiving VoFR service user is interpreting the semantics of the signal bits, it should debounce the sequence of bit values received.

▄▄ ▄▄ Annex C—Data Transfer Syntax

C.1 Reference Documents

[1] FRF.12   Frame Relay Forum Fragmentation Implementation Agreement, March 1997

[2] FRF3.1   Multiprotocol Encapsulation Implementation Agreement, June 1995

[3] RFC 1490   Multiprotocol Interconnect over Frame Relay, 1993

C.2 Data Transfer Structure

This annex describes a transfer syntax to support transport of data frames between two voice over frame relay service users. The contents of the frames are transparent to the voice over frame relay service. Typical applications include the transport of common channel signalling messages, RFC1490 packets [3], and FRF3.1 packets [2].

All data sub-frames contain the fragmentation header.

The payload type is set to primary payload type.

For more information on the fragmentation procedure refer to [1].

C.3   Data Payload Format

Figure C-1 shows the sub-frame payload format.

Figure C-1
Data transfer syntax
payload format.

Bits								
8	7	6	5	4	3	2	1	Octet
VoFR Sub-frame Header								1
B	E	0	Sequence number (upper 5 bits)					P
Sequence number (lower 8 bits)								P+1
Payload Fragment (variable length)								P+2 ⋮ P+N

C.4   Data Procedures

The sub-frame payload will consist of a data frame received from a VoFR service user.

The frame is transmitted on the data link connection in one or more data fragments as defined in [1].

Upon receipt of a sub-frame containing the data transfer syntax, the fragments are re-combined using the procedures of [1], and the frame is delivered to the VoFR service user.

All frames received from the VoFR service user are conveyed without interpretation. Information transmitted using this transfer syntax is transparent to the VoFR service.

The maximum fragment size is governed by the maximum frame size supported by the Q922 data link connection.

Annex D—Fax Relay Transfer Syntax

D.1   Reference Documents

[1]   ITU T.4   Standardization of group 3 facsimile apparatus for document transmission, March 1993

[2] ITU T.30   Terminal Equipment and Protocol for Telematic Service/Procedure for Facsimile General Switch Networks, November 1994

[3] ITU V.17   A 2-wire modem for facsimile applications with rates up to 14,400bit/s, February 1991

[4] ITU V.21   300 bit/s duplex modem standardized for use in general switched telephone network Blue Book Fasc. VIII.1, October 1994

[5] ITU V.27   4800/2400 bit/s modem standardized for use in general switched telephone network Blue Book Fasc. VIII.1, November 1994

[6] ITU V.29   9600 bit/s modem standardized for use in point-to-point 4-wire leased telephone-type circuits Blue Book Fasc. VIII.1, November 1988

[7] ITU V.33   14400 bit/s modem standardized for use in point-to-point 4-wire leased telephone-type circuits Blue Book Fasc. VIII.1, November 1988

D.2   FAX Transfer Structure

The Fax Relay Transfer Syntax is comprised of the Fax Relay Payload Format and the Fax Relay Transfer Procedure. The fax relay transfer syntax provides transfer syntax for fax.

D.3   Fax Relay Payload Format

D.3.1 Modulation Turn-On Payload

The Modulation Turn-On Payload has the modulation types defined in the octet following the time stamp. If Modulation Type is single Frequency Tone, Frequency MS:LS bytes will specify the frequency. Fre-

Figure D-1
Modulation Turn-On Payload.

				Bits				
8	7	6	5	4	3	2	1	Octet
EI1=1		Sequence Number			Relay Command=001			P
Time Stamp LS byte								P+1
EI2=0		Time Stamp MS byte						P+2
HDLC	reserved				Modulation Type			P+3
Frequency LS byte								P+4
Frequency MS byte								P+5

*LS=least significant, MS=most significant

quency MS:LS bytes should be set to zero if the Modulation Type is not Single Frequency Tone.

D.3.2 Modulation Turn-Off Payload

The Modulation Turn-Off Payload has the following structure.

Figure D-2
Modulation Turn-Off Payload.

				Bits				
8	7	6	5	4	3	2	1	Octet
EI1=1		Sequence Number			Relay Command=000			P
Time Stamp LS byte								P+1
EI2=0		Time Stamp MS byte						P+2

D.3.3 T.30 Payload

The T.30 Payload has 3 bytes of demodulated and HDLC de-framed data.

Figure D-3
T.30 Payload.

				Bits				
8	7	6	5	4	3	2	1	Octet
EI1=0		Sequence Number			Relay Command = 010,011or 100			P
Data [I]								P+1
Data[I-1]								P+2
Data[I-2]								P+3

D.3.4 T.4 Payload

The T.4 Payload should be sent once every 40ms. The Relay Command = 010 (Data). Use of the Relay Command 011 and 100 for T.4 Payload is for further study.

Figure D-4
T.4 Payload.

				Bits				
8	7	6	5	4	3	2	1	Octet
EI1=0		Sequence Number			Relay Command = 010			P
Data[I]								P+1
Data[I-1]								P+2
•								•
Data[I-N-1]								P+N

Each payload should have the following number of raw demodulated data bytes according to the modulation rate:

Figure D-5
Modulation rates.

Modulation Rate	Bytes per Payload (N)
14400	72
12000	60
9600	48
7200	36
4800	24
2400	12

D.3.5   Relay Command

The following is a list of code-points for Relay Commands.

■■■ ■■■ ■■■ ■■■
Figure D-6
Relay Commands.

Code	Relay Command
000	Modulation-Off
001	Modulation-On
010	Data
011	HDLC-End-Of-Frame
100	HDLC-Frame-Abort
101 - 111	reserved

D.3.6   Modulation Type

The following is an encoding table for the Modulation Type. However, it is optional to support all the types.

■■■ ■■■ ■■■ ■■■
Figure D-7
Modulation Type.

Code	Modulation Type
0000	Single Freq Tone
0001	V.21 300bps
0010	V.27ter 2400bps
0011	V.27ter 4800bps
0100	V.29 7200bps
0101	V.29 9600bps
0110	V.33 12000bps
0111	V.33 14400bps
1000	V.17 7200bps
1001	V.17 9600bps
1010	V.17 12000bps
1011	V.17 14400bps
1100 - 1111	reserved

D.3.7   HDLC

HDLC = 1 indicates that HDLC de-framing is being applied. HDLC = 0 indicates that HDLC de-framing is not used. De-framed packets are the content that remains after removing flags, extra bits inserted for transparency, and the frame check sequence.

D.3.8   Sequence Number

This sequence number is incremented for each new packet independent of the value of Relay Command.

The sequence number is reset at the beginning of each modulation type when the Modulation-On Relay Command is sent. It wraps around when it reaches a maximum count.

D.3.9   Time Stamp

The Time Stamp information represents the relative timing of events on the analog (or equivalent) input to the demodulator. The unit for Time Stamp is 1 ms. The accuracy of Time Stamp should be within 65 ms.

The Time Stamp is mandatory in the packet header when the Modulation-On or Modulation-Off Relay Commands are sent. It is optional with any other Relay Command.

The Time Stamp clocks free-run on each end and there is no synchronization between them. The Time Stamp wraps around when it reaches the maximum count.

D.3.10   EI1 and EI2

These are header Extension Indicator bits.

EI1 = 1 indicates that the two Time Stamp bytes exist and immediately follow the first header byte. EI1 = 0 indicates that there is no Time Stamp bytes.

EI2 is reserved for future use and should be set to 0.

D.3.11   Frequency LS & MS Bytes

These are the least significant (LS) and most significant (MS) bytes for the Single Frequency Tone in unit of Hertz (Hz) within ±1.5%.

D.3.12   Data

Data is packed into the packet with the latest byte first and the oldest byte last. Within each byte, the MSB is the most recent bit and LSB is the oldest bit.

D.4   Fax Relay Transfer Procedures

D.4.1   Procedure for Transmission of T.30 Data

When the preamble is detected, at least three identical Modulation Turn-On payloads should be sent with Relay Command = 001 (Modulation-On), Sequence Number = 0, EI1 = 1, Modulation Type = V.21 and HDLC = 1. The same Time Stamp should be use in all three payloads.

When the first byte of HDLC data is being demodulated and deframed, it should be sent with Relay Command = 010 (Data) and Sequence Number = 1. Data [I] is the first byte. Data [I-1] and Data [I-2] should be set to all 1's.

When the second byte of HDLC data is being demodulated and deframed, it should be sent with Relay Command = 010 (Data) and Sequence Number = 2. Data [I] is the second byte, Data [I-1] is the first byte and Data [I-2] is set to all 1's.

When the third byte of HDLC data is being demodulated and deframed, it should be sent with Relay Command = 010 (Data) and Sequence Number = 3. Data [I] is the third byte, Data [I-1] is the second byte and Data [I-2] is the first byte.

Subsequently, a new payload should be sent after every byte being demodulated. The payload is sent with Relay Command = 010 (Data) and the Sequence Number incremented by 1. The most current byte should be immediately after the header, followed by the recent byte and then the previous byte.

At the end of each HDLC frame, if there is no CRC error, the last payload should be sent three times with Relay Command = 011 (HDLC-End-Of-Frame). If a CRC error was detected by the sender, the last payload should be sent three times with Command = 100 (HDLC-Frame-Abort). In both cases, all three payloads should have the same three bytes of data as the previous data payload. All three payloads should have the sequence number (N_{EOF}). The previous data payload should have sequence number $N_{EOF}-1$.

The first data payload of the following HDLC frame should have sequence number $N_{EOF}+1$. The data bytes Data [I-1] and Data [I-2} in the first data payload of the following frame are the last two data bytes from the previous frame.

If the modulation turns off, three identical payloads should be sent with Command = 000 (Modulation-Off). All three payloads should have the same sequence number, which is one more than the last data payload, EI = 1 and the same two bytes of Time Stamp.

D.4.2   Procedure for Transmission of T.4 Data

When modulation (non-single frequency tone) for the T.4 procedure is detected, at least three Modulation Turn-On payloads should be sent with Relay Command = 001 (Modulation-On), Sequence Number = 0, EI1 = 1, Modulation Type = the codepoint of the detected modulation type and HDLC = 0. Use of HDLC = 1 is for further study. The same Time Stamp should be use in all three payloads.

Subsequently, when data is available, a payload should be sent every 40 ms with relay Command = 010 (Data) and the sequence number should be incremented by 1. Use of Relay Command 011 and 100 is reserved for further study.

When the modulation turns off, three identical payloads should be sent with Command = 000 (Modulation-Off) and EI1 = 1. These last three payloads should have the same sequence number and the same Time Stamp. The sequence number should be one larger than the last data.

D.4.3 Handling of Non-Standard Facilities (NSF) Frame

Procedures for disabling the NSF frame are for further study.

Annex E—CS-ACELP Transfer Syntax

E.1 Reference Document

[1]	ITU G.729/	Coding of Speech at 8 kbit/s using Conjugate Structure-Algebraic Code
	ITU G.729	Excited Linear Predictive (CS-ACELP) Coding, March 1996
	Annex A	

E.2 CS-ACELP Transfer Protocol

When the VoFR service user offers a frame of sampled speech it is immediately transmitted using the transfer structure described below.

E.3 CS-ACELP Transfer Structure

CS-ACELP produces 80 bits for each 10 ms frame of sampled speech. The list of the transmitted parameters used by the CS-ACELP algorithm is provided below. In order to allow the frame relay device to adjust its transmission rate, the CS-ACELP transfer syntax structure will permit multiples of 10 ms frames to be packed into the voice information field. An integer number of 10 ms frames will be packed into the voice information field to form a M*10 ms payload. For each M*10 ms of compressed speech, M*80 bits or M*10 octets will be produced. Support of M = 2 is required. A range of 1 to 6 can optionally be supported.

Figure E-1
List of transmitted parameters.

Symbol	Description	Bits
LSP0	Switched predictor index of LSP quantizer	1
LSP1	First stage vector of LSP quantizer	7
LSP2	Second stage lower vector of LSP quantizer	5
LSP3	Second stage lower vector of LSP quantizer	5
P1	Pitch period (Delay)	8
P0	Parity check of pitch period	1
C1	Fixed Code-Book – 1st sub-frame	13
S1	Signs of pulses –1st sub-frame	4
GA1	Gain Code-Book (stage 1) – 1st sub-frame	3
GB1	Gain Code-Book (stage 2) – 1st sub-frame	4
P2	Pitch Period (Delay) - 2nd sub-frame	5
C2	Fixed Code-Book – 2nd sub-frame	13
S2	Signs of pulses –2nd sub-frame	4
GA2	Gain Code-Book (stage 1) – 2nd sub-frame	3
GB2	Gain Code-Book (stage 2) – 2nd sub-frame	4
Total	Per 10 ms frame	80

*LSP = Line Spectrum Pairs

Figure E-2
CS-ACELP bit packing structure for each frame.

Octet	MSB Bit Packing LSB
1	LSP0, LSP1[7...1]
2	LSP2[5..1], LSP3[5..3]
3	LSP3[2,1], P1[7..3]
4	P1[2,1], P0, C1[13..9]
5	C1[8..1]
6	S1[4..1], GA1[3...1], GB1[4]
7	GB1[3...1], P2[5..1]
8	C2[13...6]
9	C2[5...1], S2[4..2]
10	S2[1], GA2[3..1], GB2[4..1]

Figure E-3
CS-ACELP transfer structure.

7	6	5	4	3	2	1	0	
LSP0	LSP1[7]	LSP1[6]	LSP1[5]	LSP1[4]	LSP1[3]	LSP1[2]	LSP1[1]	Octet P
LSP2[5]	LSP2[4]	LSP2[3]	LSP2[2]	LSP2[1]	LSP3[5]	LSP3[4]	LSP3[3]	Octet P+1
LSP3[2]	LSP3[1]	P1[8]	P1[7]	P1[6]	P1[5]	P1[4]	P1[3]	Octet P+2
P1[2]	P1[1]	P0	C1[13]	C1[12]	C1[11]	C1[10]	C1[09]	
C1[08]	C1[07]	C1[06]	C1[05]	C1[04]	C1[03]	C1[02]	C1[01]	
S1[04]	S1[03]	S1[02]	S1[01]	GA1[03]	GA1[02]	GA1[01]	GB1[04]	
GB1[03]	GB1[02]	GB1[01]	P2[05]	P2[04]	P2[03]	P2[02]	P2[01]	Frame 1
C2[13]	C2[12]	C2[11]	C2[10]	C2[09]	C2[08]	C2[07]	C2[06]	
C2[05]	C2[04]	C2[03]	C2[02]	C2[01]	S2[04]	S2[03]	S2[02]	
S2[01]	GA2[03]	GA2[02]	GA2[01]	GB2[04]	GB2[03]	GB2[02]	GB2[01]	

⋮

LSP0	LSP1[7]	LSP1[6]	LSP1[5]	LSP1[4]	LSP1[3]	LSP1[2]	LSP1[1]	
LSP2[5]	LSP2[4]	LSP2[3]	LSP2[2]	LSP2[1]	LSP3[5]	LSP3[4]	LSP3[3]	
LSP3[2]	LSP3[1]	P1[8]	P1[7]	P1[6]	P1[5]	P1[4]	P1[3]	
P1[2]	P1[1]	P0	C1[13]	C1[12]	C1[11]	C1[10]	C1[09]	Frame M
C1[08]	C1[07]	C1[06]	C1[05]	C1[04]	C1[03]	C1[02]	C1[01]	
S1[04]	S1[03]	S1[02]	S1[01]	GA1[03]	GA1[02]	GA1[01]	GB1[04]	
GB1[03]	GB1[02]	GB1[01]	P2[05]	P2[04]	P2[03]	P2[02]	P2[01]	
C2[13]	C2[12]	C2[11]	C2[10]	C2[09]	C2[08]	C2[07]	C2[06]	Octet P+N-2
C2[05]	C2[04]	C2[03]	C2[02]	C2[01]	S2[04]	S2[03]	S2[02]	Octet P+N-1
S2[01]	GA2[03]	GA2[02]	GA2[01]	GB2[04]	GB2[03]	GB2[02]	GB2[01]	Octet P+N

Where:
P = First octet of payload
M = Number of 10 ms Frames
N = Number of octets in Voice Information Field = M*10

E.4   Transfer Characteristics

Packetization Time: M*10 ms

Figure E-4
CS-ACELP transfer
characteristics.

Algorithm Name	Reference Document	Compression Rate	Frame Size
CS-ACELP	ITU G.729	8 kbit/s	M*10

E.5   Optional Sequence Number

Transmission of sequence numbers may be configured on a sub-channel basis. When enabled, the voice transfer syntax defined in Figure E-3 is encapsulated in the Voice Transfer Structure field of the Active Voice Payload shown in Figure F-2. The Sequence Number of Figure F-2 shall be incremented every 10 msec. The Coding Type field of Figure F-2 shall be set to 0000.

Annex F—Generic PCM/ADPCM Voice Transfer Syntax

F.1   Reference Documents

[1]   ITU G.711   Pulse Code Modulation of Voice Frequencies, 1988

[2]   ITU G.726   40, 32, 24, 16 kbit/s Adaptive Differential Pulse Code Modulation (ADPCM), March 1996

[3]   ITU G.727   5-, 4-, 3-, and 2-bits Sample Embedded Adaptive Differential Pulse Code Modulation, November 1994

[4]   ITU G.764   Voice packetization—Packetized voice protocols, December 1990

F.2   Voice Transfer Structure

Encoded voice samples—G.711 (PCM), G.726 (ADPCM), or G.727 (EAD-PCM)—shall be inserted into the structure defined by Figure F-1. The

Figure F-1
PCM/ADPCM/EAD-
PCM Voice Transfer
Structure (showing
case of M = 1).

Bit number	8	7	...	1	
MSB block	MSB/S8	MSB/S7	...	MSB/S1	P+5
			·		
			·		
	MSB/S40	MSB/S39	...	MSB/S33	
MSB-1 block	(MSB-1)/S8	(MSB-1)/S7	...	(MSB-1)/S1	
			·		
			·		
	(MSB-1)/S40	(MSB-1)/S39	...	(MSB-1)/S33	
· · ·			· · ·		
LSB block	LSB/S8	LSB/S7	...	LSB/S1	
			·		
			·		
	LSB/S40	LSB/S39	...	LSB/S33	Octet N

transfer of PCM/ADPCM/EADPCM is inspired by ITU-T Recommendation G.764. The following sections define two payload types and the Voice Transfer Structure.

The voice transfer structure contains blocks arranged according to the significance of the bits. The first block contains the MSBs of all the encoded samples; the second contains the second MSBs and so on. Within a block, the bits are ordered according to their sample number. Since the 5 ms encoding interval corresponds to 40 samples, each block contains 5 octets.

A particular feature of this structure is that non-critical (enhancement) information is placed in locations where it can easily be discarded, without impacting the critical (core) information. For example, if 32 kbit/s EADPCM (G.727 (4, 2)) is used, then there will be four blocks corresponding to four bits of varying significance (msb, msb-1, msb-2, lsb). The least significant blocks (msb-2, lsb) are the enhancement blocks and may be discarded under congestion conditions.

Annex G describes a related way of placing the critical and non-critical information into separate frames, so that the enhancement blocks can be marked with Discard Eligibility.

The size of the voice transfer structure depends on the packing factor M and the coding type, as shown in Figure F-4. The packing factor is a multiple from one to 12. The value of M is configured identically at transmitter and receiver. It is typically, but not necessarily, the same in both directions. Equipment complying with this transfer syntax shall be configurable to support the default value M = 1.

When M is greater than 1, the voice transfer structure contains a first set of blocks, ordered from MSB to LSB, followed by a second set of blocks, ordered likewise, and so on up to the Mth set of blocks.

F.3 Active Voice Payload

When the Payload Type is Primary Payload, other fields in the sub-frame are as shown. The voice transfer structure containing encoded voice samples is defined in section F.2.

Figure F-2
PCM/ADPCM/EAD-
PCM Steady State
Payload

Bits

8	7	6	5	4	3	2	1	Octet
Sequence Number				Coding Type				P
Voice Transfer Structure								P+1

F.3.1 Coding Type

The coding type field indicates the method of encoding PCM/ADPCM/EADPCM voice samples into the voice transfer structure.

The transmitting end-system shall only encode using algorithms for which there is decode support at the receiving end-system. The algorithms supported by the receiver are known by mutual configuration.

Values of the Coding Type field are defined in Figure F-4.

F.3.2 Sequence Number

The sequence number is used to maintain temporal integrity of voice played out by the receiving end-system. For PCM/ADPCM/EADPCM, the underlying encoding interval is 5 ms. Voice samples are processed with this periodicity and the sequence number is incremented by 1. After a count of 15 is reached the sequence number rolls back to 0.

The sequence number is incremented every 5 milliseconds, even when there is no active voice to be sent. This would be the case during a silence insertion period, if voice activity detection were operational. The peer end-system expects to receive voice samples in sequence and within a certain time period. If voice activity detection is operational and no active voice is received, the peer end-system will continue increment its expected sequence number every 5 ms.

When multiple voice samples are received in a single subframe (M > 1), the next expected sequence number is incremented by M.

F.4   Silence Insertion Descriptor (SID) Payload

When the Payload Type is Primary Payload with Silence Insertion, other fields in the sub-frame are as shown in Figure F-3.

Figure F-3
PCM/ADPCM/EAD-PCM Silence Insertion Descriptor (SID) payload.

				Bits				
8	7	6	5	4	3	2	1	Octet
Sequence Number				Reserved				P
Reserved		Noise Level						P+1

F.4.1   Reserved

This field is set to 000000 by the transmitter and is ignored at the receiver.

F.4.2   Sequence Number

This field is the same as defined in F.3.2.

F.4.3   Noise Level

The background noise level is expressed in -dBm0. The receiver can use this field to play out an appropriate level of background noise in the absence of active voice.

Additional sub-frames of this type may be sent if the noise level changes or may be sent redundantly to increase the probability of being received.

This payload type should not be sent if voice activity detection is not operational.

F.5   Transfer Characteristics

Encoding interval: 5 ms

Packing factor: M = 1 to 12

Support of M = 4 is required. A range of 1 to 12 can optionally be supported.

Figure F-4
PCM/ADPCM/
EADPCM transfer
characteristics.

Coding Type	Algorithm Name	Reference Document	Compression Bit Rate (kbit/s)	Voice Transfer Structure (Octets)
0000	PCM A-law	ITU G.711	64	40*M
0001	"	"	56	35*M
0010	"	"	48	30*M
0011	PCM u-law	"	64	40*M
0100	"	"	56	35*M
0101	"	"	48	30*M
0110	ADPCM	ITU G.726	40	25*M
0111	"	"	32	20*M
1000	"	"	24	15*M
1001	"	"	16	10*M
1010	EADPCM (5,2)	ITU G.727	40	25*M
1011	(4,2)	"	32	20*M
1100	(3,2)	"	24	15*M
1101	(2,2)	"	16	10*M

Annex G—G.727 DISCARD-ELIGIBLE EADPCM VOICE Transfer Syntax

G.1 Reference Documents

[1] ITU G.727   5-, 4-, 3-, and 2-bits Sample Embedded Adaptive Differential Pulse Code Modulation, November 1994

G.2 Voice Transfer Structure

The voice transfer structure is the same as defined in Annex F.

G.3 Active Voice Payload

The G.727 EADPCM compression algorithm outputs core and enhancement information. This information is separately assembled into blocks.

Core information is inserted into frames with low discard eligibility (DE = 0), and enhancement information inserted into frames with high discard eligibility (DE = 1).

Core and enhancement information, if required by a particular traffic type, may be combined within a single frame with DE = 0.

When the Payload Type is Primary Payload, other fields in the sub-frame are as shown in Figure G-1. The voice transfer structure containing encoded voice samples is defined in Annex F.

Figure G-1 shows only two sub-frames, one each for core and enhancement information, but transmitters are explicitly allowed to use the VoFR header to pack multiple sub-frames of the same kind of information into each frame, with DE = 0 or 1, correspondingly.

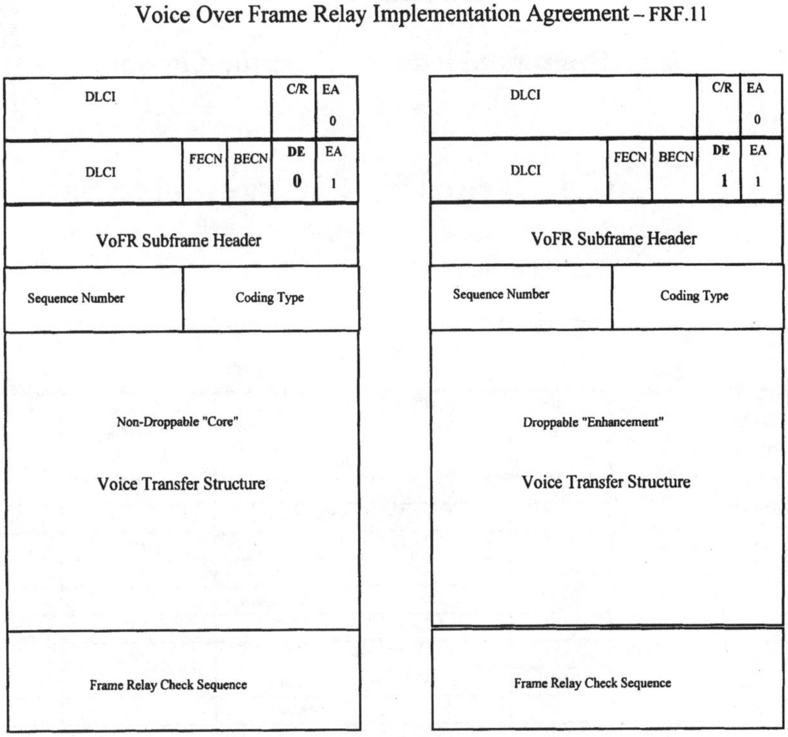

Figure G-1
Discard-Eligible EAD-PCM Steady State Payload (showing single sub-frames).

Voice Over Frame Relay Implementation Agreement – FRF.11

G.3.1 Coding Type

The coding type field indicates the method of encoding EADPCM voice samples into the voice transfer structure.

The transmitting end system shall only encode using algorithms for which there is decode support at the receiving end system. The algorithms supported by the receiver are known by mutual configuration.

Values of the Coding Type field are defined in Figure G-2.

G.3.2 Sequence Number

This field is the same as defined in Annex F.

G.4 Silence Insertion Descriptor (SID) Payload

This payload is the same as defined in Annex F.

G.5 Transfer Characteristics

Encoding interval: 5 ms

Packing factor: M = 1 to 12

Figure G-2
Discard-eligible
EADPCM transfer
characteristics.

Coding Type	Algorithm Name	Type of Information	Compression Bit Rate (kbit/s)	Voice Transfer Structure (Octets)
0000	EADPCM (2,2)	Core	16	10*M
0001	(3,2)	Enhancement	8	5*M
0010	(4,2)	"	16	10*M
0011	(5,2)	"	24	15*M
0100	(3,2)	Combined	24	15*M
0101	(4,2)	"	32	20*M
0110	(5,2)	"	40	25*M
0111	EADPCM (3,3)	Core	24	15*M
1000	(4,3)	Enhancement	8	5*M
1001	(5,3)	"	16	10*M
1010	(4,3)	Combined	32	20*M
1011	(5,3)	"	40	25*M
1100	EADPCM (4,4)	Core	32	20*M
1101	(5,4)	Enhancement	8	5*M
1110	(5,4)	Combined	40	25*M

Annex H—G.728 LD-CELP Transfer Syntax

H.1 Reference Documents

[1] ITU G.728   Coding of Speech At 16 kbit/s Using Low-Delay Code
                    Excited Linear Prediction, November 1994

H.2 Voice Transfer Structure

Voice samples that are compressed using 16 kbit/s LD-CELP (G.728) will be inserted into the voice transfer structure defined in Figure H-1. The LD-CELP compression algorithm produces a 10-bit code-word vector for every 5 samples of input speech from an 8000 sample/sec. stream. The 10 bits are reformatted to fit within the octet structure of the Voice Transfer Structure. Every group of five octets contains four, 10-bit code-words resulting in a 2.5 ms duration sub-frame. Two of these 2.5 ms groups are combined into a 5 ms block for transmission. The MSB of the first 10-bit code-word is aligned with the MSB of the first octet in the block. Subsequent bits of the code-word are placed in descending bit locations of the first octet with the other bits of subsequent code-words being bit packed into the remaining octets. Each block consists of eight 10-bit code-words which are mapped into 10 octets.

H.3 Transfer Protocol

The size of the voice transfer structure depends on the packing factor M. The packing factor is a multiple from 1 to 12. The value of M is configured identically at transmitter and receiver. It is typically, but not necessarily, the same in both directions. Equipment complying with this transfer syntax shall be configurable to support the value M = 1 to 12.

When M is greater than 1, the voice transfer structure contains multiple blocks, starting with the first encoded voice sample and ending with the last encoded voice sample.

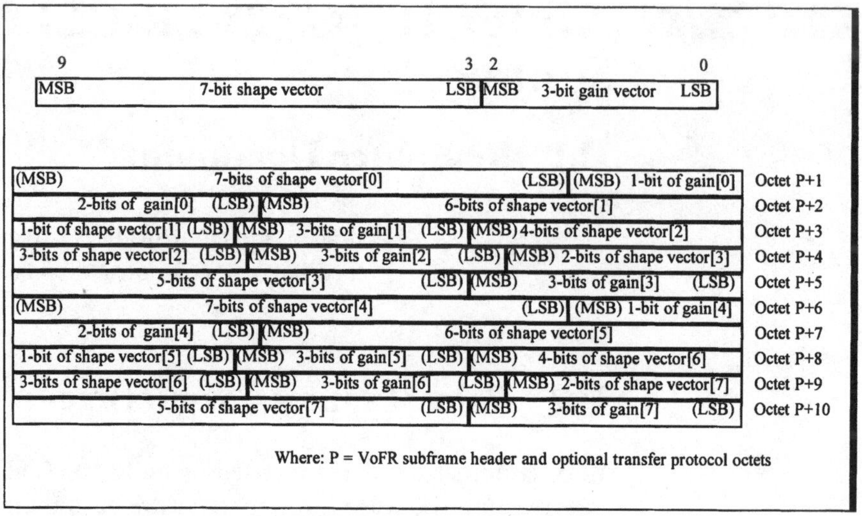

Figure H-1
LD-CELP Voice
Transfer Structure
(showing case of
M = 1).

9			3	2		0
MSB	7-bit shape vector		LSB	MSB	3-bit gain vector	LSB

(MSB) 7-bits of shape vector[0] (LSB) (MSB) 1-bit of gain[0]	Octet P+1
2-bits of gain[0] (LSB) (MSB) 6-bits of shape vector[1]	Octet P+2
1-bit of shape vector[1] (LSB) (MSB) 3-bits of gain[1] (LSB) (MSB) 4-bits of shape vector[2]	Octet P+3
3-bits of shape vector[2] (LSB) (MSB) 3-bits of gain[2] (LSB) (MSB) 2-bits of shape vector[3]	Octet P+4
5-bits of shape vector[3] (LSB) (MSB) 3-bits of gain[3] (LSB)	Octet P+5
(MSB) 7-bits of shape vector[4] (LSB) (MSB) 1-bit of gain[4]	Octet P+6
2-bits of gain[4] (LSB) (MSB) 6-bits of shape vector[5]	Octet P+7
1-bit of shape vector[5] (LSB) (MSB) 3-bits of gain[5] (LSB) (MSB) 4-bits of shape vector[6]	Octet P+8
3-bits of shape vector[6] (LSB) (MSB) 3-bits of gain[6] (LSB) (MSB) 2-bits of shape vector[7]	Octet P+9
5-bits of shape vector[7] (LSB) (MSB) 3-bits of gain[7] (LSB)	Octet P+10

Where: P = VoFR subframe header and optional transfer protocol octets

H.4 Transfer Characteristics

Encoding interval: 5 ms

Packing factor: M = 1 to 12

Other Capabilities:

In-Band Tone Handling—Can pass 2400 baud Modem Signals & DTMF

Figure H-2
LD-CELP transfer
characteristics.

Algorithm Name	Reference Document	Compression Bit Rate	Voice Transfer Structure
LD-CELP	ITU G.728	16 kbit/s	10*M octets

H.5 Optional Sequence Number

Transmission of sequence numbers may be configured on a sub-channel basis. When enabled, the voice transfer syntax defined in Figure H-1 is encapsulated in the Voice Transfer Structure field of the Active Voice Payload shown in Figure F-2. The Sequence Number of Figure F-2 shall be incremented every 10 msec. The Coding Type field of Figure F-2 shall be set to 0000.

Annex I—G.723.1 MP-MLQ Dual Rate Speech Coder

I.1   Reference Document

[1]   ITU G.723.1   Dual Rate Speech Coder for Multimedia Communications Transmitting at 5.3 & 6.3 kbit/s, March 1996

I.2   Transfer Structure

Voice samples that are compressed using the 6.3 kbit/s MP-MLQ algorithm (G.723.1 high rate) and 5.3 kbit/s ACELP algorithm (G.723.1 low rate) yield a frame of packed parameters for every 240 samples of input speech from a 8000 sample/sec stream. Some of these parameters are based on an analysis of the entire frame; others are based on the analyses of each of the four component 60 sample sub-frames. Figure I-1 shows of list of transmitted parameters for both MP-MLQ and ACELP.

For MP-MLQ, the resulting 191-bit frame is formatted to fit within the 24 octet structure of the Voice Information Field (one bit is unused) as defined in Figure I-2. For ACELP, the resulting 160-bit frame is formatted to fit within the 20 octet structure of the Voice Information Field as defined in Figure I-1. In Figure I-2 and Figure I-3, each bit of transmitted

Figure I-1
List of transmitted parameters.

Name	Transmitted parameters	high rate	low rate # bits
LPC	LSP VQ index	24	24
ACL0	Adaptive Code-Book Lag	7	7
ACL1	Differential Adaptive Code-Book Lag	2	2
ACL2	Adaptive Code-Book Lag	7	7
ACL3	Differential Adaptive Code-Book Lag	2	2
GAIN0	Combination of adaptive and fixed gains	12	12
GAIN1	Combination of adaptive and fixed gains	12	12
GAIN2	Combination of adaptive and fixed gains	12	12
GAIN3	Combination of adaptive and fixed gains	12	12
POS0	Pulse positions index	20*	12
POS1	Pulse positions index	18*	12
POS2	Pulse positions index	20*	12
POS3	Pulse positions index	18*	12
PSIG0	Pulse sign index	6	4
PSIG1	Pulse sign index	5	4
PSIG2	Pulse sign index	6	4
PSIG3	Pulse sign index	5	4
GRID0	Grid index	1	1
GRID1	Grid index	1	1
GRID2	Grid index	1	1
GRID3	Grid index	1	1

*Note: The 4 msb of these code-words are combined to form a 13 bit index, msb Position

▬ ▬ ▬ ▬

Figure I-2

Octet Packing for the
6.3 kbps MP-MLQ
codec.

TRANSMITTED	PARx_By, ...
1	LPC_B5...LPC_B0, VADFLAG_B0, RATEFLAG_B0
2	LPC_B13...LPC_B6
3	LPC_B21...LPC_B14
4	ACL0_B5...ACL0_B0, LPC_B23, LPC_B22
5	ACL2_B4...ACL2_B0, ACL1_B1, ACL1_B0, ACL0_B6
6	GAIN0_B3...GAIN0_B0, ACL3_B1, ACL3_B0, ACL2_B6, ACL2_B5
7	GAIN0_B11...GAIN0_B4
8	GAIN1_B7...GAIN1_B0
9	GAIN2_B3...GAIN2_B0, GAIN1_B11...GAIN1_B8
10	GAIN2_B11...GAIN2_B4
11	GAIN3_B7...GAIN3_B0
12	GRID3_B0, GRID2_B0, GRID1_B0, GRID0_B0, GAIN3_B11...GAIN3_B8
13	MSBPOS_B6...MSBPOS_B0, UB
14	POS0_B1, POS0_B0, MSBPOS_B12...MSBPOS_B7
15	POS0_B9...POS0_B2
16	POS1_B2, POS1_B0, POS0_B15...POS0_B10
17	POS1_B10...POS1_B3
18	POS2_B3...POS2_B0, POS1_B13...POS1_B11
19	POS2_B11...POS2_B4
20	POS3_B3...POS3_B0, POS2_B15...POS2_B12
21	POS3_B11...POS3_B4
22	PSIG0_B5...PSIG0_B0, POS3_B13, POS3_B12
23	PSIG2_B2...PSIG2_B0, PSIG1_B4...PSIG1_B0
24	PSIG3_B4...PSIG3_B0, PSIG2_B5...PSIG2_B3

Voice Over Frame Relay Implementation Agreement – FRF.11

▬ ▬ ▬ ▬

Figure I-3

Octet Packing for
the 5.3 kbps ACELP
codec.

TRANSMITTED OCTETS	PARx_By, ...
1	LPC_B5...LPC_B0, VADFLAG_B0, RATEFLAG_B0
2	LPC_B13...LPC_B6
3	LPC_B21...LPC_B14
4	ACL0_B5...ACL0_B0, LPC_B23, LPC_B22
5	ACL2_B4...ACL2_B0, ACL1_B1, ACL1_B0, ACL0_B6
6	GAIN0_B3...GAIN0_B0, ACL3_B1, ACL3_B0, ACL2_B6, ACL2_B5
7	GAIN0_B11...GAIN0_B4
8	GAIN1_B7...GAIN1_B0
9	GAIN2_B3...GAIN2_B0, GAIN1_B11...GAIN1_B8
10	GAIN2_B11...GAIN2_B4
11	GAIN3_B7...GAIN3_B0
12	GRID3_B0, GRID2_B0, GRID1_B0, GRID0_B0, GAIN3_B11...GAIN3_B8
13	POS0_B7...POS0_B0
14	POS1_B3...POS1_B0, POS0_B11...POS0_B8
15	POS1_B11...POS1_B4
16	POS2_B7...POS2_B0
17	POS3_B3...POS3_B0, POS2_B11...POS2_B8
18	POS3_B11...POS3_B4
19	PSIG1_B3...PSIG1_B0, PSIG0_B3...PSIG0_B0
20	PSIG3_B3...PSIG3_B0, PSIG2_B3...PSIG2_B0

parameters is named PAR(x)_By: where PAR is the name of the parameter and x indicates the G.721 sub-frame index if relevant and y stands for the bit position starting from 0 (lsb) to the msb.

The expression PARx_ByPARx_Bz stands for the range of transmitted bits from bit y to bit z. The unused bit is named UB (value = 0). RATE-

FLAG_B0 tells whether the high rate (0) or the low rate (1) is used for the current frame. VADFLAG_B0 tells whether the current frame is active speech (0) or non-speech (1). The combination of RATEFLAG and VAD-FLAG both being set to 1 is reserved for future use. Octets are transmitted in the order in which they are listed in Figure I-2 and Figure I-3. Within each octet shown, the bits are ordered with the most significant bit on the left.

I.3   Transfer Protocol

When the VoFR service user offers a frame of sampled speech it is immediately transmitted using the transfer structure described above in Section I.2.

I.4   Transfer Characteristics

Packetization Time: 30 ms

Other Capabilities:
    In-Band Tone Handling—Can pass DTMF

Figure I-4
MP-MLQ and
ACELP transfer
characteristics.

Algorithm Name	Reference Document	Compression Rate	Frame Size
MP-MLQ	ITU G.723.1	6.3 kbit/s	24 octets
ACELP	ITU G.723.1	5.3 kbit/s	20 octets

I.5   Optional Sequence Number

Transmission of sequence numbers may be configured on a sub-channel basis. When enabled, the voice transfer syntax defined in Section I.2 is encapsulated in the Voice Transfer Structure field of the Active Voice Payload shown in Figure F-2. The Sequnce Number of Figure F-2 shall be incremented every 10 msec. The Coding Type field of Figure F-2 shall be set to 0000.

APPENDIX B

APPENDIX B

To facilitate reference to the Application Notes found throughout the text, this appendix provides a compilation of all the Notes.

APPLICATION NOTES

1. Introduction

   If using access control lists, move your voice-related   **14**
   statements toward the top of the list.

   Encryption adds to the delay of packets transporting   **16**
   digitized voice and should be employed only when
   absolutely necessary.

   Understanding the delays associated with access and egress .   **25**
   lines, different voice-compression methods, and the network
   provides the ability to consider different techniques to reduce
   overall latency

2. IP and Related Protocols

   Within an IP network, routers periodically transfer the   **40**
   contents of their routing tables, during which time the
   transmission of data, including voice-digitized packets, is
   suspended. Because edge routers commonly are connected
   only to an ISP router, you should consider configuring the
   edge router for static routing. This will preclude the transfer
   of router table entries and the resulting delays to traffic such
   table transfers cause.

   For transporting voice over IP, you will normally be more   **44**
   concerned with the effect of delay than with that of periodic
   packet dropping, because real-time voice cannot be
   retransmitted. For this reason, you should configure your
   application to set the TOS field in the Service Type byte to a
   value of 1000, which minimizes delay.

   The translation of IP addresses by a router or firewall adds a **53**
   slight delay to packets as they flow through the device. If

your voice over IP application is stretched toward the maximum amount of tolerable delay, you may wish to consider placing stations that depend upon the application on their own network, which avoids the necessity of network address translation and its delay.

Although modern routers are based on relatively fast microprocessor technology, it is important to remember that most networks include routers manufactured three, four, or even five years ago. Although they may provide a high level of support for traditional data transfer operations, if you are using subnetting, the extra cycles may add several milliseconds of delay that could represent the figurative straw that breaks the back of a real-time voice transport application. Instead of replacing the router, you might want to consider placing stations requiring real-time voice transport on their own network, thus avoiding the extra cycles associated with subnet processing.

59

Many routers and workstations run operating systems that dynamically update the ARP cache. This means that old entries are purged to make space available for new entries. This also means that if an entry for a voice gateway is purged, and then the layer 2 address requires resolution for an inbound packet transporting digitized voice, there will be a delay as a router attempts to resolve the layer 3 address to a layer 2 address so it can transmit the packet to the gateway.

69

To avoid ARP delays to devices that operate on digitized voice packets, consider configuring permanent ARP entries in your router that support communications to such devices. Doing so will eliminate the delay associated with the address resolution protocol and may shave a few additional milliseconds off end-to-end communications.

There are currently no standards concerning the use of different UDP port numbers for the transmission of digitized voice. This means that there exists a high degree of probability that different applications will use different UDP ports. This also means that if you use a router access list or firewall to enable certain applications to flow into

73

and out of your private network, you will have multiple statements that require checking, adding a delay to delay-sensitive digitized voice packets. The best way to minimize this delay is to standardize on one or two products instead of having your router or firewall administrator enter literally dozens of statements to support a large number of products. Another technique is to move your UDP checking statements toward the top of your access list statements, positioning them directly below any antispoofing address statements to minimize delay

3. Frame Relay

When considering voice over frame relay, the ability to initiate a service-level agreement (SLA) that guarantees a maximum end-to-end latency through the network enables you to develop a predictable voice transport mechanism. **93**

When considering a service-level agreement covering delay, make sure the agreement covers latency on an end-to-end basis. **96**

If you have a choice between using a FRAD and a router to access a frame relay network and intend to transmit voice, use a FRAD. Doing so will eliminate IP encapsulation, which results in a significant degree of overhead that especially adds to latency when access to the network occurs over relatively low-speed fractional T1 lines. **100**

4. Understanding Voice

Although PCM has the highest bandwidth of all voice coding techniques, its encoding latency is practically negligible, with an encoding delay under 1 microsecond, which for comparison purposes is several thousand times lower than low-delay hybrid coders. **126**

The predictor and summation operations performed by ADPCM increase its latency over PCM by approximately 25 percent. However, this results in only a 125 µs delay, which is relatively insignificant when compared to the delay associated with many hybrid coding techniques. **130**

G.728-compatible coders are referred to as *Low Delay* CELP (LD-CELP) because their 2.5-ms latency is the lowest of all members of the CELP family of coders.

137

Although the use of a CS-ACELP coder results in half the bandwidth of LD-CELP, the coding delay increases from approximately 2.5 ms to 15.0 ms.

138

5. Telephone Operations

To prevent disruptive echo from being returned to the speaker, voice-compliant routers, FRADs, and gateways should perform echo cancellation when used to establish a voice over IP or voice over frame relay transmission path that exceeds 50 miles in length.

149

When planning to interconnect a voice gateway to the switched telephone network in a foreign country, you should determine the make/break ratio and pulses-per-second rate required for pulse dialing.

152

Prior to connecting equipment to a PBX or the switched network in a foreign location, it is important to verify the compatibility of the equipment with call-progress signaling frequencies. Doing so ahead of time can alleviate a considerable amount of potential frustration.

153

6. Voice over IP Networking

Consider varying the use of different audio codecs as a mechanism to determine if a more suitable codec is available for use.

176

Coordinate the use of Internet telephony products on a LAN with your organization's firewall and router administrators. Many times, Internet telephony products will fail to operate due to the ports they use being blocked by a router access list and/or a firewall.

179

Many gateways and other Internet telephony products include a selectable jitter buffer, with users able to set a delay from 0 (disabled) to 255 ms or more. When setting a selectable jitter buffer, it is important to remember that

190

while an increase in the jitter buffer setting can improve the clarity of small blocks of reconstructed speech, the increase adds to the overall one-way delay. If there is too much delay, a person on one side of the conversation may believe the other party has stopped speaking and so may begin to talk, thus creating a "voice clash" and a requirement for both parties to listen.

7. Voice over Frame Relay

GLOSSARY

Address resolution process The conversion of a layer 3 address to a layer 2 address and vice versa.

Address signaling A type of signaling that provides the telephone number that enables calls to be routed to their destination. Two types of address signaling are *dial pulse* and *dual-tone multifrequency.*

ADPCM Adaptive Differential Pulse Code Modulation. A waveform voice digitization technique in which a predictor is used to estimate sample height, allowing data rates of 32, 24, and 16 Kbps.

Antispoofing A technique that prevents a person from being able to transmit data into a network using the source address or RFC 1918 addresses in their packets.

Authentication The process of verifying the originator of a transmission. One common method for authentication is the assignment of a password to a userid, with a person entering his or her userid and then being prompted to enter a password.

Backbone network The major transmission path for a network interconnection.

Backward-explicit congestion notification (BECN) A bit setting in a frame relay frame used to indicate congestion. The notification flows backward to the originator of the transmission.

Broadband A data transmission technique allowing multiple high-speed signals to share the bandwidth of a single cable via frequency division multiplexing.

Broadcast A method of communications in which the source sends a single copy of a message that is read by each station on the network.

Broadcast domain The part of a network that receives the same broadcasts.

Call control operations Procedures that control the establishment and teardown of a call.

Call management Information concerning the activity of calls, including time of day and duration, that is used by management for analysis.

Call-progress signaling Signaling that indicates the progress of a voice call, such as fast busy, busy, and ringing.

Call-waiting　A signal placed on an active telephone line to inform the party that another call has arrived and is presently on hold.

Carrier Sense Multiple Access with Collision Detection (CSMA/CD)　The channel access method used by Ethernet networks. Under CSMA/CD, a station listens for an idle channel and then begins transmission. If two or more stations transmit at the same time, a collision occurs that, when detected, results in a random period of waiting for each station prior to attempting to retransmit.

CELP　Code Excited Linear Predictor. A series of voice coding techniques based on analysis and synthesis of speech.

Central office (CO)　A term used to reference a location where telephone company switches are located. The central office that is directly connected to subscribers is commonly referred to as an *end office*.

Channel　The data path between two nodes.

Channel service unit (CSU)　A device that converts unipolar signaling into bipolar signaling and inserts framing bits according to the requirements of the digital transmission facility to which CSU is attached.

Charge-back　The process of billing users for services used.

Class A IP address　A 32-bit address that uses the first 8 bits to define the network and the following 24 bits to define the host on the network.

Class B IP address　A 32-bit address that uses the first 16 bits to define the network and the following 16 bits to define the host on the network.

Class C IP address　A 32-bit address that uses the first 24 bits to define the network and the following 8 bits to define the host on the network.

Class D IP address　A 32-bit address used to define a multicast session. Class D IP addresses are in the range 224.0.0.0 to 239.255.255.255.

Class E IP address　A 32-bit address used for experimental purposes.

Client　The requestor or initiator of data, typically from a server.

Command-line interface　A method of interacting with a computer program by typing commands.

Committed burst size (B_c)　The amount of data in bits per second that a frame relay network agrees to transfer under normal network conditions.

Committed information rate (CIR)　The guaranteed transmission rate on a frame relay private virtual channel (PVC).

Common associated signaling A method of voice signaling in which bit positions in the digitized voice stream are "robbed" to convey the signaling information.

Common channel signaling The transmission of signaling information on a separate channel from that used to convey voice.

Conference A multiparty conversation.

Congestion notification (CN) A bit position in the ATM cell set in which the network is experiencing congestion.

Connection A transport layer virtual circuit established between two programs for the purpose of communications.

Connectionless protocol A type of network protocol that allows a host to transmit a message without first having to establish a connection with the recipient. UDP and the Simple Network Management Protocol (SNMP) are examples of connectionless, best-effort protocols.

Connection-oriented protocol A protocol that requires the establishment of a channel between the sender and recipient prior to data being transferred. The telephone, TCP, and the HyperText Transmission Protocol (HTTP) are examples of connection-oriented protocols.

CPE Customer-premises equipment.

CVSD Continuously variable slope delta modulation. A waveform voice-digitization technique in which the relative height of the analog signal sample is encoded in 1 bit. A 0 is encoded if the voltage is less that the reference level, while a 1 is encoded if the voltage is greater than the reference.

Data circuit terminating equipment (DCE) An interface included in modems and similar devices that provides clocking as well as compatibility with the DTE.

Data Exchange Interface (DXI) A protocol that permits frame relay to be carried over an ATM network, with a CSU/DSU providing the frame-to-cell conversion.

Datagram Under Ipv4, the term represents the format of a packet, including the IP header, the layer 4 header, and subsequent data.

Data terminal equipment (DTE) An interface typically included in routers and terminal devices that governs the manner by which signaling and data transfer occurs from the DTE.

Dial register An area within a PBX or telephone company switch where dialed digits are stored.

Digital signal processors (DSPs)   A specially designed chip that converts analog signals to digital.

Discard eligible (DE)   A bit setting in a frame relay frame that indicates the frame can be discarded when the network experiences congestion.

Domain Name Service (DNS)   The name service of the TCP/IP protocol suite that provides translation between host names and IP addresses. DNS also represents an Internet hierarchical database that provides the address translation capability.

DTE/DCE   The interface between data terminal equipment (DTE) and data circuit terminating equipment (DCE).

E lead   The "ear" lead on a telephone handset.

E&M signaling   The most common type of analog trunk signaling. There are five types of E&M signaling.

E1   The European basic digital line structured to transport 30 voice-digitized conversations, each operating at 64 Kbps, and separate signaling and control channels, each also operating at 64 Kbps, for a bit rate of 2.048 Mbps.

Echo cancellation   A technique used to isolate and filter unwanted reflected or echoed signal energy typically resulting from hybrids that convert two-wire to four-wire circuits.

Excess burst size (B_e)   The maximum amount of uncommitted data in bits above the committed burst size that a frame relay network will attempt to deliver during time interval T_c, which is normally a 1-second time interval.

Far-end echo   The reflection of energy by the hybrid located in the central office serving the called party.

Fast Ethernet   The name used to reference the 100-Mbps version of Ethernet.

Forward-explicit congestion notification (FECN)   A bit setting in a frame relay frame transmitted upstream to indicate the network experienced congestion.

Fragment   A portion of a packet or frame. Often a part of an Ethernet frame resulting from a collision. In IP terminology, *fragment* means a packet resulting from the subdivision of a larger packet into a series of smaller ones.

Fragmentation   The process of breaking a frame that exceeds a predefined length into two or more smaller frames to minimize their effect upon frames transporting voice.

Frame In telecommunications, a unit of data that is transmitted between network points complete with addressing and necessary protocol control information.

Frame-based User-to-Network Interface (FUNI) A protocol that permits frame relay to be transported over an ATM network, with the conversion of frames to cells occuring at the ATM switch.

Frame loss handling The method by which vendor equipment compensates for lost frames carrying voice. Some equipment does nothing, generating a period of silence. Other equipment generates noise or uses the contents of the prior frame in an interpolation process to generate speech.

Frame relay A packet switching technique that operates at layer 2 of the OSI Reference Model and does not provide error checking at nodes or flow control, discarding packets when network congestion occurs.

Frame Relay Forum An association that promotes the use of frame relay and develops implementation agreements (IAs) to facilitate interoperability between different vendor equipment.

Frequency The rate of signal oscillation in hertz (Hz).

FS 1016 The U.S. Department of Defense standardized version of CELP that operates at 4.8 Kbps.

Full-duplex The ability to simultaneously transmit and receive data.

Gateway A device that converts the format of packets and/or their contents so they can flow from one network to another.

Glare A condition in which a trunk is seized from both sides.

Ground-start signaling A trunk signaling method that modifies local loop-start signaling by providing a current-detection method at each end of the trunk to eliminate the possibility of both ends being seized at the same time.

G.711 The ITU standard for PCM.

G.721 The ITU standard for ADPCM.

G.723.1 The ITU standard for a version of CELP for transmission via packet networks, supporting both 5.3- and 6.3-Kbps operating rates.

G.728 The ITU standard for a 16-Kbps low-delay version of CELP.

G.729 The ITU standard for a low-bit-rate version of CELP that operates at 8 Kbps.

Half-duplex The ability to transmit or receive; however, only one action can occur at a time.

Hertz   A frequency unit equal to one cycle per second.

Hybrid   A two- to four-wire converter used to connect subscriber loops to trunks.

Hybrid coding   A voice coding method that attempts to match analyzed speech parameters via synthesis, resulting in high-quality, low-bit-rate digitized voice.

IEEE   Institute of Electrical and Electronic Engineers.

Immediate-start signaling   A trunk signaling method in which the originating switch places the trunk in an off-hook condition and maintains that condition for at least 150 ms, after which the switch outputs the address digits.

Informational signaling   Signaling that informs the originator of the status of a dialed call. Also referred to as *call-progress signaling*.

iNOW!   An organization that promotes interoperability of Internet telephony standards.

Internet Assigned Numbers Authority (IANA)   The central coordinator for the assignment of unique parameter values for Internet protocols. The Internet Society (ISOC) and the Federal Network Council (FNC) charter the IANA to act as the clearinghouse to assign and coordinate the use of numerous Internet protocol parameters.

Internet datagram   The unit of data exchanged between an Internet module and the higher-level protocol together with the Internet header.

Internet Engineering Task Force (IETF)   An international group of network designers, operators, vendors, and researchers, closely aligned to the Internet Architecture Board and chartered to work on the design and engineering of TCP/IP and the global Internet. The IETF is divided into groups or areas, each with a manager, and is open to any interested individual.

Internet Group Management Protocol (IGMP)   Multicast routers use this protocol to learn the existence of host group members on their directly attached subnets. IP hosts use IGMP to report their host group memberships to any immediately neighboring multicast routers. IGMP messages are encapsulated in IP datagrams, with an IP protocol number of 2. RFC1112 describes IGMP, which is considered as an extension to ICMP and occupies the same place in the IP protocol stack.

Internet Protocol (IP)   The protocol or standard at the network level of the Internet that defines the packets of information and routing them to remote nodes, and the method of addressing remote computers and routing packets to remote hosts.

Internet service provider (ISP)   A business that provides subscription services, such as online information retrieval software, bulletin boards, electronic mail, and so on to users for a fee. ISPs are domains under the control of a single administration that share their resources with other domains.

Internetwork Packet Exchange protocol (IPX)   A datagram protocol found in Novell NetWare networks. It is similar to UDP and together with SPX provides connectionless services similar to UDP/IP.

InterNIC   A collaborative project between AT&T and Network Solutions, Inc. (NSI) supported by the National Science Foundation. The project currently offers four services to users of the Internet.

IP multicast   A one-to-many transmission described in RFC 1112. The RFC describes IP multicasting as "the transmission of an IP datagram to a 'host group,' a set of zero or more hosts identified by a single IP destination address. A multicast datagram is delivered to all members of its destination host group with the same 'best-efforts' reliability as regular unicast IP datagrams. The membership of a host group is dynamic; that is, hosts may join and leave groups at any time. There is no restriction on the location or number of members in a host group. A host may be a member of more than one group at a time."

IP multicast datagram   A datagram delivered to all members of the multicast host group. Such datagrams are delivered with the same best-efforts reliability as regular unicast IP datagrams.

IP multicast router   A router supporting IGMP and one or more of the multicast routing protocols, including Distance DVMRP, MOSPF, PIM-DM, CBT, and PIM-SM.

Ipv4   The current version of the Internet Protocol.

Ipv6   The next version of the Internet Protocol, which is currently being tested.

IPX   *See* Internetwork Packet Exchange protocol.

ISO   International Standards Organization, a special agency of the United Nations that is charged with the development of communication standards for computers. Membership in the ISO consists of representatives from international standards organizations throughout the world.

ISP   Internet service provider.

ITU   International Telecommunication Union.

Jitter   A delay that results in the late arrival of a frame.

Jitter buffer   An area of memory in which arriving frames transporting voice are first placed. Frames are then extracted to remove the random arrival times between frames, making reconstructed voice more natural-sounding.

Kbps   Kilobits per second.

LAN   A local area network; a communication network that spans a limited geographical area. LANs can differ from one another in topology or arrangement of devices on the network, the protocols they use, and the media, such as twisted-pair wire, coaxial cables, or fiber-optic cables used to connect the devices on the network.

Latency   The transmission delay of the network or the minimum amount of time it takes for any one of those bits or bytes to travel across the network.

LLC   Logical link control.

Local loop   The line from a subscriber to the telephone company central office.

Logical link   A temporary connection between source and destination nodes or between two processes on the same node.

Logical link control (LLC)   Part of the data-link layer of the OSI model and the link-layer control specification for the IEEE 802.x series of standards. It defines the services for the transmission of data between two stations with no intermediate switching stations. There are three versions: LLC1 is connectionless; LLC2 is connection-oriented; and LLC3 is connectionless with acknowledgment.

Logical link multiplexing   A frame relay transmission technique that enables frames transporting voice and data to share the same PVC.

Loop-start signaling   The flow of current when a telephone goes off-hook.

Low-bit-rate encoder   A voice digitizer that converts speech to a digital data rate typically at or under 8 Kbps.

MAC address   The unique media access control 6-byte address that is associated with the network adapter card and identifies the machine on a particular network. A MAC address is also known as an *Ethernet address, hardware address, station address,* or *physical address.*

Make/break period   In dial pulse signaling, the ratio of circuit closure to the time a circuit is open.

Mask   A means of subdividing networks using address modification. A mask is a dotted quad specifying which bits of the destination are significant.

Maximum transmission units (MTU)   The largest amount of data that can be transferred across a network; size is determined by the network hardware.

Mbone   A virtual multicast backbone network layered on top of the physical Internet. In existence for about five years, the Mbone supports routing of IP multicast packets.

Mbps   Megabits per second.

Media stream   A single media instance (e.g., an audio stream or a video stream as well as a single whiteboard or shared application group). When using RTP, a stream consists of all RTP and RTCP packets created by a source within an RTP session. This is equivalent to the definition of a DSM-CC stream.

M lead   The wire connected to the mouthpiece in a telephone headset.

Modulation   The process in which the characteristics of one wave or signal are varied in accordance with another wave or signal. Modulation can alter frequency, phase, or amplitude characteristics.

Multiaccess network   A physical network that supports the attachment of more than two routers. Each pair of routers on such a network can communicate directly.

Multicast   Method of transmitting messages from a host using a single transmission to a selected subset of all the hosts that can receive the messages; also, a message that is sent out to multiple devices on the network by a host. *See also* **broadcast** and **IP multicast.**

Multicast group   A group set up to receive messages from a source. These groups can be established based on frame relay or IP in the TCP/IP protocol suite as well as in other networks.

Multicast interface   An interface to a link over which IP multicast or IP broadcast service is supported.

Multicast link   A link over which IP multicast or IP broadcast service is supported. This includes broadcast media such as LANs and satellite channels, single point-to-point links, and some store-and-forward networks such as SMDS networks.

Multicast Open Shortest Path First (MOSPF)   RFC 1584 defines MOSPF as an extension to the OSPF link-state unicast routing protocol that provides the ability to route IP multicast traffic. Some portions of the Mbone support MOSPF. MOSPF uses the OSPF link-state metric to determine the least-cost path and calculates a spanning tree for routing multicast traffic with the multicast source at the root and the group members as leaves.

Multicast Transport Protocol (MTP) This protocol gives application programs guarantees of reliability. The MTP protocol could be useful when developing some types of applications, for example, with distributed databases that need to be certain that all members of a multicast group agree on which packets have been received.

Multiplex Combining signals of multiple channels into one channel. This process provides multiple users with access to a single conductor or medium by transmitting in multiple distinct frequency bands (*frequency division multiplexing,* or FDM) or by assigning the same channel to different users at different times (*time division multiplexing,* or TDM).

Multiplexer A device that allows several users to share a single circuit and funnels different data streams into a single stream. At the other end of the communications link, another multiplexer reverses the process by splitting the data stream back into the original streams.

Multiplexing A repeater, either standalone or connected to standard Ethernet cable, for interconnecting up to eight thin-wire Ethernet segments.

Near-end echo The reflection of energy at the hybrid in the caller's serving central office.

Network Access Point (NAP) An Internet hub where national and international ISPs connect with one another. An NAP router has to know about every network on the Internet.

Network Service Access Point (NSAP) The network address or the node address of the machine where a service is available.

Node Any intelligent device connected to the network. This includes terminal servers, host computers, and any other devices (such as printers and terminals) directly connected to the network. A node can be thought of as any device that has a hardware address.

NSP Network service provider.

Open Settlement Protocol (OSP) A mechanism for the charge-back of Internet telephony use among Internet service providers.

Packet A package of data with a header that may or may not be logically complete. A series of bits containing data and control information, including source and destination node addresses, formatted for transmission from one node to another. A packet is more often a physical packaging than a logical packaging of data.

Packet-by-packet An implementation of layer 3 switching that uses industrywide, standard routing protocols to examine all packets and forward them to their destination entirely in layer 3.

PCM Pulse code modulation. A waveform voice-digitization technique that converts voice into a 64-Kbps digital data stream.

Permanent virtual circuit (PVCP) A permanent logical connection set up with packet data networks such as frame relay.

Phase modulation A technique that changes the characteristics of a generated sine wave or signal so that it will carry information.

Physical layer The physical channel implements layer 1, the bottom layer of the OSI model. The physical layer insulates layer 2 (the data-link layer) from medium-dependent physical characteristics such as baseband, broadband, or fiber-optic transmission. Layer 1 defines the protocols that govern transmission of media and signals.

Physical topologies These define the arrangement of devices and the layout of the wiring.

Ping A TCP/IP utility program that determines the round-trip delay to a specified destination address.

Plosive sound Sound resulting from the closure of our vocal tract, resulting in air pressure becoming extremely high behind the closure.

Point-to-point network A network joining a single pair of routers—for example, a 56-Kb serial-line network.

POTS An acronym for plain old telephone service.

POTS splitter A passive filter that separates voice traffic from data traffic.

Predictive congestion management A technique under which the lengths of queues are varied in response to traffic to reduce the probability of congestion adversely affecting frames presented to a network.

Presentation A set of one or more streams presented to the client as a complete media feed, using a presentation description. In most cases in the RTSP context, this implies aggregate control of those streams.

Presentation description   A presentation description contains information about one or more media streams within a presentation, such as the set of encodings, network addresses, and information about the content.

Protocol   The set of rules to send and receive data and govern activities within a specific layer of the network architecture model. Protocols regulate the transfer of data between layers and across links to other devices and define procedures for handling lost or damaged transmissions or packets. Protocols also determine whether the network uses peer-to-peer or client/server architecture.

Protocol-Independent Multicast (PIM) Routing Protocol   Developed by an IETF working group, PIM provides a standard multicast routing protocol that supports scalable interdomain multicast routing across the Internet independent of the mechanisms provided by any particular unicast routing protocol. PIM has two modes: dense and sparse.

Public switched telephone network (PSTN)   A telephone system through which users can be connected by dialing specific telephone numbers.

QoS   Quality of service.

Random delay   The random amount of time a transmission is delayed to prevent multiple nodes from transmitting at exactly the same time or to prevent long-range periodic transmissions from synchronizing with each other.

Real-Time Streaming Protocol (RTSP)   This application-level protocol provides control for the delivery of data with real-time properties. RTSP enables controlled on-demand delivery of real-time data, such as audio and video.

Real-Time Transport Protocol (RTTP)   RTTP provides end-to-end network transport functions for applications that transmit real-time data over multicast or unicast network services. Such applications can include audio, video, or simulation data applications.

Regional Bell operating company (RBOC)   A telecommunication company formed as a result of the divestiture of AT&T. RBOCs oversee Bell operating companies.

Regular Pulse Excited (RPE)   A hybrid coding method that results in high-quality digitized speech at a 13-Kbps data rate. RPE is used in the Global System for Mobile Communications digital radio system.

Request for Comment (RFC)   An official document used by the IETF to create standards for use in the Internet.

ReSerVation Protocol (RSVP)   A method developed by the IETF to assist in providing QoS characteristics to communications over an IP network. The name refers to the fact that it allows the end stations to reserve bandwidth on the network. This protocol supports requests for a specific QoS from the network for particular data streams or flows.

Response   An RTSP response. If an HTTP response is meant, that is explicitly indicated.

Reverse Address Resolution Protocol (RARP)   An Internet protocol that can be used by diskless hosts to find their Internet address.

Ring   The pair of wires that conveys voltage from the battery.

RIP (Routing Information Protocol)   An early BSD Unix routing protocol that has become an industry standard.

RISC   An acronym for reduced instruction set computing.

RMON   An acronym for remote monitoring.

Router   A device that connects two networks at the network layer (layer 3) of the OSI model; operated like a bridge but also can choose routes through a network.

Routing   In networking, routing is the process of moving a packet of data from source to destination. A dedicated device called a *router* usually performs routing. Routing is a key feature of the Internet and enables messages to pass from one computer to another and eventually reach the target machine. Each intermediary computer performs routing by passing along the message to the next computer. Part of this process involves analyzing a routing table to determine the best path.

RSVP   Resource ReSerVation Protocol.

RTSP session   A complete RTSP "transaction" (e.g., the viewing of a movie). A session typically consists of a client setting up a transport mechanism for the continuous media stream, starting the stream with Play or Record, and closing the stream with Teardown.

Sequenced Packet Exchange (SPX)   A connection-oriented protocol found in Novell NetWare networks. This transport-layer protocol is similar to TCP and together with IPX provides connection services similar to TCP/IP.

Shared Ethernet   An Ethernet configuration in which a number of segments are bound together in a single collision domain; hubs produce this type of configuration, where only one node can transmit at a time.

Side tone   A design of the hybrid within a telephone set that allows a portion of speech to "bleed" over the earpiece or receiver, allowing people to hear themselves talk.

Simple Network Management Protocol (SNMP)   Allows a TCP/IP host running an SNMP application to query other nodes for network-related statistics and error conditions. The other hosts, which provide SNMP agents, respond to these queries and allow a single host to gather network statistics from many other network nodes.

SLA   Service-level agreement.

SNAP   Subnetwork Access Protocol.

Station-loop signaling   Signaling that informs a central office switch of the status of the telephone on the subscriber loop.

Subchannel multiplexing   A frame relay multiplexing technique under which portions of multiple voice conversations are combined within one frame.

Subscriber loop   The pair of wires from a switch or PBX to the telephone.

Supervisory signaling   Signaling used to inform a telephone instrument and ports on the central office switch or PBX of the status of the local loop and any connected trunks between switches and PBXs.

Switch hook   A connector on a telephone that allows current to flow when the handset is lifted.

T1   A circuit used in North America that operates at 1.544 Mbps. A channelized T1 consists of 24 time slots, each operating at 64 Kbps and 8000 framing bits per second.

Time division multiplexing   A digital transmission method that combines signals from multiple sources by time onto a common transmission facility.

Tip   The pair of wires that permits current detection.

Tone-start signaling   A trunk signaling method in which the originating side of the trunk is placed in an off-hook condition, causing the receiving side to generate a dial tone.

Traceroute   A TCP/IP utility program that traces the route to a destination address.

Twisted pair Telephone system cabling that consists of copper wires loosely twisted around each other to help cancel out any induced noise in balanced circuits.

UDP User Datagram Protocol.

Unvoiced sounds Sounds produced when our vocal folds are open, allowing air to pass from our lungs to the rest of our vocal tract.

UTP Unshielded twisted pair.

Vocoding A method of voice digitization based on modeling speech.

Voiced sounds Sounds produced when our vocal cords vibrate.

Wink-start signaling A trunk signaling method in which the originating trunk is placed in an off-hook condition and the remote switch responds with an off-hook pulse, after which the switch returns to an idle or on-hook state.

INDEX

INDEX

ABOUT THE AUTHOR

Gil Held is an award-winning author and lecturer who specializes in the application of computer and communications technology. He is the author of more than 40 books and 300 technical articles covering personal computers and data communications. Gil's books have been translated into over 20 languages and he has represented the United States at technical conferences ranging from Moscow to Jerusalem. Mr. Held was selected by Federal Computer World as one of the top 100 persons in government, industry, and academia who have made a difference in the acquisition and use of computer systems.